UNITED STATES DEPARTMENT OF COMMERCE · Luther H. Hodges, *Secretary*
NATIONAL BUREAU OF STANDARDS · A. V. Astin, *Director*

Ellipsometry in the Measurement Of Surfaces and Thin Films

Symposium Proceedings
Washington 1963

Symposium held September 5-6, 1963, at the National Bureau of Standards, Washington, D.C.

Edited by E. Passaglia, R. R. Stromberg, and J. Kruger

National Bureau of Standards Miscellaneous Publication 256

Issued September 15, 1964

For sale by the Superintendent of Documents, U.S. Government Printing Office
Washington, D.C., 20402 - Price $2.25

Abstract

A Symposium on the Ellipsometer and its Use in the Measurement of Surfaces was held at the National Bureau of Standards in September 1963. This volume contains 19 of the papers included in the program, together with any discussions which followed oral presentation. Topics covered include historical review, theory, computational techniques, measurement techniques, and the use of ellipsometry in measuring metal surface oxide films and organic films.

Library of Congress Catalog Card Number: 64-60043

II

Foreword

An important responsibility of the National Bureau of Standards is the development and improvement of measurement techniques and the dissemination of information on them. For many years the Bureau has supported work in the study and measurement of properties of surfaces and, as part of this activity, sponsored a "Symposium on the Ellipsometer and its Use in the Measurement of Surfaces and Thin Films." The Symposium was held at NBS in Washington, D.C. on September 5 and 6, 1963 and was attended by approximately 200 scientists. Partial financial support was provided by the Army Research Office (Durham).

This volume contains most of the papers presented at the Symposium as well as the discussions that followed the presentations. The papers represent contributions from a number of laboratories in this country and abroad. Primary responsibility for their technical content must rest, of course, with the individual authors and their organizations.

A. V. Astin
Director

Preface

The study of surfaces and films is important in many branches of physics, physical chemistry, and engineering. The measurement of the changes in polarization upon the reflection of light from a surface is a very sensitive technique for studying the properties of a surface and any films overlaying it. This technique is commonly called "ellipsometry" since it involves measurement of the state of polarization of elliptically polarized light. While the theory of the method is old and well-known, it is only relatively recently that serious and concerted application of the method to various surface problems has been made. This has been occasioned by recent developments in instrumentation and computational techniques, and particularly by the general availability of electronic computing facilities.

The Symposium, which was held to summarize developments in this field of measurement, consisted of 20 technical papers. Eighteen of the papers were presented orally and two others were submitted but not presented because the authors were unable to attend. Most of these papers are published together in these Proceedings to provide in one volume a "state of the art" for this measurement technique. The papers include historical review, theory, computational techniques, measurement techniques, and the use of ellipsometry in studying metal surfaces, oxide films, and organic films. As this book is a group of papers rather than a series of integrated chapters, each paper is written to be self-supporting. An introduction by the Chairman provides scientific background and discusses the differences, similarities, and interrelationships among the various contributions.

We, the members of the Symposium Committee, wish to express our appreciation to those who contributed to this conference, the authors and the discussants.

E. Passaglia, *Chairman*
R. R. Stromberg
J. Kruger
Ellipsometer Symposium Committee
National Bureau of Standards

IV

Contents

	Page
Foreword	III
Preface	IV
Introduction	1

1. **Historical Review**
   Measurements of the thickness of thin films by optical means, from Rayleigh and Drude to Langmuir, and the development of the present ellipsometer. ALEXANDRE ROTHEN — 7

2. **Theory**
   Optical study of a thin absorbing film on a metal surface. ANTONÍN VAŠÍČEK — 25
   Optical properties of inhomogeneous films. FLORIN ABELÈS — 41

3. **Techniques**
   Computation
   Computational techniques for the use of the exact Drude equations in reflection problems. FRANK L. McCRACKIN and JAMES P. COLSON — 61
   Factors influencing the experimental sensitivity of the Drude technique. RICHARD C. SMITH and MICHAEL HACSKAYLO — 83
   Instrumentation
   Increased scope of ellipsometric studies of surface film formation. A. B. WINTERBOTTOM — 97
   Electronic polarimeter techniques. JEROME M. WEINGART and ALAN R. JOHNSTON — 113
   On determining optical constants of metals in the infrared. SHEPARD ROBERTS — 119

4. **Applications**
   Oxidation and Corrosion of Metals
   Use of ellipsometry for *in situ* studies of the oxidation of metal surfaces immersed in aqueous solutions. JEROME KRUGER — 131
   An assessment of the suitability of the Drude-Tronstad polarized light method for the study of film growth on polycrystalline metals. P. C. S. HAYFIELD and G. W. T. WHITE — 157
   Studies of thin oxide films on copper crystals with an ellipsometer. J. V. CATHCART and G. F. PETERSEN — 201
   Optical study of the formation and stability of anodic films on aluminum. M. A. BARRETT — 213
   Ellipsometry in electrochemical studies. A. K. N. REDDY and J. O'M. BOCKRIS — 229
   Application of ellipsometry to the study of phenomena on surfaces prepared in ultra-high vacuum. J. F. DETTORRE, T. G. KNORR, and D. A. VAUGHAN — 245

Adsorption

Measurement of the physical adsorption of vapors and the chemisorption of oxygen and silicon by the method of ellipsometry. R. J. ARCHER _____ 255

Application of ellipsometry to the study of adsorption from solution. ROBERT R. STROMBERG, ELIO PASSAGLIA, and DANIEL J. TUTAS _____ 281

Determination of thickness and refractive index of thin films as an approach to the study of biological macromolecules. J. B. BATEMAN _____ 297

Other

Blood coagulation studies with the recording ellipsometer. L. VROMAN _____ 335

Ellipsometry for frustrated total reflection. T. D. YOUNG and J. M. FATH _____ 349

VI

Introduction

Elio Passaglia

National Bureau of Standards, Washington, D.C., 20234

The study of surfaces and thin films overlaying them has been carried out for many years, but recently has become increasingly important in several fields of study. Notable among these are the physics and physical chemistry of adsorption, metallurgy (where the concern is with oxidation and corrosion processes), and the general field of solid-state electronics, where surface phenomena are of crucial importance.

With such interest, an old and very elegant optical method for the study of surfaces has been further developed and applied to various problems. The method has been called by several names, among them "ellipsometry" and "polarization spectrometry," and is based upon the classic theory of Paul Drude [1] [1] concerning the change in the state of polarization of light upon reflection from a bare surface or a surface with a film on it. By measuring the change in the state of polarization, it is possible to measure the optical constants of a bare surface, or, if these are known and the surface is covered by a dielectric film, it is possible to calculate the thickness and refractive index of the film. The method involves only the measurement of polarization and not photometry, which makes it relatively simple in application

Although the theory and equations of Drude are exact, the exact equations are cumbersome in form. They cannot be solved in closed form for the desired quantities (refractive index and thickness of film) in terms of the measured change in state of polarization, as represented by $\tan \psi$, the ratio of the magnitude of the reflection coefficient for light polarized in the plane of incidence to that polarized normal to the plane of incidence, and Δ, the relative phase difference for these two polarizations. Thus trial-and-error and iteration methods must be used, and before the availability of electronic computers the routine application of the exact equations was almost impossible. Thus Drude and many subsequent workers used only the first linear terms in the expansion of the equations relating $\tan \psi$ and Δ to refractive index and thickness, and it is these approximate equations which are (unfortunately) often referred to as the "Drude equations." This limited the application of the Drude theory to films which are very thin in comparison to the wavelength of light. However, with modern electronic computers the use of the exact equations is routine, once the initial programming is complete. Most workers have some kind of computational facilities, and programs have been described by Archer [2] and McCrackin et al. [3].

The collection of papers in this volume is intended both to serve as an introduction to the method of ellipsometry for the worker who is

---

[1] Figures in brackets indicate the literature references on p. 4.

embarking on a study of surfaces and thin films, and to present for the expert a summary of some of the latest theoretical and experimental achievements. The papers are collected into three categories: Theory, Techniques, and Applications, and a historical review is provided by Rothen, who reviews the history of optical studies of surfaces and gives the physical basis of the method of ellipsometry. It is the purpose of this introduction to give a brief summary of the content of each of the three categories so that the reader may go directly to the papers of interest.

1. Theory

Professor Vašíček gives a review of his theory of reflection from a film-covered surface and applies it to an absorbing film on a metal surface. For absorbing films this theory differs somewhat from the theory of Drude, which is well described in several places [4, 5] and in this volume by many of the authors, notably Hayfield and White.

Professor Abelès in his paper gives a discussion of the very important problem of inhomogeneous films, and gives the differential equations for the case in which the refractive index of a film varies only in the direction normal to the surface. For the case of exponential variation he presents an exact solution for Δ and ψ from these equations, and points out how numerical solutions may be obtained for other cases by considering the inhomogeneous film to be a stack of very thin homogeneous films (a so-called stratified medium).

2. Techniques

The method just described has been applied by McCrackin and Colson in computing the properties of films whose refractive index varies in an exponential, linear, and Gaussian manner with distance from the surface, and thereby relating average quantities of these films to the average refractive index and thickness which would be measured experimentally by ellipsometry. These authors also consider various methods for determining thickness and the real and imaginary parts of the complex refractive index of absorbing films— something which cannot in general be done by a single measurement. (Also see the paper by Hayfield and White.) This paper illustrates the essential role of the electronic computer in modern studies of the optical properties of surfaces.

The experimental technique of ellipsometry has been described in the literature [4] and in this volume by Rothen. However, extensions of it are continuing. Thus Winterbottom describes certain ways in which automatic ellipsometers might be made. This is not simply a problem of reducing the labor of taking measurements (which is very small), but of increasing the speed of the method so that fast surface reactions might be followed. (The use of convential ellipsometers to study fast reactions is illustrated in the papers by Reddy and Bockris and by Vroman.)

Weingart and Johnston present elegant electronic techniques for measuring very accurately the state of polarization of light. For certain values of the parameters of film, substrate, and surrounding medium, ellipsometry has a calculated senistivity of only a fraction of an Angstrom [4, p. 47] even for ordinary means of measuring state of polarization. However, in other cases experimental sensitivity is of essential importance (see, for example, the paper by Stromberg, Passaglia, and Tutas) and the application of some of the methods discussed by Weingart and Johnston would be of very real value in these problems. The whole question of sensitivity is very thoroughly discussed by Smith and Hacskaylo for thin films where the thin film approximation of the Drude equation is applicable. A less thorough discussion for thicker films has been given by McCrackin et al. [3a].

An extension of ellipsometry to measuring the optical constants of metals in the infrared is given by Roberts. This is very difficult as compared to measurements in the visible range, and involves making photometric measurements at selected azimuths of incident linearly polarized light and analyzing prisms in the reflected beam.

3. Applications

One of the most widely exploited applications of ellipsometry is the study of metal surfaces and oxidation and corrosion processes on them. In all of this work the object is to identify the process occurring and its rate by measuring the refractive index of the film formed and the change in its thickness with time.

The papers by Kruger and by Hayfield and White present reviews of this subject describing the type of information that can be obtained from these studies. The latter authors represent these data by making a polar plot of ρ (called Z by them) which is the (complex) ratio of the reflection coefficient for light polarized in the plane of incidence to that polarized normal to the plane of incidence. This has the advantage that a closed curve indicates a dielectric film, whereas a nonclosing curve represents an absorbing film with a finite value of the imaginary part of the refractive index. The same type of representation is used by Barrett in her study of the corrosion of aluminum.

The oxidation of copper is described in papers by Cathcart and Petersen and by Dettorre, Knorr, and Vaughan. The former authors, studying specific surfaces of single crystal specimens, show the presense of epitaxially induced strains in the oxide film, resulting in optical anisotropy of the film. This illustrates very clearly the type of detail which can be obtained by use of this method.

Reddy and Bockris illustrate the application of ellipsometry in electrochemical studies. In this study one of the parameters varied is the electric potential of the surface, and electrochemical processes at the surface may be studied as a function of this potential.

As previously mentioned, one of the common problems in all these studies is that of rapidity of measurement. Often the processes involved in oxidation, corrosion, or electrochemical processes are extremely rapid, and the finite time necessary to take measurements is a distinct handicap. This clearly calls for some type of automatic ellipsometer, perhaps like one of the designs described by Winterbottom.

Another widely exploited application is the study of adsorption. Archer describes a very thorough study of the adsorption of several vapors on silicon surfaces, taking specific account of the roughness of the surfaces, and deriving the dependence of Δ and ψ on surface coverage and thickness from two points of view: (1) considering the film to have a refractive index which is the average of the refractive index of the film, substrate, and surrounding medium, and (2) considering the film to be a two-dimensional collection of Hertzian oscillators. This important problem is also discussed by Hayfield and White.

Adsorption of macromolecules is described in papers by Stromberg, Passaglia, and Tutas, and by Bateman. In both cases the aim of the work is to determine the conformation of the adsorbed macromolecule. The former workers, working with synthetic polymers, used a strictly ellipsometric technique, while Bateman used the stepped interference reflector method described by Rothen in his paper.

A novel use of the ellipsometer is described by Vroman, who used this method for studying the coagulation of blood. By calibration with barium stearate layers, Vroman is able to convert measurements of intensity of extinction to equivalent thickness of barium stearate. This gave him a very fast instrument to study the rapid changes occurring in this process.

Young and Fath also describe an interesting application of ellipsometry. They studied the thickness and refractive index of wringing films between metallic gage blocks and optically flat transparent glass surfaces. The angle of the incident light in the glass was greater than the critical angle, resulting in frustrated total reflection from the glass-film surface.

It is hoped that the present collection of papers will fulfill its aim of being useful to both experts and new workers in ellipsometry. By illustrating the many different fields of application, the potentialities of this technique have been demonstrated. It is hoped that new applications will be forthcoming, perhaps stimulated by this volume.

4. References

[1] P. Drude, Ann. Physik. **272,** 532 (1889); ibid. **272,** 865 (1889); ibid. **275,** 481 (1890).
[2] R. J. Archer, J. Opt. Soc. Am. **52,** 970 (1962).
[3a] F. L. McCrackin, E. Passaglia, R.R. Stromberg, and H. L. Steinberg, J. Res. NBS **67A,** 363 (1963).
[3b] F. L. McCrackin and J. P. Colson, NBS Tech. Note 242 (1964).
[4] A. B. Winterbottom, "Optical Studies of Metal Surfaces," The Royal Norwegian Scientific Society Report No. 1, 1955, published by F. Bruns, Trondheim, Norway.
[5] M. Born and E. Wolf, Principles of Optics (Pergamon Press, 1959).

1. Historical Review

Measurements of the Thickness of Thin Films by Optical Means, From Rayleigh and Drude to Langmuir, and the Development of the Present Ellipsometer

Alexandre Rothen

The Rockefeller Institute, N.Y.

The historical review begins at the end of the last century when Rayleigh remarked that "having proved that the superficial viscosity of water was due to a greasy contamination whose thickness might be much less than one millionth of a millimeter, I too hastily concluded that films of such extraordinary tenuity were unlikely to be of optical importance." The fundamental work of Drude is then discussed. In the thirties, Blodgett and Langmuir used a very simple and beautiful interferometric method to measure the thickness of very thin films. The review ends by summarizing how in order to obviate definite drawbacks of this method, the ellipsometer was developed in 1944.

1. Early Studies of Elliptically Polarized Light

Before going over the historical development of this chapter of optics, it might be well to define the term "ellipsometry." Ellipsometry is the art of measuring and analyzing the elliptical polarization of light. This is a definition in the broadest possible sense, no restriction being placed on the cause of the elliptical polarization. Methods for analyzing elliptical polarization go way back to Sénarmont in the middle of the nineteenth century, and more recently, Skinner, from the National Bureau of Standards, in 1925 published a comprehensive article describing an apparatus which he called a universal polarimeter permitting the determination of the ellipticity and orientation of an ellipse characterizing a state of polarization [1].[1]

I shall limit the discussion on ellipsometry to the case where elliptical polarization is caused by reflection from the surface of a dielectric or a metal coated with a film, and we shall be concerned chiefly with the measurement of the thickness of these films or transition layers. Genuine ellipsometry does not involve any photometric measurements. One measures angles, ratio of amplitude vectors, and phase differences.

Without the fundamental work of the great Augustin Fresnel early in the nineteenth century, there would be no "ellipsometer," because the Fresnel formulas are the foundations upon which ellipsometry could be constructed. The Fresnel formulas indicate that when light is reflected, let us say, at the air-water interface, the two components vibrating in and perpendicular to the plane of incidence, generally called r_p and r_s, undergo a phase shift of 180° or 0°, and furthermore, that r_p becomes zero at a certain angle called the Brewsterian angle.

---

[1] Figures in brackets indicate the literature references on page 21.

I might mention parenthetically that the use of the subscript s to refer to the component vibrating perpendicularly to the plane of incidence comes from the German word *senkrecht*, meaning "perpendicular." In testing these formulas experimentally, Jamin [2] and others found that, in the neighborhood of the Brewsterian angle, the reflection of light from many liquids and solids deviates sensibly from Fresnel's law, and that an appreciable amount of ellipticity was present. (It is interesting to notice that Jamin described the failure of the component r_p to vanish at the Brewsterian angle and the ellipticity in its neighborhood as two phenomena of different natures.) In other words, if the incident light was plane polarized at 45° to the principal planes, after reflection at the Brewsterian angle, the ratio K of the reflected amplitudes in and perpendicular to the plane of incidence was called ellipticity. For instance, Jamin found in the case of water a K as large as 0.006. The values of K were either positive or negative, depending on the liquid. No explanation was available for this departure from Fresnel's law, and from Jamin's own words, it was "impossible to find the cause of the ellipticity in an abnormal molecular constitution."

Then, ten years before the end of the last century, two men, Lord Rayleigh [3] in England and Paul Drude [4] in Germany, found the correct explanation for the failure of Fresnel's law. It resulted from the presence of thin films deposited at the solid or liquid interface. These two great physicists had opposite temperaments. In their respective papers dealing with this subject, Rayleigh emerges as an outstanding experimentalist. Rayleigh was experimenting at the time with surface viscosity of different liquids repeating some of Plateau's work. "Having proved," said he, "that the superficial viscosity of water was due to a greasy contamination whose thickness might be much less than one-millionth of a millimetre, I too hastily concluded that films of such extraordinary tenuity were unlikely to be of optical importance, until prompted by a remark of Sir G. Stokes, I made an actual estimate of the effect to be expected." And then Rayleigh started his famous experiments on the state of polarization of light reflected at the Brewsterian angle from clean water and water covered by a greasy contamination. His apparatus, at first, was very simple. The sun was his light source, a porcelain dish contained the water, and he observed the image of the sun through a nicol. "Thus encouraged, I returned to the attack and, on October 2, 1890, examined the image of the sun as reflected from water at the polarizing angle," and "on June 26th, the dish was placed on a table below the window of an undarkened room and the passage of the spot across the sun's disk was watched. The spot was central at about 4^h 0^m and the instant of centrality could be determined to within 10^s."

The simple and precise description of his experiment reminds one of Newton's optics. For instance, one reads in Newton's *Opticks*, "In a very dark chamber, at a round hole about one-third part of an inch broad, made in the shut of a window, I placed a glass prism, whereby the beam of the sun's light which came in at the hole might be refracted upwards toward the opposite wall of the chamber."

This could just as well have been written by Rayleigh. And thus, the great Rayleigh was experimenting in a lucky period where the scientists were small in number and the periodicals not too crowded. One might imagine the reaction of today's editors of a scientific journal if they received an article with the dates and the hours at which the experiments were performed. The general conclusion drawn by Rayleigh was that the ellipticity of the light reflected by clean liquids was very much less than that of a contaminated surface, and he made the final statement that "it is even possible that there would be no sensible ellipticity for the surface of a chemically pure body. But the surfaces of bodies are the field of very powerful forces of whose action we know but little." A very prophetic remark.

At about the time that Rayleigh was investigating the optical properties of the light reflected from the surface of liquids, Drude, in Germany, was testing the optical properties of the light reflected from solids. In two fundamental articles published in 1889 and 1890, he was able to correlate quantitatively the optical thickness of a film and the optical constants of the material upon which the film was deposited with two parameters characterizing the ellipse representing the reflected light. The two parameters were the ratio, $\tan\psi = \dfrac{\rho^p}{\rho^s}$ and $\Delta = \delta^p - \delta^s$; where ρ^p and ρ^s are the reflection coefficients of the components in and perpendicular to the plane of incidence after reflection; δ^p and δ^s, the absolute phase shifts of the same two components, brought about the reflection. Drude started from the Maxwell equations and the appropriate boundary conditions. He obtained a most general equation, valid for films of any thickness deposited on metallic surfaces, which reads:

$$\rho^{p,s}e^{i\delta^{p,s}} = \frac{I_r^{p,s}}{I_i^{p,s}}e^{i\delta^{p,s}} = \frac{r_f^{p,s} + r_m^{p,s}e^{-ix}}{1 + r_f^{p,s}r_m^{p,s}e^{-ix}}, \tag{1}$$

where $I_r^{p,s}$ represents the amplitudes of the electric vector in (p) and perpendicular to (s) the plane of incidence after reflection, and $\delta^{p,s}$ represents the corresponding absolute phase shifts. $I_i^{p,s}$ are the amplitudes of the components before reflection, $r_f^{p,s}$ and $r_m^{p,s}$ are the Fresnel coefficients for reflection at the film and the metal surface, respectively. The variable x is equal to $4n\pi\cos\varphi\dfrac{l}{\lambda}$, l being the thickness of the film; n, its index of refraction, and φ, the angle of incidence. The superscripts, p and s, indicate that this formula holds for each component separately. Writing the above formula for the two components p and s separately and taking the ratio, Drude obtained:

$$\tan\psi e^{i\Delta} = \frac{(r_f^p + r_m^p e^{-ix})(1 + r_f^s r_m^s e^{-ix})}{(1 + r_f^p r_m^p e^{-ix})(r_f^s + r_m^s e^{-ix})}. \tag{2}$$

The values of ψ and Δ can be obtained experimentally from ellipsometric measurements, that is, by measurements of orientation of amplitude vectors. No photometric measurements are involved. In order to test his theoretical results for the case of extremely thin films, much thinner than the wavelength of light, Drude developed the terms containing e^{-ix} in a serial development, using only the first term $\frac{l}{\lambda}$. Thus, he obtained the two following linear equations, one relating the change in the ratio $\tan \psi = \frac{\rho^p}{\rho^s}$ and the other, the change in the difference of phase $\Delta = \delta^p - \delta^s$ brought about by the film. These equations are:

$$\Delta - \Delta' = -A\left(1 - \frac{1}{n^2}\right)\frac{l}{\lambda}$$

and (3)

$$2\psi - 2\psi' = B(1-C)\left(1 - \frac{1}{n^2}\right)\frac{l}{\lambda},$$

where the primes refer to the values obtained in the absence of films. In these equations, A and B are functions of the angle of incidence and the optical constants of the support and $C = n^2 \cos \varphi$, n being the index of refraction of the film.

These equations are commonly called the Drude equations valid for very thin films only. Unfortunately, it is not always recognized nowadays that Drude also obtained the most general equation (2) given above. The name of Drude should be attached to this equation, as it was done by Hauschild [5] in 1920, who used a two-term serial development of Drude's formulation. It is to be regretted that in his recent book on Optics of Thin Films [6] Vašíček does not make it clear that the general equation can be found in Drude's work.

2. Early Studies of Thin Film Thicknesses

Tronstad [7] was the first one in 1935 to test Drude's first-term expressions for films of known thickness. He measured the thickness of monomolecular films of fatty acids adsorbed on a mercury surface and found good agreement with the theoretical values.

In the late thirties, chemists' interest in surface films was suddenly aroused by one of the most important single developments in the technique of surface films since the introduction of the spreading trough by Langmuir. It was the discovery made in Langmuir's laboratory by Katherine Blodgett [8] that coherent films formed on a water surface could easily be transferred to solid slides if they were maintained at a certain minimum pressure during the transfer. In many cases, a large number of monomolecular layers could be transferred on top of each other, a process akin to the building up of a crystal, layer by layer. This opened up a vast field for experimentation which has not yet been completely covered. I still remember the great enthusiasm created by this new technique. I believe that the scientific spirit of Langmuir's laboratory was close to that which must have permeated Rayleigh's.[2]

With this new technique mainly developed by Blodgett [9], a large amount of experimenting went on in many laboratories with all kinds of materials, from proteins to viruses and bacteria, capable of being spread and transferred. One of the main characteristics of a film is, of course, its thickness. From the historical background which I have just reviewed, one would think that the next step would have been to use the basic formulation of Drude to measure the thickness of all the films now available. Nothing happened for the following reason. Blodgett and Langmuir built up on glass slides multilayers sufficiently thick to have shown interference colors. But there were no interference colors. This puzzled Blodgett and Langmuir for a while, until they realized that the refractive index of their slides was not what they expected it to be. When they deposited multilayers of stearic acid on glass of high index of refraction or on chromium-plated slides, they observed indeed, the most brilliant colors.[3]

Being accustomed to build films thick enough to show interference colors, Blodgett and Langmuir developed in a most ingenious way a method to measure the thickness of films whose thicknesses comprised a very small fraction of the wavelength of light. It consisted in building on a slide multilayers of barium stearate in a series of steps; the difference in thickness of two adjacent steps corresponded to a double layer of stearate ($\approx 48A$). The slide was coated with 35 up to 55 monolayers of stearate. Monochromatic plane polarized light vibrating perpendicularly to the plane of incidence was reflected at such an angle that two adjacent steps appeared equally dark. If a very thin film of unknown thickness was then deposited on the slide, the angle of incidence had to be increased to maintain equal darkness of the same adjacent steps. From this change in the angle of incidence, it was possible to estimate the thickness of a film. If the unknown film had the thickness of two monolayers of stearate, the angle of incidence remained the same, but equal darkness occurred for the pair of steps directly below the one matched before the deposition of the unknown film, for instance, between 47 and 45 layers instead of 49 and 47. The method, extremely simple, permitted an accuracy of 3 to 4 Å at best, but very often differences as large as 10 Å occurred, when the matching had to be made between two different pairs of steps, before and after the deposition of the film.

[2] I shall always remember the essentially practical laboratory of Langmuir in one of the old buildings of G.E. in Schenectady. Langmuir liked to work with simple apparatus. His genius more than compensated for his primitive tools. Rayleigh also used simple apparatus, and both men made important discoveries. I visualized Blodgett and Langmuir experimenting with a large trough covered with a film of stearic acid and noticing the sudden change in surface tension when a slide was dipped into the trough, as I visualize Rayleigh forty years before, investigating properties of surface films of greasy material on top of the water contained in his porcelain dish, with the same enthusiasm and keen sense of observation displayed by his successors in Schenectady.

[3] I wish to mention here a detail so typical of Langmuir's practical sense. When he and Blodgett started using chromium-plated slides, they bought from the 5 and 10 cent store electrical appliances consisting of rectangular chromium-plated brass sheets with a hole in the middle used to cover ordinary house switches. They sawed pieces, roughly 1 in. × 3 in., with reflecting properties suitable for their optical studies on film transfers. This practical sense reminds one of Millikan's when he made his first apparatus to determine the charge of the electron.

Most of the experiments with films carried out in this country just before 1940 were made by chemists or biologists not especially familiar with the field of optics. Blodgett and Langmuir had shown what could be done with their simple method which could be mastered without difficulty. This is why the work of Drude and his direct successors was ignored in this country, at least for the time being, and why most of the experimenters used the elegant interference method developed by the Schenectady scientists.

At that time, I became very much interested in Langmuir's work and had the good fortune to spend a few days in his laboratory. I wished to pursue some biochemical investigation with surface films, mostly protein films. This involved many measurements of film thickness, and for each measurement by the Langmuir technique it meant the deposition of some 50 odd layers of stearic acid. This was time-consuming. Also, it was desirable to have a method permitting a greater accuracy by one order of magnitude, if possible. Finally, for certain experiments, it was very objectionable to have a large number of stearate films on the slides. Thus, I had to turn my back to the beautifully colored slides of Blodgett and Langmuir as I recalled the experiments of Drude, done at the end of the last century. I had a little more experience in optics than most chemists, having built one of the first polariscopes for the ultraviolet range, and I decided to develop an apparatus according to the fundamental principles of Drude.

Let me summarize the situation with the help of figure 1, in which the plane of the paper is perpendicular to the light beam. A light

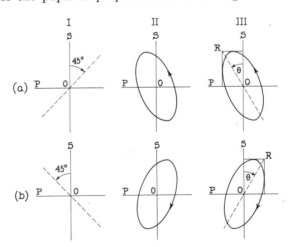

FIGURE 1. *Representation of polarized light before and after reflection.*
I_a and I_b represent the incident plane polarized light in the two positions vibrating at 45° to the plane of incidence. II_a and II_b represent the ellipses obtained after reflection. Their orientation and ellipticity are functions of the angle of incidence and the optical constants of the metal. The two ellipses, II_a and II_b, are symmetrically oriented with respect to the plane of incidence and they have opposite sense of rotation. III_a and III_b show the parameters, θ and R, which are required to analyze the ellipse. (Reproduced from [12].)

beam plane polarized at 45° to the plane of incidence impinges on a metalized slide. (It might be in order at this point to recall that, in optics, following a tradition which goes back to the early part of the nineteenth century, the plane of polarization is perpendicular to the plane of vibration of the electric vector. The radio engineers call the plane of vibration "plane of polarization." Certain authors, in recent articles on ellipsometry have adopted this definition, thus creating unnecessary confusion.) Before reflection, the two components, OP, OS, that is, in the plane of incidence and perpendicular to it, are in phase and of equal magnitude. After reflection, each of them suffers a phase shift (δ^p, δ^s) and the ratio ψ of their amplitudes, which is now equal to tan ψ, is decreased. For most metals at about 70° incidence, the phase shift $\Delta = \delta_p - \delta_s$ is greater than 90°. The light has become elliptically polarized. The ellipticity is defined, contrary to the custom of geometers, as the ratio of minor to major axis. If a film is present on the slide, the orientation of the ellipse and its ellipticity are both changed. Drude's equations correlate the change in ψ and the change in Δ with the film thickness. If the orientation of the ellipse and its ellipticity are known, ψ and Δ are easily calculated, as was shown a hundred years ago by Sénarmont.

One should then analyze the ellipse. By placing, for instance, a $\lambda/4$ plate oriented with its principal directions along the axis of the ellipse, the light becomes again plane polarized. The position of the $\lambda/4$ plate determines the orientation of the ellipse. The reestablished plane polarized light can be extinguished with an analyzer whose position with respect to the axis of the ellipse determines the ellipticity. The only art is to determine accurately the position of the $\lambda/4$ plate and of the analyzer, if the method is to be sensitive. No photomultiplier tubes were available at the time I was investigating the question. Hauschild, in 1920, had used a Savart plate which would tell by the disappearance of interference fringes produced by the plate whether the analyzer was properly oriented. The only difficulty with this method is that one should observe the beam while focusing at infinity. The presence of scratches on the slides disturbed the measurements so much that, for easily scratched slides, the method was useless.

3. Development of Early Ellipsometer

A visual method had to be used which would permit focusing on the slide so that the eye would ignore the scratchy or defective areas of the surface in the same way as the eye focuses on the slide in the Blodgett-Langmuir method. It occurred to me that a halfshade device analogous to the halfshade device of Lippich could be used. In the Lippich polarimeter, the polarizing unit is made up of two nicols so oriented that the field is divided into two half fields, each half field transmitting plane polarized light whose direction of vibration makes a small angle of about 3° with the direction of vibration transmitted by the other half field. Both half fields appear of the

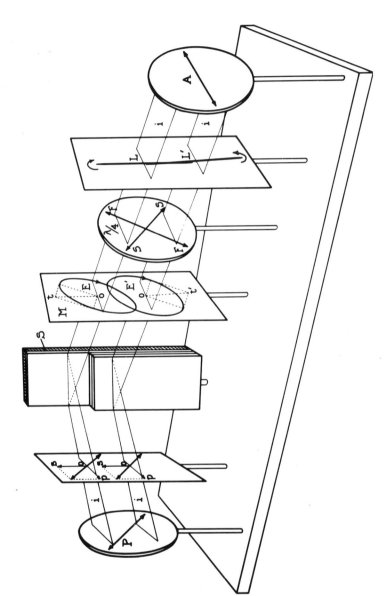

FIGURE 2.   *Schematic representation of the halfshade ellipsometer.*

P is the polarizer, *I*, a plane representing the state of polarization before reflection for two light beams to be reflected, one from the upper part of the slide *S* and the other from the lower part; *M*₁, a plane representing the state of polarization after reflection. λ/4, quarter-wave plate, which changes the two ellipses *E* and *E'* into very elongated ellipses, *L* and *L'*.   *A*₁ is the analyzer.   (Reproduced from [10].)

same intensity when the analyzer bisects the angle made by the directions of vibration transmitted by the components of the polarizer. The idea was to make the halfshade device on the slide itself by depositing, let us say, one monolayer of stearate on the upper part and three monolayers on the lower part of the slide. Then the λ/4 plate would be oriented with its principal directions bisecting the angle made by the axis of the ellipses characterizing the light after reflection from the upper and lower parts respectively.

With the help of Drude's approximate formulas, one can calculate that under such conditions the light, after passage through the λ/4 plate, becomes nearly plane polarized, with an ellipticity of about 0.5°, and that the major axes of these two elongated ellipses, characterizing the light from the upper and lower parts of the slide, make an angle of about 3°, the best angle for a visual halfshade device. The analyzer is placed in the position for which both half fields appear equally illuminated (see fig. 2). When an unknown film is deposited on the slide, the analyzer has to be turned by a certain angle which can be estimated within ±0.01° to reestablish the equality of intensity of the two half fields. The angle of rotation is a measure of the thickness. The simplest way is to correlate angles of rotation versus thickness of known films. The apparatus did work indeed according to these simple theoretical considerations, and the aim to better the interferometric method of Blodgett and Langmuir by one order of magnitude had been achieved. My own original contribution was limited to the halfshade device. The apparatus was described in the Review of Scientific Instruments [10], and I had to give it a name.

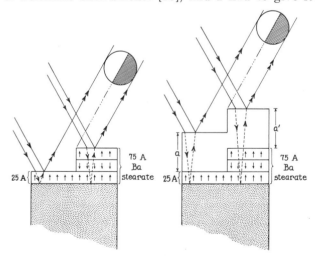

When a=a'   Correct measurement
When a < or > a'   Incorrect measurement

FIGURE 3.   *Measurements of film thickness with the half-shade device.*
Material placed on top of barium stearate indicated by a and a'.

Up to that time, methods for measurements of states of polarization were called polarimetric methods. I could not call the apparatus a polarimeter because it simply was not one according to the chemist's vocabulary. So I hit upon the word "ellipsometer." Thus, in the year 1944, the term "ellipsometer" was born. Apparently, it was a good choice, because the word was adopted and it was a very satisfying feeling for me to find out that the word "ellipsometer" was in the title of this symposium.

There is one point I should like to discuss with the help of figure 3, in connection with the halfshade device. The diagram represents the cross section of a slide upon which one and three monolayers of barium stearate have been deposited stepwise. If the added unknown film or layer formed on top of the two steps is of uniform thickness, then the halfshade method gives a correct measurement. But there are some cases in which this is not so, and whereby the halfshade device yields incorrect results. I shall mention but one example. A few layers of protein are deposited on both steps and heated to 75° C [11]. A thin membrane of formvar is placed on top. The slide is treated with a solution of trypsin for a few minutes, then the membrane is dissolved, and finally a solution of antibodies homologous to the protein film is smeared on the slide. It is found that the protein layers deposited on three layers have not been much inactivated by trypsin and that they can adsorb a thick layer of antibodies, whereas those deposited on one layer of stearate have been completely hydrolyzed and are unable to adsorb an appreciable amount of antibodies, as illustrated in figure 4. This is a very nice illustration of the influence of supposedly inert layers serving as anchorage on the interaction between protein layers and enzymes across a protective membrane. It is one example among many others which shows that chemical reactions taking place at interphases cannot be predicted by our knowledge of chemical reactions taking place in a homogeneous liquid phase. If the Blodgett-Langmuir

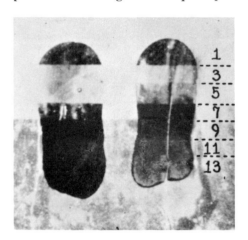

FIGURE 4. *Action of tryspin through a membrane of formvar 70 Å thick on three double layers of protein deposited on 1, 3, 5, 7, 9, 11, and 13 monolayers of barium stearate.*
The protein layers deposited on 3 and 5 monolayers of barium stearate have been very little acted upon by trypsin. (Reproduced from [11], p. 155.)

technique had been used, this most interesting result could not have been observed.

After the end of the war, the photomultiplier tube became available. The tube was substituted for the eye, and the halfshade device became obsolete. The advantage realized by the substitution of the tube for the eye was an increase in the sensitivity of the apparatus by a factor of two. This is easily explained by the following considerations. Using the limiting laws of Drude, it can be shown that a 48 Å thick barium stearate film on chrome brings about a change of 3° in the ellipticity and a rotation of 2.3° in the orientation of the ellipse characterizing the reflected light. With the half shade method, the λ/4 plate remains stationary, and the angle by which the analyzer has to be turned in order to bring back equal intensity of the half fields is about 3°. On the other hand, with a phototube in conjunction with a photometer used as a null instrument, both plate and analyzer can be turned simultaneously to bring back the intensity of the reflected light to a minimum, with the result that the analyzer has to be rotated by $2.3+3=5°$. It means that the optical thickness can be measured within ± 0.1 Å, since, with a good instrument, the position of the analyzer to obtain a minimum intensity of the light can be determined within $\pm 0.01°$. It is important to notice that the compensation of the ellipse has to be done with the proper orientation of the λ/4 plate, the fast direction alined with the retarded axis of the ellipse. If the compensation is done with the slow direction of the plate alined with the retarded axis, a 180° phase shift is introduced. The two angles, 2.3° and 3°, characterizing the change in the ellipse of the reflected light become of opposite sense, and the analyzer has to be turned by their difference, $3°-2.3°=0.7°$, instead of their sum. The method under these conditions is several times less accurate.

4. Measurement

Shortly after the birth of the term "ellipsometer," Vašíček published a long series of articles on the optical properties of thin films. It was his merit to show that the Drude general equation could be developed in a usable form without approximation. He did it in the case of glass reflection, and I did it afterwards for metallic reflection. Not only could Δ be plotted for any film thickness (see fig. 5), but the individual values of δ^p and δ^s, which cannot be determined experimentally, could be calculated as shown in figure 6 [12]. These curves gave an explanation of some observations made earlier by Blodgett and Langmuir when they were experimenting with their interferometric method. In this method the light is polarized either in or perpendicular to the plane of incidence.

The component I^s is used preferably to I^p for two main reasons. The first reason is that, in order to achieve a 180° phase difference between light reflected from the air-film interface and that reflected

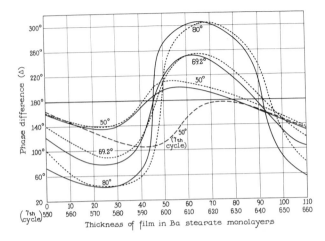

FIGURE 5.   *Phase shift produced by films of barium stearate at 50°, 69.2°, and 80° incidence.*

The dotted curves are theoretical and the solid and dashed lines are experimental.   (Reproduced from [12].)

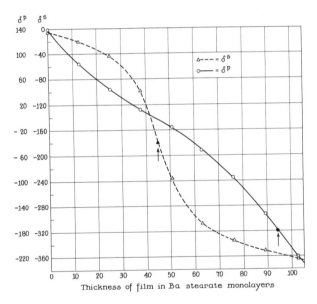

FIGURE 6.   *Absolute phase shift, δ^p, δ^s of each component produced by films of barium stearate at 69.2 incidence.*

(Reproduced from [12].)

from the metal, the necessary number of layers of barium stearate is about 45 layers when I^s is used, in accordance with the relation $n \times 45 \times 24 \cos r = \lambda$. This means that the phase shift for δ^s produced by the bare metal is close to zero at about 75° incidence. On the other hand, there is a phase shift close to 140° for the component δ^p. This phase shift δ^p diminishes with increasing thickness of a film; when the thickness of the film is equal to 45 layers of stearate, δ^p equals zero and reaches the desired 180° when 95 layers of stearate have been deposited on the slide. Thus, if one wishes to measure an unknown film using the I^p component, the optical gage must have twice as many layers as when I^s is utilized.

The second reason for using I^s instead of I^p comes from the fact that Blodgett and Langmuir had observed that measurements with I^s could be made between 68° and 85° incidence, whereas the range of angles of incidence was limited between 77° and 85° when the measurements were made with I^p, on account, said the authors, of lower contrast. The curves of δ^p and δ^s versus thickness shown in figure 6 gave an explanation for this lower contrast. The tangent to the curve for a thickness corresponding to 180° phase shift is a measure of the sensitivity of the method; it measures the contrast mentioned by Blodgett and Langmuir. One can see that the theoretical curves corresponding to δ^p and δ^s have not the same shape and that the

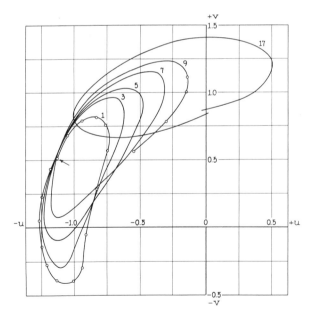

FIGURE 7. *Ellipticity of reflected light at 69.2° incidence, produced by films of barium stearate from 0Å up to 5 wavelengths of light.*

Arrow indicates beginning of first circle. $u + iv = \cot\psi e^{i\Delta}$, $u = \cot\psi \cos\Delta$, $v = \cot\psi \sin\Delta$. (Reproduced from [12].)

tangent at 180° phase shift is much steeper for the component r^s than for r^p. These theoretical considerations explain nicely the observations of Blodgett and Langmuir.

In one way, the method of Blodgett and Langmuir is theoretically simpler than the ellipsometric method which uses both r^s and r^p for a single measurement. If the film is optically equivalent to a uniaxial crystal with its optic axis perpendicular to the surface of the slide, as in the case of barium stearate layers which form a positively bire-fringent crystal, only one index of refraction n_o^s is involved for any angle of incidence when the component r^s is used. In the case of ellipsometric measurements, two indices are involved, n_o^s and n_e^p, the value of n_e^p varying between two extreme values, n_0 and n_1, with $n_0 < n_1$. In the Drude formula, an average n is introduced. Thus, one should not expect the Drude method to be very precise for these films. A second periodicity is introduced due to the birefringence of the film. The birefringence of barium stearate films is $n_e - n_0 = 1.551 - 1.491 = 0.06$. At 50° incidence, the value of n_e is 1.528. One can thus estimate this longer period to be $N \simeq 3800$, N being the number of layers of stearate in the longer period. A plot of the experimental values of ψ and Δ can be seen in figure 7 for films up to 765 monolayers. One cycle corresponds obviously to an optical path of λ. From the rate of precession of each cycle, it can be estimated that the 46th cycle should come close to the first one, as predicted by the preceding formula.

Shortly after the incorporation of the photomultiplier tube in the ellipsometer, Trurnit followed a rate of adsorption by using a recording device. This involved a mixed method; it is partially ellipsometric and partially photometric. At the beginning of the experiment, one compensates partially or completely the ellipse representing the reflected light and measures the increase in the intensity of the reflected light which occurs as the adsorption proceeds, since both the orienta-tion of the ellipse and its ellipticity change. In order to estimate a thickness, a calibration curve has to be prepared with films of known thickness. With a light source that is powerful and stable enough, which is a difficult thing to achieve, the method may become extremely sensitive, and differences in optical thickness much smaller than 0.1 Å can be detected.

I wish to end this review by mentioning two entirely different applications of the ellipsometer.

In 1949, Jackson and Burge [13] in England were able to measure with an ellipsometer the thickness of the creeping film of helium ii which was found, roughly, 150 Å thick.

The second application is the use of the ellipsometer to follow immunological reactions, based on the fact that an antigen deposited on a slide is capable of adsorbing specifically a relatively thick layer of antibodies from a homologous antiserum. This I have shown years ago in the case of systems giving a precipitin reaction [14]. Quite recently, we have taken up the matter again in collaboration with Dr. J. Casals of The Rockefeller Foundation and Mr. Christian

Mathot of our laboratory, for systems which do not give precipitin reactions. The method looks very promising and would be very much faster than either the hemagglutinin test or the complement fixation test, which are commonly used in this field of immunology.

5. References

[1] C. Skinner, J. Opt. Soc. Am. **10,** 491 (1925).
[2] J. Jamin, Ann. Chim. **31,** 165 (1851).
[3] Rayleigh, Phil. Mag. **33,** 1 (1892).
[4] P. Drude, Ann. Physik Chemie **39,** 481 (1890).
[5] H. Hauschild, Ann. Physik Chemie **63,** 816 (1920).
[6] A. Vašíček, Optics of Thin Films, North Holland Publ. Co., Amsterdam (1960).
[7] L. Tronstad, Trans. Faraday Soc. **31,** 1151 (1935).
[8] K. B. Blodgett, J. Am. Chem. Soc. **56,** 495 (1934).
[9] K. B. Blodgett, J. Opt. Soc. Am. **24,** 313 (1934).
[10] A. Rothen, Rev. Sci. Instr. **16,** 26 (1945).
[11] A. Rothen, Physical Chemical Techniques in Biological Research, II, p. 194, Academic Press (1956).
[12] A. Rothen, Ann. N.Y. Acad. Sci. **53,** 1054 (1951).
[13] L. C. Jackson and E. J. Burge, Nature, **164,** 660 (1949).
[14] A. Rothen and K. Landsteiner, J. Exp. Med. **76,** 437 (1942).

2. Theory

Optical Study of a Thin Absorbing Film on a Metal Surface

Antonin Vašíček

Institute of Solid State Physics of J. E. Purkyně University, Brno, Czechoslovakia

The classical theory of the reflection of light from a metal with a thin superficial film was deduced by Drude for very thin films up to about 100 Å. The author deduces from the interference of light in a thin absorbing film the formulae for the reflection of light from a metal with such an absorbing thin film. The formulae fulfill the energy conditions on both boundaries of the absorbing film. The apparatus, the methods of measuring the elliptically polarized light, and some experimental results obtained by this polarimetric method are mentioned.

1. Introduction

The optical studies of a thin superficial film on a metal have recently become a branch of physics, although such problems are not new. As much as 75 years ago Drude examined the influence of a thin superficial film produced on a metal on the measured optical quantities [1].[1] These formulae of Drude's were completed by Tronstad. These formulae of Drude-Tronstad are very often applied, e.g., in the literature about the corrosion of metal, in the following form [2]:

$$\Delta - \bar{\Delta} = -\frac{4\pi d}{\lambda} \frac{(\cos\varphi_0 \sin^2\varphi_0(n_1^2 - n_0^2))}{(\cos^2\varphi_0 - n_0^2 a)^2 + n_0^4 a'^2}\left[(\cos^2\varphi_0 - n_0^2 a)\left(\frac{1}{n_1^2} - a\right) + n_0^2 a'^2\right], \quad (1)$$

$$2\psi - 2\bar{\psi} = \sin 2\bar{\psi}\,\frac{4\pi d}{\lambda}\frac{\cos\varphi_0 \sin^2\varphi_0(n_1^2 - n_0^2)}{(\cos^2\varphi_0 - n_0^2 a)^2 + n_0^4 a'^2}$$

$$\left[n_1^2 a'\left(\frac{1}{n_1^2} - a\right) - (\cos^2\varphi_0 - n_0^2 a)a\right], \quad (1')$$

where $\bar{\psi}$ indicates the azimuth, $\bar{\Delta}$ the phase difference measured on a clean metal surface, ψ and Δ the same quantities measured on a metal with a thin, superficial, transparent (nonabsorbing) film. In the previous formulae, d denotes the thickness of the film, n_1 its refractive index, n_0 the refractive index of the first medium (usually the air having refractive index $n_0 = 1$). These formulae also include the angle of incidence φ_0 of monochromatic light having the wavelength λ. The expressions a, a' are determined by the formulae

---

[1] Figures in brackets indicate the literature references on p. 39.

$$a=\frac{1-\overline{K}^2}{\overline{n}^2(1+\overline{K}^2)},\qquad(2)$$

$$a'=\frac{2\overline{K}}{\overline{n}^2(1+\overline{K}^2)},\qquad(3)$$

where $\overline{n}$, $\overline{K}$ are Drude's optical constants computed for the normal incidence of light. The complex refractive index of a metal can then be written in the form $N=\overline{n}(1-i\overline{K})=\overline{n}-i\overline{k}$.

The formulae (1) and (1′) may be written briefly in the form

$$\Delta-\overline{\Delta}=-Cd,\qquad(4)$$

$$2\psi-2\overline{\psi}=C'd.\qquad(4')$$

It is evident that with increasing thickness of the thin film the measured azimuth increases linearly, but the phase difference decreases linearly. Recently the Drude-Tronstad formulae have been considered as a special case of the more general formulae, being deduced from the interference of light in a thin film. We show later that the validity of Drude's formulae may be assumed up to a thickness of about 100 Å, i.e., for the thinnest film. Drude-Tronstad's formulae are simpler and more convenient for practical calculations of the refractive index and of the thickness of a thin transparent film than more general formulae, which are true for greater film thicknesses, because they are deduced supposing the interference of light in a thin film. In this time of rapid computers this greater complexity of the general formulae is no obstacle to the determination of the corresponding optical quantities.

2. Theory

2.1. The Determination of the Optical Constants of a Clean Metal Surface

When light incident on a plane boundary between two dielectrics (air and glass) is plane polarized, the reflected light is also plane polarized. If a thin superficial film is present on a dielectric, the reflected light is elliptically polarized. In this case it is very easy to decide whether or not a very thin superficial film is present on the surface of dielectric. According to the author, it is possible to determine the refractive index and the thickness of a thin film from the ellipticity of the reflected light by the polarimetric method [3, 4].

A new situation occurs at the reflection of light from a metallic medium, because the reflected light is elliptically polarized. The measure of this ellipticity is the angle γ, determined by the ratio of the two semi-axes of the ellipse according to the relation $\tan \gamma = b/a$. For aluminium, at an angle of incidence of $60°$, this ellipticity angle is about $15°$, for silicon only about $30'$. A thin superficial film on a metal surface changes this ellipticity in a certain way. Therefore the determination of a clean surface of metals (without any superficial film) is more difficult than in the case of dielectrics. We mention this problem again in the experimental part.

According to the author, the optical constants of a clean metal are determined as follows: We start from the relation for the square of the complex refractive index of a metal [5]

$$N^2 = n^2 - k^2 - i2nk \cos \varphi_1 = (\bar{n} - i\bar{k})^2, \qquad (5)$$

where n, k are the optical constants of the metal for the angle of refraction in the metal φ_1, for the angle of incidence φ_0, respectively, $\bar{n}$ and $\bar{k}$ are Drude's optical constants for the normal incidence of light $(\varphi_0 = 0°)$.

Denoting by n_0 the refractive index of the first medium, ψ the azimuth defined by the relation $\tan \psi = \dfrac{r_p}{r_s}$ and $\Delta = \delta_p - \delta_s$ the phase difference, then the refractive index of the metal is calculated from the formula

$$n^2 = n_0^2 \sin^2 \varphi_0 \left[1 + \frac{\tan^2 \varphi_0 \cos^2 2\bar{\psi}}{(1 + \sin 2\bar{\psi} \cos \bar{\Delta})^2} \right] \qquad (6)$$

and the absorption coefficient

$$k = \frac{n_0 \tan \varphi_0 \sin \varphi_0 \sin 2\bar{\psi} \sin \bar{\Delta}}{1 + \sin 2\bar{\psi} \cos \bar{\Delta}}. \qquad (7)$$

The optical constants of the metal depend upon the angle of refraction φ_1 and also on the angle of incidence φ_0, because the light waves propagating in a metal are nonhomogeneous. Therefore it is necessary to calculate these optical constants always for the normal incidence of light according to the formulae

$$\bar{n}^2 = \frac{(A^2 + B^2)^{1/2} + A}{2}, \qquad (8)$$

$$\bar{k}^2 = \frac{(A^2 + B^2)^{1/2} - A}{2}, \qquad (9)$$

$$A = n^2 - k^2 = \bar{n}^2 - \bar{k}^2, \qquad (10)$$

$$B = 2nk \cos \varphi_1 = 2\bar{n}\bar{k}. \qquad (11)$$

The angle of refraction in a metal is determined by the formula

$$\cos^2 \varphi_1 = \frac{n^2 - n_0^2 \sin^2 \varphi_0}{n^2} = \frac{\tan^2 \varphi_0 \cos^2 2\bar{\psi}}{(1 + \sin 2\bar{\psi} \cos \bar{\Delta})^2 + \tan^2 \varphi_0 \cos^2 2\bar{\psi}}. \quad (12)$$

2.2. The Calculation of the Amplitudes r_p, r_s and of phases δ_p, δ_s of Light Reflected on a Metal from n, k, φ_0

For these calculations the starting points are the generalized Fresnel relations

$$r_p e^{i\delta_p} = \frac{\tan(\varphi_0 - \Phi_1)}{\tan(\varphi_0 + \Phi_1)} = \frac{N^2 \cos \varphi_0 - n_0 N \cos \Phi_1}{N^2 \cos \varphi_0 + n_0 N \cos \Phi_1}$$

$$= \frac{N^2 \cos \varphi_0 - n_0(n \cos \varphi_1 - ik)}{N^2 \cos \varphi_0 + n_0(n \cos \varphi_1 - ik)}, \quad (13)$$

$$r_s e^{i\delta_s} = -\frac{\sin(\varphi_0 - \Phi_1)}{\sin(\varphi_0 + \Phi_1)} = \frac{n_0 \cos \varphi_0 - N \cos \Phi_1}{n_0 \cos \varphi_0 + N \cos \Phi_1} = \frac{n_0 \cos \varphi_0 - (n \cos \varphi_1 - ik)}{n_0 \cos \varphi_0 + (n \cos \varphi_1 - ik)}, \quad (14)$$

where we substitute for the complex expression $N \cos \Phi_1$ the relation

$$N \cos \Phi_1 = n \cos \varphi_1 - ik. \quad (15)$$

Direct calculation from the complex amplitude $r_p e^{i\delta_p}$ is very difficult. It is more convenient to calculate the ratio of the two complex amplitudes first

$$r e^{i\bar{\Delta}} = \frac{r_p}{r_s} e^{i(\delta_p - \delta_s)} = -\frac{\cos(\varphi_0 + \Phi_1)}{\cos(\varphi_0 - \Phi_1)} = -\frac{n \cos \varphi_0 \cos \varphi_1 - n_0 \sin^2 \varphi_0 - ik \cos \varphi_0}{n \cos \varphi_0 \cos \varphi_1 + n_0 \sin^2 \varphi_0 - ik \cos \varphi_0} \quad (16)$$

and to determine $r = \tan \bar{\psi} = \dfrac{r_p}{r_s}$ and the phase difference $\bar{\Delta} = \delta_p - \delta_s$.

Snell's law is also valid for the complex quantities in the form

$$n_0 \sin \varphi_0 = N \sin \Phi_1. \quad (17)$$

After the calculations we obtain the following formulae:

$$r_s^2 = \frac{(n_0 \cos \varphi_0 - n \cos \varphi_1)^2 + k^2}{(n_0 \cos \varphi_0 + n \cos \varphi_1)^2 + k^2}, \quad (18)$$

$$r^2 = \frac{(n \cos \varphi_0 \cos \varphi_1 - n_0 \sin^2 \varphi_0)^2 + k^2 \cos^2 \varphi_0}{(n \cos \varphi_0 \cos \varphi_1 + n_0 \sin^2 \varphi_0)^2 + k^2 \cos^2 \varphi_0}, \quad (19)$$

$$r_p = r \cdot r_s, \tag{20}$$

$$\tan \delta_s = \frac{2 n_0 k \cos \varphi_0}{-[n^2 + k^2 - n_0^2]}, \tag{21}$$

$$\tan \bar{\Delta} = \frac{2 n_0 k \sin \varphi_0 \tan \varphi_0}{-[n^2 + k^2 - n_0^2 \tan^2 \varphi_0]}, \tag{22}$$

$$\delta_p = \bar{\Delta} + \delta_s. \tag{23}$$

It is evident that the author does not calculate with Drude's optical constants of a metal $\bar{n}$, $\bar{k}$, but with the optical constants n,k for a certain angle of incidence $\varphi_0 (\varphi_0 \neq 0°)$.

2.3. The Reflection of Light on a Metal With a Weak Absorbing Film

Experience has shown that many oxide films on metals, e.g., oxide films on steel, have weak absorption. Therefore it is necessary to present the theory of the reflection of light from a thin film on a metal in the most general form, i.e., for a thin absorbing film. This theory was published by the author in 1961 [6]. In this case both amplitudes on the boundaries of the absorbing film are complex quantities (fig. 1).

For the reflection of light from a metal with a thin absorbing film, the following formulae are valid:

$$r_p e^{i\delta_p} = \frac{r_p' e^{i\delta_p'} + r_p'' e^{i\delta_p''} e^{-x'} e^{-ix}}{1 + r_p' e^{-i\delta_p'} r_p'' e^{i\delta_p''} e^{-x'} e^{-ix}} = \frac{r_p' e^{i\delta_p'} + r_p'' e^{-x'} e^{-i(x - \delta_p'')}}{1 + r_p' r_p'' e^{-x'} e^{-i(x + \delta_p' - \delta_p'')}}, \tag{24}$$

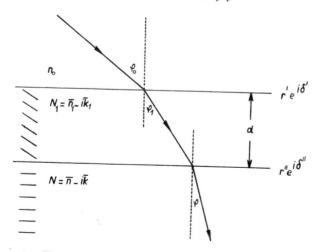

FIGURE 1.   *The reflection of light from a metal with a thin absorbing film.*

$$r_s e^{i\delta s} = \frac{r'_s e^{i\delta'_s} + r''_s e^{-x'} e^{-i(x-\delta''_s)}}{1 + r'_s r''_s e^{-x'} e^{-i(x+\delta'_s-\delta''_s)}}. \tag{24'}$$

The phase difference of the light rays in an absorbing film is the complex expression, which in the previous formulae is divided into two parts:

the real phase difference independent of the absorption

$$x = \frac{2\pi}{\lambda} 2n_1 d \cos \varphi_1 \tag{25}$$

and the imaginary part

$$x' = \frac{2\pi}{\lambda} 2k_1 d \tag{26}$$

being used in the expression

$$e^{-x'} = e^{-\frac{2\pi}{\lambda} 2k_1 d}. \tag{26'}$$

The last expression determines the damping of the amplitude owing to the absorption.

Formulae (24) and (24') can be written in the form

$$r_p e^{i\delta p} = \frac{\alpha_1 + i\beta_1}{\alpha_2 + i\beta_2}, \tag{27}$$

$$r_s e^{i\delta s} = \frac{\alpha_3 + i\beta_3}{\alpha_4 + i\beta_4}. \tag{27'}$$

In the latter expression it is necessary to substitute

$$\left.\begin{array}{l} \alpha_1 = r'_p \cos \delta'_p + r''_p e^{-x'} \cos (x-\delta''_p), \\[4pt] \alpha_2 = 1 + r'_p r''_p e^{-x'} \cos (x+\delta'_p-\delta''_p), \\[4pt] \alpha_3 = r'_s \cos \delta'_s + r''_s e^{-x'} \cos (x-\delta''_s), \\[4pt] \alpha_4 = 1 + r'_s r''_s e^{-x'} \cos (x+\delta'_s-\delta''_s), \\[4pt] \beta_1 = r'_p \sin \delta'_p + r''_p e^{-x'} \sin (x-\delta''_p), \\[4pt] \beta_2 = r'_p r''_p e^{-x'} \sin (x+\delta'_p-\delta''_p), \\[4pt] \beta_3 = r'_s \sin \delta'_s + r''_s e^{-x'} \sin (x-\delta''_s), \\[4pt] \beta_4 = r'_s r''_s e^{-x'} \sin (x+\delta'_s-\delta''_s). \end{array}\right\} \tag{28}$$

Multiplying the formulae (27) and (27') by the complex conjugates $r_p e^{-i\delta p}$ and $r_s e^{-i\delta s}$, we get

$$r_p^2=\frac{\alpha_1^2+\beta_1^2}{\alpha_2^2+\beta_2^2}=\frac{r_p'^2+r_p''^2e^{-2x'}+2r_p'r_p''e^{-x'}\cos\,(x+\delta_p'-\delta_p'')}{1+r_p'^2r_p''^2e^{-2x'}+2r_p'r_p''e^{-x'}\cos\,(x+\delta_p'-\delta_p'')},\qquad(29)$$

$$r_s^2=\frac{\alpha_3^2+\beta_3^2}{\alpha_4^2+\beta_4^2}=\frac{r_s'^2+r_s''^2e^{-2x'}+2r_s'r_s''e^{-x'}\cos\,(x+\delta_s'-\delta_s'')}{1+r_s'^2r_s''^2e^{-2x'}+2r_s'r_s''e^{-x'}\cos\,(x+\delta_s'-\delta_s'')}.\qquad(29')$$

The azimuth ψ, determined by optical measurements, is

$$\tan\psi=\frac{r_p}{r_s}.\qquad(30)$$

The amplitudes r_p and r_s, as the absolute values, are always positive.

Calculating the phase δ_p we introduce the auxiliary angles ξ_p and η_p according to the formulae

$$\tan\xi_p=\frac{\beta_1}{\alpha_1},\qquad\tan\eta_p=\frac{\beta_2}{\alpha_2}.\qquad(31)$$

Similarly, calculating the phase δ_s we introduce the angles ξ_s and η_s by the relations

$$\tan\xi_s=\frac{\beta_3}{\alpha_3},\qquad\tan\eta_s=\frac{\beta_4}{\alpha_4}.\qquad(32)$$

The phases are then

$$\delta_p=\xi_p-\eta_p,\qquad\delta_s=\xi_s-\eta_s,\qquad(33)$$

and the phase difference, as the quantity following from the optical measurements, is finally

$$\Delta=\delta_p-\delta_s=(\xi_p-\xi_s)-(\eta_p-\eta_s).\qquad(34)$$

The amplitudes r_p, r_s and the phases δ_p, δ_s completely determine the optical characteristic of the system—a thin absorbing film on a metal—at the reflection of light.

The author points out that the formulae (24) and (24') differ from Murmann's formulae for light reflected from a thin metallic film. The formulae following from (24) and (24') fulfil the corresponding energy conditions on both boundaries of the absorbing film, but Murmann's formulae fail in the energy conditions [7].

The preliminary calculations require the determination of the phase difference according to the formula (25) and of the expression (26') for the damping of the amplitude. The amplitudes r_p', r_s' and the phases δ_p', δ_s' are calculated from formulae (18) to (23); we merely substitute the quantities n_1, k_1 for n, k.

The amplitudes r_p'', r_s'' and the phases δ_p'', δ_s'' are calculated separately from the supposition that for the thickness of the film $d\rightarrow0$, $x\rightarrow0$, $x'\rightarrow0$, respectively, the reflection of the light is the same as from a clean metal without any superficial film. Then the formulae

(24) and (24′) are simplified as follows:

$$r_{0, p}e^{i\delta_{0, p}} = \frac{r'_p e^{i\delta'_p} + r''_p e^{i\delta''_p}}{1 + r'_p e^{-i\delta'_p} r''_p e^{i\delta''_p}}, \tag{35}$$

$$r_{0, s}e^{i\delta_{0, s}} = \frac{r'_s e^{i\delta'_s} + r''_s e^{i\delta''_s}}{1 + r'_s e^{-i\delta'_s} r''_s e^{i\delta''_s}}. \tag{35'}$$

Because the calculations are the same for both components of light, we calculate the corresponding formulae for one component only; e.g., for the p-component.

From the formula (35) we calculate the complex amplitude $r''_p e^{i\delta''_p}$, as the unknown quantity. We obtain

$$r''_p e^{i\delta''_p} = \frac{r_{0, p}e^{i\delta_{0, p}} - r'_p e^{i\delta'_p}}{1 - r_{0, p}r'^p e^{-i(\delta_{0, p} - \delta'_p)}}. \tag{36}$$

From the last formula we get the final relations

$$r''^2_p = \frac{r^2_{0, p} + r'^2_p - 2r_{0, p}r'_p \cos (\delta_{0, p} - \delta'_p)}{1 + r^2_{0, p}r'^2_p - 2r_{0, p}r'_p \cos (\delta_{0, p} - \delta'_p)}, \tag{37}$$

$$\tan \delta''_p = \frac{r_{0, p} \sin \delta_{0, p} - r'_p(1 + r^2_{0, p}) \sin \delta'_p - r_{0, p}r'^2_p \sin (\delta_{0, p} - 2\delta'_p)}{r_{0, p} \cos \delta_{0, p} - r'_p(1 + r^2_{0, p}) \cos \delta'_p + r_{0, p}r'^2_p \cos (\delta_{0, p} - 2\delta'_p)}. \tag{38}$$

Similar formulae are also written for the s-component.

The amplitudes of the light reflected from a clean metal $r_{0, p}$, $r_{0, s}$ and their phases $\delta_{0, p}$, $\delta_{0, s}$ are given by the formulae (18) to (23). Then all the quantities in the formulae for the reflection of light from a metal with a thin absorbing film are determined.

The reflection of light from metal with a thin absorbing film expresses the most general case, where $k_1 \neq 0$, $k \neq 0$, and therefore $x' \neq 0$, $\delta'_p \neq 0$, $\delta'_s \neq 0$, $\delta''_p \neq 0$, $\delta''_s \neq 0$.

For the reflection of light from metal with a thin dielectric film $k_1 = 0$, $k \neq 0$. Then we have $x' = 0$, $\tan \delta'_p = 0$, $\tan \delta'_s = 0$. The corresponding phases δ'_p and δ'_s are 0 or π. For the phases δ''_p and δ''_s we have $\delta''_p \neq 0$, $\delta''_s \neq 0$.

The simplest case is the reflection of light from a dielectric (glass) with a thin dielectric (transparent) film, where $k_1 = 0$, $k = 0$. Then $x' = 0$, $\tan \delta'_p = \tan \delta'_s = \tan \delta''_p = \tan \delta''_s = 0$, and the corresponding phases δ'_p, δ'_s, δ''_p, δ''_s are 0 or π.

When calculating the Fresnel amplitudes on the boundary between two dielectrics (these amplitudes are real quantities), it is more convenient to start from the formulae for the first boundary

$$r'_p = \frac{\tan (\varphi_0 - \varphi_1)}{\tan (\varphi_0 + \varphi_1)}, \tag{39} \qquad\qquad r'_s = -\frac{\sin (\varphi_0 - \varphi_1)}{\sin (\varphi_0 + \varphi_1)} \tag{39'}$$

and for the second boundary

$$r''_p = \frac{\tan\,(\varphi_1-\varphi)}{\tan\,(\varphi_1+\varphi)},\tag{40}$$

$$r''_s = -\frac{\sin\,(\varphi_1-\varphi)}{\sin\,(\varphi_1+\varphi)}.\tag{40'}$$

We obtain the amplitudes with positive or negative sign. The positive amplitude means the phase 0 or 2π; the negative amplitude is actually the positive amplitude with phase π according to the relation $re^{\pm i\pi} = -r$.

3. Experiment

3.1. Apparatus for Measurement of Elliptically Polarized Light

When studying reflection in polarized light we use the polarization spectrometer, which is also called an ellipsometer. Measurements with this apparatus have been made by the author since 1937. It is a spectrometer furnished with polarization equipment—polarizer, analyzer, and compensators. One compensator is placed on the side of the polarizer, the other on the side of the analyzer. The schematic arrangement of this apparatus is seen in figure 2. The third compensator is not necessary. Sénarmont's compensators (quarter-wave mica plates) are used. The author's measurements were made in half-shade using Nakamura's double-plate placed in front of the analyzer. The subjective measurements by this half-shade method are more sensitive than the original arrangement in the dark field of a telescope. Using a detector photocell or photomultiplier tube, we come back to the original arrangement, because these measurements can be made with very high exactness without the half-shade arrangement.

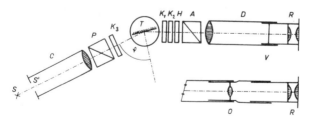

Figure 2. *Schematic diagram of the polarization spectrometer:*

S—source of monochromatic light, S^1—slit; C—collimator; P—polarizer; T—rotating table; K_1, K_2, K_3—compensators; D—Nakamura's double-plate; A—analyzer; D—telescope, (a) R—eyepiece for measurements in a dark field, (b)—telescope O with eyepiece R for measurements in half-shade.

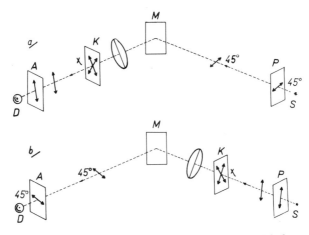

FIGURE 3.   *Measurement of elliptically polarized light.*

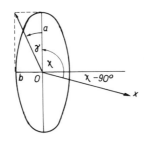

FIGURE 4.   *Measurement of the optical quantities χ and γ.*

The axis x is the plane of incidence.

The measurements of the elliptically polarized light can be made in two ways:

(a) From the polarizer the parallel rays of the plane polarized light are incident on the metallic mirror. The polarizer is set at 45° (fig. 3a). The light reflected from a metallic mirror is elliptically polarized. We rotate the compensator circle on the side of the analyzer and the analyzer, until we get the smallest intensity of the reflected light. The vibration direction of the compensator determines the angle χ between the great semi-axis of the ellipse and the plane of incidence. The difference between the position of the compensator and the analyzer gives the ellipticity angle γ, where $\tan \gamma = \dfrac{b}{a}$ (fig. 4). This measurement can be made in other ways, where the analyzer is set at 45° and we rotate the polarizer and the compensator on the side of the analyzer, until the detector gives the minimum of the reflected light (fig. 3b). The roles of the analyzer and polarizer are changed.

Because the azimuth ψ and the phase difference Δ are deduced from the theoretical formulae, but with the optical methods the angles χ and γ are measured, we perform the calculations according to the formulae.

$$\cos 2\psi = \cos 2\gamma \cos 2\chi, \tag{41}$$

$$\tan \Delta = \frac{\tan 2\gamma}{\sin 2\chi} \tag{42}$$

and reciprocally

$$\tan 2\chi = \tan 2\psi \cos \Delta, \tag{43}$$

$$\sin 2\gamma = \sin 2\psi \sin \Delta. \tag{44}$$

(b) The second way of measuring elliptically polarized light is described by Archer [8, 9]. With this method the compensator (on the side of the analyzer or on the side of the polarizer) is set so that the direction of the fast vibration is at 45°. If we consider the compensator placed on the side of the analyzer (fig. 5a), then we rotate the polarizer and analyzer until we obtain the minimum of the reflected light. The corresponding position of the polarizer is indicated by P and the corresponding position of the analyzer is indicated by A. Then we set the compensator (the direction of the fast vibration) at 135°. The corresponding position of the analyzer at the minimum of the reflected light is A'. For the calculations Archer and Winterbottom [10] give the following formulae

$$\tan^2 \psi = \tan A \tan A', \tag{45}$$
$$\tan \psi = \cot L \tan A = \tan L \tan A', \tag{46}$$
$$\cos 2 L = -\cos t \, \epsilon \cos 2 P, \tag{47}$$
$$\tan \Delta = \sin \epsilon \cot 2P, \tag{48}$$

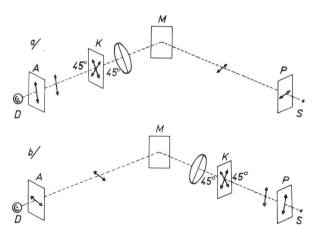

FIGURE 5. *Archer's method for the measurement of ellipti-cally polarized light.*

where ϵ indicates the relative retardation of the quarter-wave mica plate. For the chosen wavelength, this relative retardation is exactly $\frac{\lambda}{4}$ or $\frac{\pi}{2}$. Archer's method not only enables one to check exactness of this supposition, but also permits the application of the quarter-wave plate for other wavelengths, because the previous formulae allow a different relative retardation than $\frac{\pi}{2}$ to be taken into account. This fact is very important for Archer's method.

Similarly, Archer's method can be used in the second arrangement (fig. 5b), where the compensator placed on the side of the polarizer is set at 45° and 135°, respectively. The roles of the polarizer and and analyzer are again changed.

3.2. Measurements and Results

In our institute this polarimetric method is used to study thin transparent oxide films on aluminium and on the monocrystal plates of germanium and silicon (Sládková) [11] and thin absorbing oxide films on steel (Růžička). The most difficult problem is the determination of the optical constants of the clean metal surface. This problem is relatively simple when studying metallic mirrors evaporated in vacuo, where the measurements are made immediately after the production of these metallic mirrors. In this case it is possible to neglect the thicknesses of the thinnest natural oxide films. With the measured samples which are mechanically polished, e.g., steel, the determination of the clean metal surface is more difficult. This problem is especially difficult with semiconductors, where etching by various convenient agents is recommended. We took the cleanest metal surface to be one giving minimum value of the measured azimuth ψ and maximum value of the phase difference Δ.

The difficult and lengthy calculations of the corresponding tables (usually for angle of incidence 50° or 60°) are performed by rapid computers. The refractive index of the first medium (air) is practically $n_0 = 1$. In these calculations it is necessary to know the optical constants of the clean metal surface $N = \bar{n} - i\bar{k}$. The optical constants of the film $N_1 = \bar{n}_1 - i\,\bar{k}_1$ are chosen according to the values of the bulk material (e.g., for oxide films on steel according to hematite) or according to known values of the oxides. For example, when calculating the oxide film on silicon we take the values $n_1 = 1.40$, 1.45, 1.50, 1.55. The tables are calculated as a function of the thickness d of the measured film and the phase difference x of the light rays in the film. Figures 6 and 7 are examples of these calculations for the oxide film Al_2O_3 on aluminium having $n_1 = 1.635$, according to the author's measurements.

Because the film is nonabsorbing, these curves are periodically repeated, increasing the thickness d and the phase difference x, respectively. From the graphs in figures 6 and 7, it is evident that the initial part of these curves may be taken as linear up to thicknesses

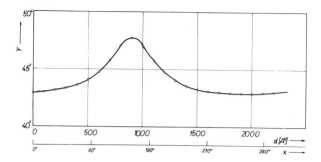

FIGURE 6. *The dependence of the azimuth ψ on the thickness* d *and on* x, *respectively, of thin* Al_2O_3 *film produced on aluminium.*

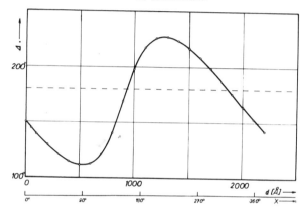

FIGURE 7. *The dependence of the phase difference Δ on the thickness* d *and on* x, *respectively, of thin* Al_2O_3 *film produced on aluminium.*

of about 100 Å in accordance with Drude's theory. According to Winterbottom, it is very useful to plot the polar curve for the film in question. The polar curve combines the two graphs (figs. 6 and 7) into one. For the transparent film, the polar curve in figure 8 is closed. Archer plots these curves in the orthogonal system ψ, Δ [9].

When calculating the optical constants of an absorbing film on a metal, the determination of the optical constants of such a film is very complicated because the number of various possible combinations of n_1 and k_1 increases. Owing to the damping of the amplitude of light in the absorbing film, the curves of the dependence ψ and Δ on the thickness d or on x are no longer periodical; they are damped to a greater or lesser degree according to the value of the absorption coefficient k_1. With increasing thickness of the film, the values ψ, Δ approach the constant values which correspond to the optical constants of the same material as the film. We can suppose that in the case of the reflection of light from a metal with a thin absorbing

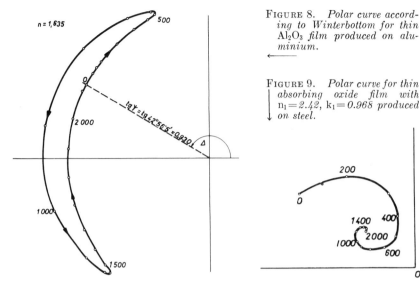

FigURE 8.   *Polar curve according to Winterbottom for thin Al₂O₃ film produced on aluminium.*

FigURE 9.   *Polar curve for thin absorbing oxide film with* $n_1 = 2.42$, $k_1 = 0.968$ *produced on steel.*

film we have few equations for the determination of the optical constants n_1 and k_1 of the film and its thickness d, and that it is necessary to determine the thickness of the measured film by another method (e.g., by the interferometric method). Because these measurements are made at various thicknesses of the film (not for one case), it is possible to determine the third unknown quantity, e.g., from the damping of the curves. In the case of the reflection of light from a metal with a thin absorbing film, Winterbottom's curves are not closed, but create spirals, which are closed the more rapidly, the greater is the absorption coefficient k_1. An example of such a spiral is shown in figure 9 according to Růžička for an oxide film with $n_1 = 2.42$, $k_1 = 0.968$ on steel.

4. Conclusion

Polarimetric measurements for the study of a thin oxide film on metals have many advantages, but they also have some disadvantages. First, it is very difficult to obtain a polished clean metal surface having the necessary optical qualities. The polarimetric measurements are also difficult, and it is also difficult to prepare the tables and evaluate the measured results from these tables. The polarimetric method can be applied as long as the surface of the sample at the production of the film reflects light. The polarimetric method enables one to determine the optical constants and the thickness of the film with great accuracy, especially for the thinnest films, where other methods fail. Recently the microbalance method was elaborated, enabling the study of the continuous increase of oxide films on metal by heating [12]. The polarimetric method will certainly retain its importance in physical and technical practice.

5. References

[1] P. Drude, Wiedeman Ann. Phys. **36,** 884, 886 (1889).
[2] U.R. Evans, Korrosion, Passivität und Oberflächenschutz, p. 715, Berlin (1939).
[3] A. Vašíček, Phys. Rev. **57,** 925 (1940).
[4] A. Vašíček, J. Opt. Soc. Am. **37,** 145 (1947).
[5] A. Vašíček, Optics of Thin Films, p. 288, Amsterdam (1960).
[6] A. Vašíček, Opt. Spectry. **11,** 128 (1961).
[7] A. Vašíček, Optik **19,** 584 (1962); **20,** 225 (1963).
[8] R. J. Archer, Phys. Rev. **110,** 354 (1958).
[9] R. J. Archer, J. Opt. Soc. Am. **52,** 970 (1962).
[10] A. B. Winterbottom, Optical Studies of Metal Surfaces, pp. 44, 57, Trondheim (1955).
[11] J. Sladkova, Czech. J. Phys. **B13,** 452 (1963).
[12] E. A. Gulbransen and K. F. Andrew, J. Electrochem Soc. **109,** 560 (1962).

Optical Properties of Inhomogeneous Films

F. Abelès

Faculté des Sciences and Institut d'Optique, Paris

The inhomogeneous films investigated in this article have a refractive index n which is a function of the single coordinate z, the axis Oz having the direction of the normal to the planes which limit the layer. The discussion is limited to non-absorbing films, although mention is made of the possibilities of using the same methods for absorbing layers. Three different methods of computation are described: (a) use of the differential wave equation; (b) WKB approximation; (c) replacement of an inhomogeneous layer by a pile of homogeneous films. A numerical example is discussed, which corresponds to a refractive index of the inhomogeneous layer given by $n = n_i \exp{(\alpha z)}$. Exact solutions are given in terms of Bessel functions and they are compared with approximate solutions. Drude's equations, valid for very thin films, are not discussed in this article.

1. Introduction

The aim of this review article is to give some information concerning the computation methods which can be used when discussing the optical properties of inhomogeneous films. Such films may be encountered quite often in physico-chemical investigations, and it may be useful to have some indications concerning their properties. We are dealing mainly with nonabsorbing films, which are such that their refractive index is a function of the coordinate z only, the direction Oz being that of the normal to the planes which limit the film. We do not discuss anisotropic films, because it would take us too far and because the mathematical investigation of this problem is only in its infancy. In fact, an inhomogeneous and isotropic film can be rather complicated in its optical properties and we do not have yet any means by which to make sure that such a film is anisotropic, at least if its anisotropy cannot already be detected by measurements in normal incidence.

We shall discuss three different methods of computation. Two of them, the use of the differential equation and the replacement of the inhomogeneous layer by a number of homogeneous layers, are quite general, which means that they can be employed in any circumstance. The third method, which is an adaptation of the well-known WKB method for the solution of second-order differential equations, can be used only when the refractive index of the film is a slowly varying function of z. We have omitted from our discussion the famous Drude equations, which are valid only when dealing with films which are very thin with respect to the wavelength of the incident light. These generally have a very rapidly varying refractive index, so that they represent the case which is the opposite of the WKB films.

It should be pointed out that the different methods described below are not specific to ellipsometry, because they enable the computation of the reflected complex amplitudes separately for the s- and the p-polarizations. We think that they are convenient, as they distinguish the quantities which concern the inhomogeneous film from those which pertain to its substrate. A modification of the substrate is easily taken into account. On the other hand, if photometric measurements are used in order to supplement the ellipsometric measurements, their results could be readily interpreted.

2. Definitions and Notations

The thin film is bounded by the planes $z=0$ and $z=d$. It is comprised between two semi-infinite media, the refractive indices of which are n_0 (for $z<0$) and n_s (for $z>d$). Light is incident on the plane $z=0$ and we shall generally have $n_0=1$, although it is possible to examine thin inhomogeneous films embedded in other media (for instance, fluids). The refractive index of the film under study, $\tilde{n}(z)$, is a complex function of z, which means that it can be absorbing. In fact, we shall discuss mainly the properties of nonabsorbing films. But the considerations which lead us to the differential equations satisfied by the function $U(z)$ (see below, eqs (4) and (8)) are valid even if the inhomogeneous layer is absorbing and so are the expressions for the reflected amplitudes (eqs (17) and (22)). It is convenient to use the dielectric constant of the film, $\epsilon(z)=\tilde{n}^2(z)$. The refractive index of the substrate, n_s, may be complex, a situation which occurs whenever it is metallic or, more generally, absorbing.

The law of refraction will be written

$$n_0 \sin \phi_0 = n_s \sin \phi_s = S$$

and it is valid even if n_s is a complex number. Here ϕ_0 is the angle of incidence and ϕ_s is the angle of refraction (a complex quantity, when n_s is complex).

3. Fields in the Layer

In the layer, the fields verify a wave equation which is a direct consequence of Maxwell's equations. Let us discuss first the s *vibration*. We shall choose the xoy coordinates in such a way as to have $\vec{E}=(E_x, 0, 0)$, which means that the plane yoz is the plane of incidence. We are looking for solutions of Maxwell's equations which are

$$E_x=U(z) \exp (i(\omega t -kSy)) \tag{1}$$

$$H_y=V(z) \exp (i(\omega t -kSy)). \tag{2}$$

We have used the notation $k=2\pi/\lambda$, λ being the wavelength of the incident light in vacuo. If, for the sake of symmetry, we imagine that our layer has a magnetic permittivity μ which is a function of z, it may be shown that

$$V(z) = \frac{i}{k\mu} \frac{dU}{dz} \qquad (3)$$

and U verifies the second-order differential equation (wave equation):

$$\frac{d^2U}{dz^2} - \frac{d \log \mu}{dz} \frac{dU}{dz} + k^2(\epsilon\mu - S^2)U = 0. \qquad (4)$$

The equations for the p *vibration* may be deduced from eqs (3) and (4) by the simultaneous interchanges of μ and ϵ and of $\vec{E}$ and $-\vec{H}$. This signifies that if $\vec{H} = (H_x, 0, 0)$, then we may set

$$H_x = U(z) \exp (i(\omega t - kSy)) \qquad (5)$$

$$E_y = -V(z) \exp (i(\omega t - kSy)) \qquad (6)$$

and now

$$V = \frac{i}{k\epsilon} \frac{dU}{dz} \qquad (7)$$

$$\frac{d^2U}{dz^2} - \frac{d \log \epsilon}{dz} \frac{dU}{dz} + k^2(\epsilon\mu - S^2)U = 0. \qquad (8)$$

We shall suppose throughout all the following that $\mu = 1$. The point in using a $\mu(z)$ was only to better show the symmetry of our wave equations for U ((4) and (8)). When $\mu = 1$, this symmetry is lost and (4) becomes

$$\frac{d^2U}{dz^2} + k^2(\epsilon - S^2)U = 0. \qquad (9)$$

4. The Reflected and Transmitted Amplitudes

Let $U_1(z)$ and $U_2(z)$ be two arbitrary solutions of the wave equation, and let us discuss first the s polarization, maintaining for the moment $\mu(z) \neq 0$. The general integrals of (3) and (4) are

$$U = aU_1(z) + bU_2(z), \qquad (10)$$

$$V = \frac{i}{k\mu(z)} (aU_1'(z) + bU_2'(z)), \qquad (11)$$

a and b being two arbitrary constants, which must be chosen in order to satisfy the boundary conditions. On the plane $z = 0$, we must have

$$E_0 = aU_1(0) + bU_2(0), \qquad (12)$$

$$H_0 = \frac{i}{k\mu(0)}(aU_1'(0) + bU_2'(0)), \tag{13}$$

E_0 and H_0 being the tangential components of the fields in the first medium on the plane $z=0$. The eqs (12) and (13) may be written in matrix notation

$$\begin{bmatrix} E_0 \\ H_0 \end{bmatrix} = \begin{bmatrix} U_1(0) & U_2(0) \\ \dfrac{iU_1'(0)}{k\mu(0)} & \dfrac{iU_2'(0)}{k\mu(0)} \end{bmatrix} \begin{bmatrix} a \\ b \end{bmatrix} = [\mathfrak{M}(0)] \begin{bmatrix} a \\ b \end{bmatrix}. \tag{14}$$

In the same way, the boundary conditions on the plane $z=d$ are

$$\begin{bmatrix} E_t \\ H_t \end{bmatrix} = [\mathfrak{M}(d)] \begin{bmatrix} a \\ b \end{bmatrix}, \tag{15}$$

E_t and H_t being the tangential components of the fields in the substrate on the plane $z=d$.

Combining (14) and (15), we may write

$$\begin{bmatrix} E_0 \\ H_0 \end{bmatrix} = [\mathfrak{M}(0)] \, [\mathfrak{M}(d)]^{-1} \begin{bmatrix} E_t \\ H_t \end{bmatrix} = [M] \begin{bmatrix} E_t \\ H_t \end{bmatrix}. \tag{16}$$

This shows that an inhomogeneous film may be characterized by a two-by-two matrix, like a homogeneous one. The advantage of this representation is that the complex reflected and transmitted (if it exists) amplitudes will have exactly the same expression as for a homogeneous film, namely

$$r_s = \rho_s \exp(i\delta_{rs}) = \frac{Y_0(m_{11} + Y_s m_{12}) - (m_{21} + Y_s m_{22})}{Y_0(m_{11} + Y_s m_{12}) + (m_{21} + Y_s m_{22})} \tag{17}$$

$$t_s = \tau_s \exp(i\delta_{ts}) = \frac{2Y_0}{Y_0(m_{11} + Y_s m_{12}) + (m_{21} + Y_s m_{22})}, \tag{18}$$

where $[M] = [m_{ij}](i, j=1, 2)$, $Y_0 = n_0 \cos\phi_0$, $Y_s = n_s \cos\phi_s$. For an absorbing substrate, Y_s is computed by using the following relation, which is a consequence of the law of refraction

$$Y_s^2 = n_s^2 - S^2.$$

The m_{ij} can be expressed by using the two functions U_1 and U_2. It is found that:

$$\Delta_s m_{11} = \frac{i}{k\mu(d)}(U_1(0)U_2'(d) - U_2(0)U_1'(d))$$

$$\Delta_s m_{12} = U_1(d)U_2(0) - U_1(0)U_2(d)$$

$$\Delta_s m_{21} = \frac{1}{k^2\mu(0)\mu(d)} \left(U_1'(d)U_2'(0) - U_1'(0)U_2'(d)\right)$$

$$\Delta_s m_{22} = \frac{i}{k\mu(0)} \left(U_1(d)U_2'(0) - U_1'(0)U_2(d)\right) \tag{19}$$

with

$$\Delta_s = \frac{i}{k\mu(z)} \left(U_1(z)U_2'(z) - U_1'(z)U_2(z)\right) = \text{constant}.$$

The value of Δ_s may be obtained by replacing z either by zero or by d, as it is a constant, independent of z. In fact, eq (17) is a homogeneous expression in the m_{ij}, so that it is unnecessary to calculate Δ_s when we are interested in the reflected (complex) amplitude only.

The value of the determinant of the matrix $[M]$ is unity, which means that

$$m_{11}m_{22} - m_{12}m_{21} = 1.$$

If we use $\Delta_s m_{11}, \ldots$ instead of m_{11}, the value of the determinant will be

$$\Delta_s^2 (m_{11}m_{22} - m_{12}m_{21}) = \Delta_s^2.$$

All that has been said concerning s-polarization may be immediately transposed to p-polarization. It should be borne in mind the fact that $[M]$ is connecting now

$$\begin{bmatrix} H_0 \\ E_0 \end{bmatrix} \text{ to } \begin{bmatrix} H_t \\ E_t \end{bmatrix},$$

contrarily to the previous situation. So, let us write

$$\begin{bmatrix} H_0 \\ E_0 \end{bmatrix} = [M] \begin{bmatrix} H_t \\ E_t \end{bmatrix}. \tag{20}$$

Then, it is easily seen that

$$\begin{bmatrix} E_0 \\ H_0 \end{bmatrix} = [N] \begin{bmatrix} E_t \\ H_t \end{bmatrix} \tag{21}$$

where $[N] = [n_{ij}] (i, j = 1, 2)$ and $n_{ij} = m_{ji}$ for $i \neq j$ and $n_{11} = m_{22}$, $n_{22} = m_{11}$.

Taking this into account, it can be shown that the reflected and the transmitted (if it exists) amplitudes are given by the following expressions

$$r_p = \rho_p \exp{(i\delta_{rp})} = \frac{-Z_0(n_{11}+Z_s n_{12})+n_{21}+Z_s n_{22}}{Z_0(n_{11}+Z_s n_{12})+n_{21}+Z_s n_{22}} \qquad (22)$$

$$t_p = \tau_p \exp{(i\delta_{tp})} = \frac{2n_0/\cos{\phi_s}}{Z_0(n_{11}+Z_s n_{12})+n_{21}+Z_s n_{22}}. \qquad (23)$$

We have used the following notations: $Z_0 = n_0/\cos{\phi_0}$, $Z_s = n_s/\cos{\phi_s}$. Z_s can be computed, when n_s is a complex quantity, by using the following relation: $Z_s = n_s^2/(n_s \cos{\phi_s})$, as $n_s \cos{\phi_s}$ has already been computed when studying the s-vibration. It is assumed that, in our case, the n_{ij} have been written in terms of U functions which are solutions of eq (8).

Although not indispensable for ellipsometry, we may remind the reader of the fact that the reflectance and transmittance (intensities) are given by

$$R_s = \rho_s^2, \ R_p = \rho_p^2, \ T_s = \frac{Y_s}{Y_0}\tau_s^2, \ T_p = \frac{Y_s}{Y_0}\tau_p^2.$$

The quantities which are measured by ellipsometry are ψ and Δ, defined by

$$(\tan{\psi}) \exp{(i\Delta)} = \frac{r_p}{r_s} = \frac{\rho_p}{\rho_s}\exp{i(\delta_{rp}-\delta_{rs})}. \qquad (24)$$

5. A Special Inhomogeneous Layer

We shall use now the general method outlined in the preceding paragraph, in order to solve a particular problem. We shall suppose that the refractive index of the inhomogeneous film has an exponential dependence on the z coordinate. More precisely, its real refractive index can be written

$$n = n_i e^{\alpha z}, \qquad (25)$$

n_i and α being two parameters. It should be remembered that n_i is the refractive index at the "entrance" of the layer, whereas α is related to its thickness d by the following relation

$$\alpha d = \log{\frac{n_1}{n_i}}, \qquad (26)$$

n_1 being the refractive index at the "exit" from the layer.

5.1. s-Polarization

The use of the new variable

$$u = k \int n dz = kn/\alpha \qquad (27)$$

transforms the wave equation (9) into the classical equation for the Bessel functions

$$\frac{d^2U}{du^2} - \frac{1}{u}\frac{dU}{du} + \left(1 - \frac{k^2S^2}{\alpha^2u^2}\right)U = 0 \cdot \tag{28}$$

Thus, by using the optical thickness for normal incidence on the layer as a new variable, we can write

$$U(z) = aJ_m(u) + bY_m(u), \tag{29}$$

J_m and Y_m being Bessel functions of the first and second kind of the variable u and of order m. We use the following notation:

$$m = kdS/\log(n_1/n_i) = kS/\alpha, \tag{30}$$

which shows that we are dealing with Bessel functions, the order m of which is a function of the angle of incidence, whereas the variable u is independent of it.

The matrix elements are

$$m_{11} = n_1(J_m(u_0)Y'_m(u_1) - Y_m(u_0)J'_m(u_1))$$

$$-im_{12} = J_m(u_0)Y_m(u_1) - J_m(u_1)Y_m(u_0)$$

$$-im_{21} = n_in_1(J'_m(u_0)Y'_m(u_1) - Y'_m(u_0)J'_m(u_1))$$

$$m_{22} = n_1(J_m(u_1)Y'_m(u_0) - J'_m(u_0)Y_m(u_1))$$

with $u_0 = kn_i/\alpha$ and $u_1 = kn_1/\alpha$.

5.2. p-Polarization

It is convenient now to use not only a change of variable but a change of function too. We shall set $U = nZ$, which is quite natural, because U is now that part of the amplitude of the magnetic vector H in the film which is a function of z, and we know that $|H| = n|E|$. The new variable will be again u, which was defined by (27). It can be shown that Z verifies the following differential equation

$$\frac{d^2Z}{du^2} + \frac{1}{u}\frac{dZ}{du} + \left(1 - \frac{1 + (kS/\alpha)^2}{u^2}\right)Z = 0, \tag{31}$$

the solutions of which are again Bessel functions of the variable u, but of order $q = (1 + m^2)^{1/2}$.

Then

$$U = n(aJ_q(u) + bY_q(u)), \tag{32}$$

where the order q of the Bessel functions is again variable with the

angle of incidence, like m previously.
The matrix elements are

$$m_{11} = n_i \left\{ J_q(u_0) \left(\frac{Y_q(u_1)}{u_1} + Y'_q(u_1) \right) - Y_q(u_0) \left(\frac{J_q(u_1)}{u_1} + J'_q(u_1) \right) \right\}$$

$$im_{12} = n_i n_1 (Y_q(u_0) J_q(u_1) - J_q(u_0) Y_q(u_1))$$

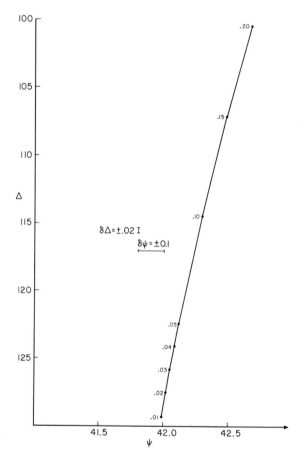

FIGURE 1 (a and b). Δ versus ψ for a thin inhomogeneous layer on a substrate with refractive index $\tilde{n}_s = 0.8 - 5.51$.

Refractive index of the layer $n(z) = 1.38 \exp(\alpha z)$. The thickness of the layer is d, and $n(d) = 2.45$. The numbers close to the curves indicate the values of $\eta = 2\pi d/\lambda$. $\delta\psi = \pm 0.1°$ and $\delta\Delta = \pm 0.2°$ are estimated limits of experimental errors.   Angle of incidence: $\phi_0 = 70°$.

$$im_{21} = \left(\frac{Y_q(u_0)}{u_0} + Y'_q(u_0) \right) \left(\frac{J_q(u_1)}{u_1} + J'_q(u_1) \right)$$

$$- \left(\frac{J_q(u_0)}{u_0} + J'_q(u_0) \right) \left(\frac{Y_q(u_1)}{u_1} + Y'_q(u_1) \right)$$

$$m_{22} = n_1 \left\{ J_q(u_1) \left(\frac{Y_q(u_0)}{u_0} + Y'_q(u_0) \right) - Y_q(u_1) \left(\frac{J_q(u_0)}{u_0} + J'_q(u_0) \right) \right\}$$

u_0 and u_1 having the same signification as for the s-vibration.

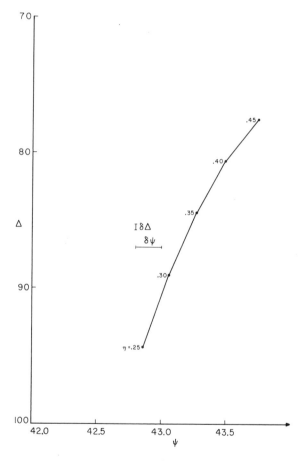

FIGURE 1—Continued.

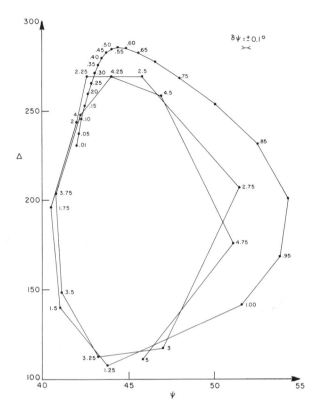

FIGURE 2.   *Same as figure 1, but for η varying from 0.01 to 5.*

The straight segments represent interpolations between computed points. δΔ is too small to be drawn.

5.3. Numerical Results

The Bessel functions are available in the IBM library, and our problem was programmed on a 7094 IBM computer. We shall give here some of the results which were obtained for a film having the following characteristics: $n_i=1.38$, $n_1=2.45$, deposited on a substrate which is characterized by $\tilde{n}_s=0.8-i5.5$.

We examine a situation where the two extreme values of n are always the same, the thickness of the film being one of the variables. In fact, it is more convenient to have a variable without dimensions and, therefore, our variable will be $\eta=2\pi d/\lambda$. If $\lambda=5460$ A (green mercury line), $d=870\eta$ Å. Figure 1 shows Δ versus ψ, when $\varphi=70°$, for very thin films ($\eta\leq0.20$, $d\leq174$ Å). If the experimental errors are $\pm0.2°$ for Δ and $\pm0.1°$ for ψ, it may be seen that only Δ is measured with sufficient accuracy for most purposes. To a change of

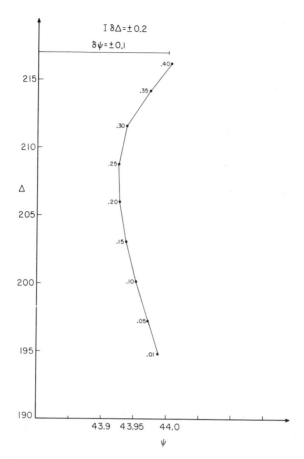

FIGURE 3.   *Same as figure 1, but for different angle of incidence,*
$\phi_0 = 45°$

$0.2°$ in ψ corresponds a change of about 0.05 in η, i.e., 45 Å in thickness if $\lambda = 5460$ Å.   For thicker films, the situation is much better, as it can be seen from figure 2.   For instance, when $\eta = 0.75$ $(d = 650$ Å for $\lambda = 5460$ Å), a change in ψ of $\delta\psi = 0.2°$ corresponds to $\delta\eta = 0.005$ $(\delta d = 4.5$ Å for the same wavelength).   The accuracy on Δ is always higher.   When $\eta = 0.75$, $\delta\Delta = 0.4°$ corresponds to $\delta\eta = 0.0014$ $(\delta d = 1.5$ Å for $\lambda = 5460$ Å).

We have chosen a relatively large angle of incidence ϕ_0, because the accuracy is higher.   Figure 3 shows the results obtained for $\phi_0 = 45°$.

It may be seen that the variation in ψ is less than 0.1 for $0 \leq \eta \leq 0.4$. This confirms the fact that small angles of incidence are less sensitive to the influence of a surface layer than large ones.   On the other hand, we have a variation of $3°$ in Δ when η changes by 0.05, at least for

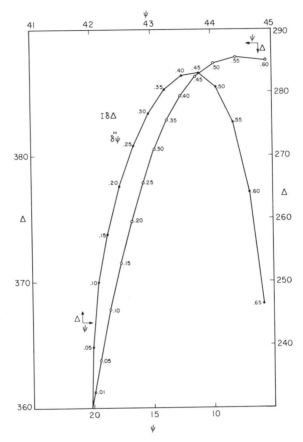

FIGURE 4. Δ versus ψ curves for the same inhomogeneous layer as previously deposited on two different substrates.

For a film on metallic substrate ($\tilde{n}_s=0.8-5.5i$); for a film on glass ($n_s=1.52$). The angle of incidence is $\phi_0=70°$. Note the different scales for the two curves.

small values of η. Again we see here that Δ is a rapidly varying function of η, so that we find the generally well-known result stating that the variation in thickness of a layer is reflected by a change of Δ.

One might ask if it is better to have the thin layer deposited on metal or on glass. In our case, and for an angle of incidence $\phi_0=70°$, we have $\partial\psi/\partial\eta=3.2°$ for very small η and a refractive index of the substrate which is either $\tilde{n}_s=0.8-i5.5$ or $n_s=1.52$. In the first instance, the substrate is an aluminum mirror, whereas $n_s=1.52$ corresponds to a glass substrate. Concerning the variation of Δ, we find $\partial\Delta/\partial\eta=175°$ for $\tilde{n}_s=0.8-5.5i$ and $\partial\Delta/\partial\eta=97°$ for $n_s=1.52$, always for very small η. This demonstrates the increased sensitivity, at least concerning Δ, for very thin inhomogeneous layers deposited on a highly reflecting mirror. For thicker films, the situation is somewhat different. Figure 4 shows Δ versus ψ curves for films deposited on both substrates ($\phi_s = 70°$).

6. Films With a Slowly Varying Refractive Index

This is the situation where the well-known WKB approximation may be used. We shall discuss it briefly, as we feel that in some instances it can give very easily and without too lengthy computations approximate results which can serve at least as a first approximation.

6.1. s-Polarization

It is useful to make a change of variable as well as a change of function. The new variable will be

$$\zeta = k \int (n^2 - S^2)^{1/2} dz. \tag{33}$$

It should be pointed out that ζ is the phase corresponding to the optical thickness, for the given angle of incidence ϕ_0, and, therefore, is not the same as the variable u which was chosen in the preceding example. The new function will be $y(\zeta)$. It is chosen in such a way that

$$U = (K(\zeta))^{1/2} y \tag{34}$$

where

$$K = (n^2 - S^2)^{-1/2}. \tag{35}$$

K is the characteristic impedance of our medium, i.e., the ratio of the tangential components of $\vec{E}$ and $\vec{H}$. The change of function is a mathematical device useful for the supression of the term containing the first derivatives in the differential equation. This can be written now

$$\frac{d^2 y}{d\zeta^2} + \left(1 - \frac{3}{4}\left(\frac{K'}{K}\right)^2 + \frac{1}{2}\left(\frac{K''}{K}\right)\right) y = 0 \tag{36}$$

the derivatives of K being taken with respect to ζ.

The WKB approximation consists in the neglect of the terms different from unity in the bracket. It shows that, when

$$|f_s| \equiv \left|\frac{1}{2}\left(\frac{K''}{K}\right) - \frac{3}{4}\left(\frac{K'}{K}\right)^2\right| = \left|\frac{1}{2}(\ln K)'' - \frac{1}{4}((\ln K)')^2\right| \ll 1, \tag{37}$$

we have

$$y = ae^{i\zeta} + be^{-i\zeta} \tag{38}$$

so that

$$U = K(ae^{i\zeta} + be^{-i\zeta}) = aU_1 + bU_2. \tag{39}$$

We may use now the method described previously, which is valid in any circumstance. The only approximation which will be made consists in writing

$$U_1' = \frac{dU_1}{dz} = \frac{dU_1}{d\zeta}\frac{d\zeta}{dz} = \frac{k}{K}\frac{dU_1}{d\zeta} \simeq \frac{ik}{\sqrt{K}}\,e^{i\zeta} \qquad (40)$$

and

$$U_2' \simeq -\frac{ik}{\sqrt{K}}\,e^{-i\zeta}.$$

We have neglected the terms containing the derivatives of K with respect to ζ, i.e. which are smaller than those which were retained by a factor K'/K.

Making use now of eqs (3), (17), and (18), we can write

$$r_s = \rho_s \exp{(i\delta_{rs})} = \frac{(Y_0 K_a - Y_s K_b)\cos\zeta_f + i(Y_0 Y_s K_a K_b - 1)\sin\zeta_f}{(Y_0 K_a + Y_s K_b)\cos\zeta_f + i(Y_0 Y_s K_a K_b + 1)\sin\zeta_f},$$

$$t_s = \tau_s \exp{(i\delta_{ts})} = \frac{2Y_0(K_a K_b)^{1/2}}{(Y_0 K_a + Y_s K_b)\cos\zeta_f + i(Y_0 Y_s K_a K_b + 1)\sin\zeta_f}. \qquad (41)$$

K_a and K_b are the values of K at the entrance and exit of the film, i.e. on the planes which limit the film and ζ_f is the value of ζ corresponding to the thickness of the film.

6.2. p-Polarization

The discussion and the results are quite analogous to the preceding case. It is only necessary to replace the previous definition of K by a new one, viz

$$K = \frac{n^2}{(n^2 - S^2)^{1/2}}. \qquad (42)$$

This change is due to the fact that U is now that part of the magnetic field which is z-dependent, and we know that $n|\vec{E}| = |\vec{H}|$. (Throughout all the discussion of the WKB approximation, it is assumed that $\mu = 1$.)

Using the eqs (22) and (23), it can be shown that:

$$r_p = \rho_p \exp{(i\delta_{rp})} = \frac{(Z_s K_a - Z_0 K_b)\cos\zeta_f + i(K_a K_b - Z_0 Z_s)\sin\zeta_f}{(Z_s K_a + Z_0 K_b)\cos\zeta_f + i(K_a K_b + Z_0 Z_s)\sin\zeta_f}, \qquad (43)$$

$$t_p = \tau_p \exp{(i\delta_{tp})} = \frac{2n_0\sqrt{K_a K_b}/\cos\phi_s}{(Z_s K_a + Z_0 K_b)\cos\zeta_f + i(K_a K_b + Z_0 Z_s)\sin\zeta_f}, \qquad (44)$$

f_p is given by the same expression as f_s in terms of K, K', K'' (see eq (37)), but K is now given by eq (42).

A straightforward computation shows that

$$f_s = -\frac{1}{2k^2(n^2-S^2)^3}\left(n(n^2-S^2)\frac{d^2n}{dz^2}-\left(\frac{3}{2}n^2+S^2\right)\left(\frac{dn}{dz}\right)^2\right),$$

$$f_p = \frac{1}{2k^2n^2(n^2-S^2)^3}\left(n(n^2-S^2)(n^2-2S^2)\frac{d^2n}{dz^2}+\left(-\frac{5}{2}n^4+9n^2S^2-4S^4\right)\left(\frac{dn}{dz}\right)^2\right).$$

One should remember that the two approximations adopted for the s- and p-polarization are: $|f| \ll 1$ and $|(dK/d\zeta)/K| \ll 1$ too. It may be shown that

$$\left(\frac{K'}{K}\right)_s = -\frac{n(dn/dz)}{k(n^2-S^2)^{3/2}}$$

and

$$\left(\frac{K'}{K}\right)_p = -\frac{n^2-2S^2}{n^2}\left(\frac{K'}{K}\right)_s,$$

so that we always have

$$\left|\left(\frac{K'}{K}\right)_p\right| < \left|\left(\frac{K'}{K}\right)_s\right|.$$

7. An Inhomogeneous Film Replaced by a Pile of Homogeneous Films

It is also possible to replace an inhomogeneous film by a super-position of homogeneous films of different refractive indices. In that case, the problem pertaining to the solution of the differential field equations is eliminated. The only difficulty is the estimation of the number of homogeneous layers which is necessary for the replacement of the inhomogeneous one. In practice, this is done by successive trials. The inhomogeneous film is replaced first by a unique layer having an average refractive index

$$\bar{n} = \frac{1}{d}\int_0^d n(z)dz$$

and the computation is done. Then the film is replaced by two, three, etc., homogeneous films and the values of ψ and Δ are computed. The refractive index of each layer is an average of the refractive indices of the portion of the inhomogeneous layer it replaces. The satisfactory result will be obtained when ψ_j, Δ_j, and ψ_{j+1}, Δ_{j+1} do not differ from each other to the desired accuracy (the index indicates the number of layers which replace the inhomogeneous film).

There are no practical difficulties when using a large and rapid computer. The computation may take some time when the variation of the refractive index is rapid.

TABLE 1. *Characteristics of multiple homogeneous layers on glass substrate* ($n_s = 1.52$), *as a function of the number of layers,* H

The total thickness of the layers is $d = \lambda/2\pi$ and the angle of incidence is $\phi_0 = 70°$

H	1	2	3	4	5	6	7	8	15	∞
R_s	0.5292	0.5682	0.5740	0.5760	0.5769	0.5774	0.5777	0.5779	0.5784	0.57855
R_p	0.0094	0.0143	0.0179	0.0193	0.0199	0.0203	0.0205	0.0206	0.0209	0.02106
ψ	7°.58	9°.02	10°.02	10°.365	10°.525	10°.61	10°.66	10°.70	10°.77	10°.80
Δ	182°.96	241°.18	245°.31	246°.40	246°.85	247°.09	247°.22	247°.31	247°.51	247°.59

TABLE 2. *Same as table 1, but for different values of the angle of incidence*

$\phi_0 = 10°$

H	1	2	3	4	∞
R_s	0.1496	0.1783	0.1827	0.1842	0.1862
R_p	0.1412	0.1695	0.1738	0.1753	0.1772
ψ	44°10'17"	44°16'29"	44°17'02"	44°17'12"	44°17'24"
Δ	−0°.1204	−0°.4905	−0°.5447	−0°.5624	−0°.5844

$\phi_0 = 40°$

H	1	2	3	4	5
R_s	0.2334	0.2697	0.2752	0.2772	0.2781
R_p	0.0798	0.1075	0.1115	0.1128	0.1134
ψ	30°.32	32°.275	32°.478	32°.54	32°.567
Δ	−1°.7040	−8°.7808	−9°.8064	−10°.1417	−10°.2928

H	6	7	8	9	15	∞
R_s	0.2786	0.2788	0.2790	0.2792	0.2795	0.27966
R_p	0.1138	0.1140	0.1141	0.1142	0.1144	0.11451
ψ	32°.583	32°.591	32°.596	32°.60	32°.612	32°.615
Δ	−10°.3739	−10°.4224	−10°.4537	−10°.4752	−10°.5266	−10°.555

$\phi_0 = 80°$

H	1	2	3	4	5	6
R_s	0.7249	0.7521	0.7561	0.7575	0.7581	0.7585
R_p	0.1673	0.1539	0.1574	0.1589	0.1597	0.1601
ψ	25°.655	24°.333	24°.511	24°.617	24°.650	24°.675
Δ	−179°.7967	−165°.9209	−163°.7149	−163°.0100	−162°.6955	−162°.5277

H	7	8	9	15	∞
R_s	0.7587	0.7588	0.7589	0.7591	0.75923
R_p	0.1603	0.1605	0.1606	0.1609	0.16104
ψ	24°.688	24°.697	24°.702	24°.717	24°.72885
Δ	−162°.4276	−162°.3631	−162°.3190	−162°.2134	−162°.15445

7.1. Numerical Example

Let us indicate here the results which are obtained for the films which were investigated and which have an exponential variation of the refractive index. The homogeneous films had the following characteristics:

total number of layers: H
refractive index of layer p:

$$n_p = \frac{1}{d} \int_{d_p}^{d_{p+1}} n(z)dz = H \times \frac{(n_1/n_i)^{(p-1)/H}(n_1-n_i)}{\ln(n_1+n_i)}$$

thickness of layer p: $d_p = d/H$.

The numerical values of the different quantities are the same as before.

It should be stressed that the average values of the n_p's are independent of the angle of incidence. They are functions of H, the total number of layers, only.

The values of n_1 and n_i are the same as in the previous example ($n_i = 1.38$, $n_1 = 2.45$), and $n_s = 1.52$.

Table 1 gives the results obtained when the incidence is $\phi_0 = 70°$ and for $\eta = 1$, i.e., for an inhomogeneous layer having a thickness d equal to $\lambda/2\pi$. (For visible light, that means a thickness of about 900 Å). It can be seen that ψ approaches the true value more rapidly than Δ. But already for six layers the difference $\Delta(\infty) - \Delta(6) = 0°.5$ is quite small. It can be even smaller for smaller angles of incidence. We have chosen $\phi_0 = 70°$, because, in our opinion, it is a convenient angle to use in ellipsometry. In order to get more insight into the rapidity of convergence, we give in table 2 the results obtained for $\eta = 1$ and $\phi_0 = 10°$, $40°$, and $80°$. It will be seen that, for large angles ϕ_0, if we decide that the largest error admitted on Δ is $0.2°$, it is necessary to replace the inhomogeneous film by at least nine homogeneous layers. As it can be expected, for small values of ϕ_0, the same accuracy is obtained with a smaller number of homogeneous layers.

8. Concluding Remarks

It is impossible to discuss all the situations which may arise when dealing with inhomogeneous layers. Our purpose was only to indicate some computational methods. We did not discuss the problem of inhomogeneous absorbing films. In principle, it is not different from those already treated, but the introduction of a complex dielectric constant leads to solutions of the differential wave equation, which are complex functions.

The special inhomogeneous layer which was examined may serve as a starting point for more complicated inhomogeneous layers. In fact, we might approximate a rather complicated law of variation of ϵ by a pile of thin films, each of them having an exponentially varying refractive index. The question is still pending as to the easiest and more accurate way of computing the ellipsometric properties of inhomogeneous layers. The replacement of an inhomogeneous film by a pile of homogeneous ones is a straight forward method, but it is impossible to know from the beginning the number of the latter which is necessary in order to know the result with a given accuracy. It would be very useful to examine the approximate methods which can be used, especially concerning the accuracy which can be expected in each case. But this is a more difficult problem than those we have discussed here.

This work has been sponsored in part by the Office of Scientific Research, O.A.R., through its European Office, United States Air Force, under Grant AF–EOAR 63–48.

Discussion

A.N. SAXENA (Fairchild Semiconductor Co.):
I want to ask you whether your calculation is restricted to inhomogeneous but transparent film only because you say nothing about k. I wonder whether you can extend this for inhomogeneous but absorbing film?

F. ABELÈS:
Yes. It can be done. As we saw on the slide one gets Bessel functions of complex variable and complex arguments, but otherwise it is exactly the same and can be extended very easily.

A. N. SAXENA:
It is good that your calculations can be extended for inhomogeneous films also; however, your present paper is restricted only to transparent films.

F. ABELÈS:
Yes, what I have done was only on transparent films.

A. N. SAXENA:
The inhomogeneity in thick transparent films on an absorbing substrate can be studied by performing ellipsometer measurements to get (ψ, Δ). Knowing the film-substrate interface optical constants, one can compute (ψ, Δ) curves for various refractive indices n_1 and thickness d of the film. From these curves then, one can determine n_1 and d. By etching the film successively to obtain smaller thicknesses and making ellipsometer measurements each time, the variation in n_1 due to inhomogeneity can be studied. We have made such measurements on SiO_2 films grown on Si, and I find that they are quite homogenous all the way from 9000 Å down to a few hundred Å. I am attempting to assign a value to the optical constants of SiO_2-Si interface which seem to be different from that of bulk Si.

J. T. BLOXSOM (Air Reduction Corporation):
Would you comment briefly on how you would modify your equations to incorporate scattering in the internal portion of your films. Would you have to use a two-dimensional function?

F. ABELÈS:
That is completely different. All that supposes that you have an inhomogeneous but isotropic film and with no scattering in the film, but if you had to have scattering, that would bring you to a completely different problem. It cannot be treated in this way.

3. Techniques

Computational Techniques for the Use of the Exact Drude Equations in Reflection Problems

F. L. McCrackin and J. P. Colson

National Bureau of Standards, Washington, D.C. 20234

The Drude equations applied to a thin film give the ellipsometer readings in terms of the refractive index and thickness of the film. A solution of these equations for the film thickness when the refractive index of the film is known, and methods of determining both the thickness and refractive index of a film from ellipsometer readings, are presented for both dielectric and absorbing films.

Ellipsometer readings for an inhomogeneous film are often analyzed as if the film were homogeneous, yielding an effective thickness and refractive index for the film. The relation of these effective quantities to various averages of thickness and refractive index of the film is investigated. In particular, the effective thickness determined by the ellipsometer is found to be greater than the root mean square average thickness of the film.

1. Introduction

When polarized light is reflected from a surface, the polarization of the light is changed. This change of polarization may be represented by the ratio of the reflection coefficient r^p, for light polarized with its electric vector parallel to the plane of incidence, to the reflection coefficient r^s, for light polarized with its electric vector perpendicular to the plane of incidence. These reflection coefficients are in general complex numbers so they express the change in both the amplitude and phase of the light, and they are given by the well-known Fresnel coefficients,

$$r^p_{12}=\frac{n_2\cos\phi_1-n_1\cos\phi_2}{n_1\cos\phi_1+n_2\cos\phi_2},$$

$$r^s_{12}=\frac{n_1\cos\phi_1-n_2\cos\phi_2}{n_1\cos\phi_1+n_2\cos\phi_2}.$$

$$(1)$$

The indexes of refraction of the medium above the surface and of the surface are n_1 and n_2, respectively, and the latter may be complex. The angle of incidence is ϕ_1, and the angle of refraction, ϕ_2, may be computed from n_1, n_2, and ϕ_1.

The changes in the polarization of light by reflection from a surface are conveniently measured by an ellipsometer. The quantity measured by an ellipsometer is the ratio of the reflection coefficients, ρ:

$$\rho=r^p/r^s=\tan\psi e^{i\Delta}. \qquad (2)$$

This ratio represents the relative attenuation, $\tan\psi$, and the difference

61

of phase shifts, Δ, for the components of the electric vector in the plane of incidence and normal to it.

The refractive index of the substrate may be computed from ρ. Solving the previous equations gives

$$n_2 = n_1 \tan \phi_1 \left[1 - \frac{4\rho \sin^2 \phi_1}{(\rho+1)^2} \right]^{1/2}. \tag{3}$$

If the substrate is absorbing, its refractive index will, of course, be complex.

If a film is now placed on the surface, the reflection coefficients of the surface are changed. The appreciable changes in the reflection coefficients for very thin films are the reason that the ellipsometer is such a sensitive instrument. The exact Drude equations [1, 2, 3] [1] for the reflection coefficients for a film-covered surface are:

$$R^p = \frac{r_{12}^p + r_{23}^p \exp D}{1 + r_{12}^p r_{23}^p \exp D}$$

$$R^s = \frac{r_{12}^s + r_{23}^s \exp D}{1 + r_{12}^s r_{23}^s \exp D} \tag{4}$$

where

$$D = -4\pi i n_2 \cos \phi_2 \ d_2/\lambda. \tag{5}$$

The subscripts 1, 2, and 3 are used for the medium, film, and substrate, respectively. The Fresnel coefficients r_{12}^p and r_{12}^s refer to reflection between the medium and film, and the coefficients r_{23}^p and r_{23}^s refer to reflection between the film and substrate. The ratio of the reflection coefficients is, as before,

$$\rho = R^p/R^s = \tan \psi e^{i\Delta}. \tag{6}$$

For a given angle of incidence, thickness of film, and indexes of refraction of surrounding medium, film, and substrate, the expected ellipsometer values ψ and Δ may be computed. First the angles of refraction in the film and substrate, then the Fresnel coefficients r_{12}^p and r_{12}^s, and finally D are computed. These are substituted in the expressions for the reflection coefficients and finally the ratio of the reflection coefficients gives the ellipsometer values of ψ and Δ. Typical results of such calculations are given in figure 1. Values of Δ and ψ are shown for films of refractive index of 1.4, 1.5, and 1.6 and thicknesses of 0 to 1000 Å on a substrate of the refractive index of chromium. The index of refraction of the medium above the film is 1.359.

The thickness of films of known refractive index may be determined from graphs such as figure 1, or from tables. From the measured values of ψ and Δ, the thickness may be read off the curve for the

---

[1] Figures in brackets refer to the literature references on p. 80.

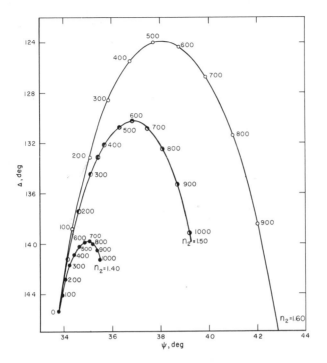

FIGURE 1. *A plot of Δ against ψ for films of refractive index n_2 as shown, in a medium with a refractive index of 1.359 on a chrome substrate.* $n_3 = 3.316 - 4.383 i$ ← P. 64
The numbers along the curves are film thicknesses in Ångstrom units.

index of refraction of the film. However, a different curve must be calculated for each set of values of the indexes of medium, film, and substrate, and for each angle of incidence. Therefore, it is usually more efficient to solve the equations for the thickness of the film in terms of the ellipsometer readings. The ratio of the reflection coefficients, ρ, is given in terms of the ellipsometry readings by eq (6). Since the thickness, d_2, of the film occurs only in the term exp D in eqs (4) and (5), we may first solve for exp D. Substituting for R^p and R^s and clearing fractions, an equation is obtained of the form:

$$C_1(\exp D)^2 + C_2(\exp D) + C_3 = 0, \qquad (7)$$

where C_1, C_2, and C_3 are complex numbers depending on the refractive indexes, angle of incidence, and measured values Δ and ψ. Solving this quadratic equation gives two solutions for exp D. From each solution, a value of D is computed and a thickness, d_2, is determined from D by eq (5). The value of d_2 that is correct must now be chosen.

Since the coefficients C_1, C_2, and C_3 are complex numbers, the film thickness calculated from this equation would also be expected to be complex. However, the correct film thickness must be a real number, as it represents a real quantity. Therefore, the calculated thickness with a zero imaginary part is the correct solution. In practice, experimental errors will result in both computed thicknesses being complex. The thickness with the smallest imaginary component is selected as the correct solution, the real part is taken as the thickness and the magnitude of the imaginary part is arbitrarily taken as a measure of error.

The real part of d is then used to compute ellipsometer values Δ and ψ by eqs (4), (5), and (6). As the imaginary part of d has been dropped, these computed values will differ from the measured values of Δ and ψ by error terms $\delta\Delta$ and $\delta\psi$. In order for the measurements and interpretation to be satisfactory, the error terms must be within the limits of experimental error.

Thus far, the refractive index of the film has been assumed to be known. The film refractive index and thickness may both be determined from ellipsometry readings, even though the equations have not been solved for the film refractive index in closed form. We consider first the case of a dielectric non-absorbing film, so that its refractive index is a real number. To determine the refractive index, several refractive indexes are assumed for the film and the film thickness and error terms computed for each refractive index. An example is shown in table 1 for a barium fluoride film on a chrome

TABLE 1.   *Thickness of evaporated barium fluoride film on chrome slide*[a, b]

Δ	$\delta\Delta$	ψ	$\delta\psi$	n_2	d
deg 133. 96	*deg* 3. 64	*deg* 36. 30	*deg* 0. 60	1. 420	$\overset{\circ}{A}$ 753
	2. 64		. 40	1. 430	726
	1. 58		. 22	1. 440	701
	1. 08		. 14	1. 445	688
	0. 58		. 07	1. 450	676
	. 28		. 03	1. 453	668
	.18		. 02	1. 454	665
	.10		. 01	1. 455	662
	. 00		. 00	1. 456	660
	.10		. 01	1. 457	657
	.20		. 02	1. 458	654
	. 28		. 03	1. 459	651
	. 38		. 04	1. 460	647
	. 70		. 38	1. 475	453

[a] Immersed in acetone, $n_1 = 1.359$, at an angle of incidence of 60°. The refractive index of the slide was $n_3 = 3.316 - 4.383i$.
[b] Film prepared by Frank E. Jones, NBS.

slide. Values from 1.42 to 1.475 were assumed for the refractive index of the film and the thickness and error terms $\delta\Delta$ and $\delta\psi$ computed for each assumed refractive index. Choosing the row with zero error terms gives a refractive index of 1.456 and a thickness of 660 Å for the barium fluoride film.

All the previously mentioned calculations have been programmed [4] in Fortran for the IBM 704, 7090, and 7094 computers and all calculations have been performed on these computers. The computer has also been programmed to determine the refractive index of a film by calculating error terms for assumed values for the index and choosing the refractive index that gives the smallest error term, so the table of error terms does not need to be examined as in the previous example. Also, the computer can use ellipsometer readings obtained by multiple reflections of the light or a compensator with arbitrary phase retardation. Calculations have also been extended to reflection from multiple films and absorbing films.

2. Determination of Complex Index of Refraction of Films

.We now consider the case of an absorbing film which has, of course, a complex index of refraction. If the imaginary part of the refractive index of the film is given, the real part of the index and the film thickness can be determined as previously by searching for the real part of the refractive index that gives zero error terms. If the real part of the refractive index of the film is given, searching over the imaginary part for zero error terms gives the solution. If the thickness of the film is given, the real and imaginary parts of the refractive index of the film may be searched until a complex refractive index is found which yields the given thickness as well as zero error terms. However, the real and imaginary parts of the refractive index and the thickness of the film *cannot* all be determined from a single set of ellipsometer readings. Since a set of ellipsometer readings consists of only two values, ψ and Δ, it cannot determine the three quantities for the film. However, by increasing the number of ellipsometer measurements, both real and imaginary parts of an unknown complex refractive index of a film may be determined.

We shall now investigate the following four means of increasing the number of ellipsometer readings:

(1) A series of ellipsometer readings is obtained for films of different but unknown thicknesses, but of the same refractive index.

(2) Ellipsometer readings are obtained on a single film for different surrounding media of known refractive index.

(3) Ellipsometer readings are obtained for a single film (or a series of films of the same refractive index) on various substrates of known refractive index.

(4) Ellipsometer readings are obtained for a single film at various angles of incidence.

The possibility of determining the complex refractive index and thickness of a film from a series of ellipsometer readings obtained by each of these methods was investigated. The series of ellipsometer data that would be obtained for an assumed complex refractive index and film thicknesses was calculated for each method. Then various schemes of determining the refractive index and thickness were tried, using these computed ellipsometer measurements, to see if they could determine the refractive index and thickness of the film that was originally used to compute the ellipsometer measurements.

2.1. Variation of Film Thickness

One method of obtaining many ellipsometer measurements is to make measurements on a series of films with the same complex refractive index but with different thicknesses. To obtain such a series of measurements, a series of films of thicknesses 40 to 100 Å, all with a refractive index of $2.5-0.5i$, was assumed. The ellipsometer readings that would be obtained by measurements on these films were calculated, as described, using eq (6). A series of measurements of this type could be obtained, for example, on a vacuum-evaporated film. Readings taken during the deposition would all be for films of the same refractive index but different, unknown, thicknesses if the structure of the film did not change during its deposition. From this series of readings, an effort was made to calculate the refractive index of the films. Values for the imaginary part of the refractive index were assumed and a value for the real part of the refractive index was computed for each assumed value of the imaginary part and for each film. The results are shown in table 2.

TABLE 2. *Calculated values of the real part of the refractive index for films from 40 to 100 A for assumed values of the imaginary part,* n_i, *of refractive index*

Thickness	Assumed n_i				
	−0.2	−0.3	−0.4	−0.5	−0.6
Å					
40	2.952	2.812	2.668	2.500	------
60	2.960	2.820	2.668	2.500	2.262
80	2.974	2.828	2.673	2.500	2.279
100	2.990	2.839	2.677	2.500	2.279

If one assumes −0.4, for example, for the imaginary part of the refractive index, the computed real part of the refractive index is seen to vary from 2.668 to 2.677 for the films from 40 to 100 Å thick. Since it is known that the refractive index is the same for all the films, the value −0.4 for the imaginary part of the refractive index is incompatible and is discarded. Examining the other columns of the table, we see that only for the value −0.5 for the imaginary part of the refractive index are constant values for the real part obtained. Therefore, the refractive index of the films is correctly determined to be $2.5-0.5i$. After the refractive index of the films is determined, the thicknesses of the films may be calculated.

This calculation shows that it is possible in principle to determine the complex index of refraction of a series of films of the same refractive index but varying thicknesses by this method, but it does not show that the method is practical. This is because exact values of the ellipsometer readings Δ and ψ were used, while in practice the readings would have experimental errors. In order to make the test of the method more realistic, random errors were added to the computed readings before they were analyzed. The errors were random normal errors with a standard deviation of 0.04° for Δ and 0.02° for ψ. The values computed for the real part, n_R, of the film refractive index from these readings with errors are shown graphically in figure 2. The computed real parts of the refractive indexes are plotted versus the film thickness for assumed values of the imaginary part, n_i. For the method to work, the computed values for n_R for $n_i = -0.5$ would have a constant value, so they would lie on a horizontal line, while the other values of n_i would give more scatter about a horizontal line. Since the graphs for all values of n_i show the same scatter about a horizontal line the method does not work for these conditions.

The method was also tried with thicker films, from 200 to 1000 Å, with errors added to the computed ellipsometer readings and the other conditions the same. The results are shown in figure 3. The range 1.5 to 3.5 was searched for values of n_R for each assumed value of n_i and film thickness. For some cases, two values of n_R were found in this range. The method worked very well in this case, since $n_i = -0.5$ gave much smaller scatter around a constant value of $n_R = 2.5$ than did $n_i = -0.54$ or -0.48. The correct value of n_R was obvious when two values were obtained. Therefore, the imaginary part of the

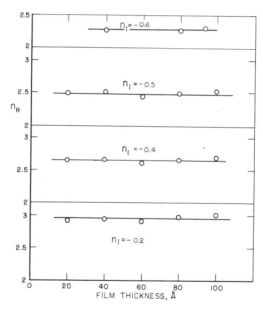

FIGURE 2. *Calculated values of the real part, n_R, of the refractive index of films from 20 to 100 Å thick for assumed values of the imaginary part, n_i, of the refractive index of the film, random errors having been added to the ellipsometer readings.*

The true index of the film is 2.5–0.5i.

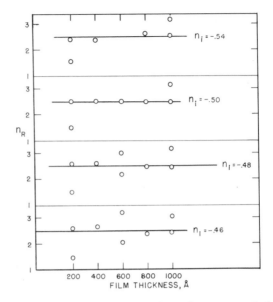

FIGURE 3.   *Calculated values of the real part,* n_R, *of the refractive index of films from 200 to 1000 Å thick for assumed values of the imaginary part,* n_i, *of the refractive index of the film, random errors having been added to the ellipsometer readings.*

The true index of the film is 2.5–0.5i.

refractive index may be determined to better than 0.02 for films up to 1000 Å thick for these conditions.

The computed values of n_R were averaged for the film thickness range 200 to 1000 Å for each assumed value of n_i. The method was applied two more times for the same conditions, except different sets of errors were added to the ellipsometer readings. This simulates repeating an experiment. The average values for n_R that were obtained for each calculation are given table 3. The spurious values of n_R were omitted.

TABLE 3.   *Average values of calculated real part of film refractive indexes for assumed values of* n_i

Assumed n_i					
−0.46	−0.48	−0.50	−0.52	−0.54	−0.56
2.513	2.508	2.504	2.492	2.483	2.470
2.516	2.510	2.498	2.492	2.491	2.474
2.510	2.504	2.502	2.489	2.480	2.463

TABLE 4. *Standard deviations of calculated real part of film refractive indexes*

Random errors added to ellipsometer readings.

Assumed n_i					
−0.45	−0.48	−0.50	−0.52	−0.54	−0.56
0.127	0.055	0.006	0.066	0.134	0.207
.129	.066	.004	.066	.130	.205
.123	.060	.012	.070	.146	.212

Table 4 gives the standard deviations of n_R computed for the various film thicknesses, choosing the values closest to the average value for each film thickness. The correct value of $n_i = -0.50$ is easily chosen, since it gives much smaller standard deviations for all three cases than the other values for n_i.

Therefore, the complex index of refraction of a series of films of varying thickness but the same index of refraction may be determined if the films are reasonably thick but not for very thin films. Of course, the thickness of films required and the accuracy to which the index is determined depend on the actual experimental conditions. For the conditions of the calculations presented here, the film refractive index could be determined for a series of films between 100 A and 1000 Å thick but not for a series of films up to 100 Å thick.

2.2. Variation of Refractive Index of Surrounding Medium

A series of ellipsometer readings may also be obtained from a single film by varying the index of refraction of the medium above the film, the index of refraction of the substrate, or the angle of incidence of the incoming light. The possibility of determining the complex refractive index of a film from a series of ellipsometer readings obtained by varying each quantity was investigated.

First, a series of ellipsometer readings was calculated for a film of 100 Å and refractive index $2.5 - 0.5i$ on a substrate with the refractive index of chromium for indexes of the surrounding medium from 1.0 to 1.6. A series of readings of this type could be experimentally obtained for a single film by placing the film on the substrate in a cell as described by Stromberg et al. [5]. By using liquids of various refractive indexes in the cell, ellipsometer readings for the film could be obtained for various refractive indexes of the surrounding medium. However, it would have to be established that the refractive index of the film did not change because of the change in the surrounding liquid, due to the film absorbing the liquid or the liquid either dissolving or depositing another film onto the film that was being investigated.

The real part, n_R, of the refractive index of the film was then computed for each surrounding medium and for assumed values from −0.3 to −0.6 for the imaginary part, n_i, of the refractive index of

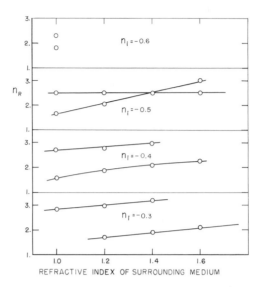

FIGURE 4.   *Calculated values of* n_R, *for a film 100 Å thick for varying refractive index of surrounding medium and assumed values for* n_i.
The true refractive index of the film is $2.5-0.5i$.

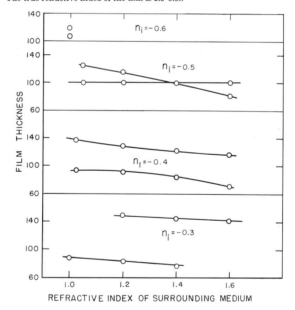

FIGURE 5.   *Calculated values of the thickness of a film for varying refractive index of surrounding medium and assumed values for* n_i.
The refractive index of the film is $2.5-0.5i$ and thickness is 100 Å.

the film. The calculated values of n_R are shown in figure 4 and the corresponding film thicknesses are shown in figure 5. From figure 4, the only value of n_i that gives constant values of n_R independent of the surrounding medium is the true value -0.5 for which the value $n_R=2.5$ is obtained. For $n_i=-0.6$ and for larger negative values, there were no solutions for n_R for these ellipsometer readings when the refractive index of the surrounding medium is greater than 1; therefore, these values of n_i may be discarded. The refractive index of $2.5-0.5i$, used for calculating the series of ellipsometer readings, has been determined from the ellipsometer readings.

The value of n_i may also be determined from the condition that calculated thickness of the film shall also be constant, independent of the refractive index of the surrounding medium, as in figure 5. The correct value of -0.5 is again obtained.

2.3. Variation of Substrate

The effect of variation of the refractive index of the substrate was investigated. The ellipsometric readings for films of refractive index 2.5–0.5i and a thickness of 100 Å on chrome, gold, silver, and steel substrates were computed, using refractive indexes of the substrates obtained from the literature. Then the real parts of the refractive index of the films for various assumed n_i were calculated and are shown in figure 6. When the correct value of -0.5 was assumed for n_i, the calculated value of n_R was 2.5 for all substrates. However, when -0.4 or -0.45 was assumed for n_i, the calculated

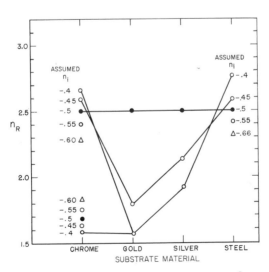

FIGURE 6. *Calculated values of* n_R *for a film 100 Å thick for varying refractive index of the substrate for assumed values of* n_i.
The true refractive index of the film is 2.5–0.5i.

value of n_R varied greatly with the substrate material, and when −0.55 or −0.60 was assumed for n_i, there was no solution for n_R for gold and silver substrates. Therefore, since all values except −0.5 are eliminated for n_i, the method works. Some spurious solutions for n_i are found for the chrome substrate, but they do not seriously interfere in the determination of n_i.

The effect of experimental error on this method was also investigated. Random normal errors with a standard deviation of 0.04° for Δ and 0.02° for ψ were added to the ellipsometer readings and the values of n_R shown in figure 7 were calculated. The correct solution of $n_i = -0.5$ is still clearly indicated as giving the most nearly constant value for n_R, even though the values of n_R show some variation due to the experimental error.

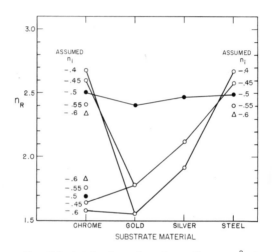

FIGURE 7.   *Calculated values of* n_R *for a film 100 Å thick for varying refractive index of the substrate and for assumed values of* n_i.
Errors have been added to ellipsometer readings.   The true refractive index of the film is 2.5–0.5i.

2.4. Variation of Angle of Incidence

A series of ellipsometer readings for a single film may also be obtained by varying the angle of incidence of the light. The analysis of such a series of ellipsometer readings has been considered by Hayfield [8]. Such a series of readings is convenient to obtain experimentally on a single film without the complications due to the possibility of changing the index of refraction of the film. Such complications occur when the substrate, or the surrounding medium, or thickness of the film are varied.

Ellipsometer readings were computed for angles of incidence from 10 to 85° for a film of 100 A thickness and index of 2.5–0.5i on a

chrome substrate in air. For each ellipsometer reading, the value
for the real part of the refractive index of the film was computed for
various assumed values of the imaginary part, n_i, of the refractive
index, as shown in table 5. In some cases two values were obtained.
It is desired to determine the true value of n_i by choosing the column
of the table which gives constant values for n_R independent of the
angle of incidence. However, the calculated values of n_R are nearly
constant with respect to the angle of incidence for all assumed
values of n_i, so the true value of n_i cannot be determined from this
information.

TABLE 5. *Calculated values of the real part of the refractive index of a 100 Å film
for varying angles of incidence and assumed values for the imaginary part, n_i,
of the refractive index of the film*

Angle of incidence	Assumed n_i				
	−0.2	−0.3	−0.4	−0.5	−0.6
deg					
10	2.994	2.853	2.684 / 1.569	2.500 / 1.672	2.284 / 1.809
20	2.994	2.839	2.677 / 1.577	2.498 / 1.689	2.264 / 1.827
30	2.994	2.841	2.681 / 1.573	2.503 / 1.683	2.274 / 1.822
40	2.990	2.839	2.677 / 1.572	2.500 / 1.682	2.277 / 1.820
50	2.990	2.839	2.677 / 1.570	2.500 / 1.679	2.279 / 1.815
60	2.988	2.837	2.677 / 1.568	2.500 / 1.677	2.281 / 1.812
70	2.988	2.837	2.677 / 1.567	2.500 / 1.675	2.282 / 1.808
80	2.988	2.836	2.676 / 1.566	2.500 / 1.674	2.283 / 1.806
85	2.987	2.856	2.676 / 1.566	2.500 / 1.673	2.282 / 1.805

The method was then repeated for film thicknesses of 500 and 1000 Å,
with the other parameters unchanged. The results are shown in
tables 6 and 7. For a film thickness of 1000 Å, some variation of the
calculated values of n_R with the angle of incidence is observed for
values of n_i different than the true value of −0.5, as may be seen from
table 7. However, this variation is still not sufficient for the method
to determine n_i accurately when the ellipsometer readings contain
experimental error.

For a film thickness of 500 Å, the method gave the surprising results
shown in table 6. Solutions for n_R were found only when the correct
value of −0.5 was used for n_i; when other values were assumed for n_i
no solutions for n_R in the range of 1.5 to 3.0 existed. Therefore, the
correct value of n_i was determined. More exactly, the value of n_i
must be between −0.4 and −0.6. To determine how closely n_i may
be determined for a 500 Å film, values of n_i from −0.4 to −0.6 in

steps of -0.02 were assumed and the results shown in table 8 were calculated. The value of n_i is between -0.40 and -0.54 by table 8.

Therefore, ellipsometry readings at various angles of incidence of a film determine the complex refractive index of the film only for a special thickness of the film (in this case 500 Å).

TABLE 6. *Calculated values of the real part of the refractive index of a 500 Å film for varying angles of incidence and assumed values for the imaginary part, n_i, of the refractive index of the film*

Angle of incidence	Assumed n_i									
	-0.1	-0.2	-0.3	-0.4	-0.5	-0.6	-0.7	-0.8	-0.9	-0.10
deg										
10					2.500					
20					2.500					
30					2.500					
					1.536					
40					2.500					
					1.588					
50					2.500					
					1.636					
60					2.500					
					1.677					
70					2.500					
					1.707					
80					2.500					
					1.726					
85					2.500					
					1.730					

TABLE 7. *Calculated values for the real part of the refractive index of a 1000 Å film for varying angles of incidence and assumed values for the imaginary part, n_i, of the refractive index of the film*

Angle of incidence	Assumed n_i							
	-0.2	-0.3	-0.4	-0.5	-0.6	-0.7	-0.8	-0.9
deg.								
10	-----	1.990	2.284	2.498	2.656	2.776	2.871	2.944
20	1.550	2.012	2.293	2.500	2.654	2.775	2.870	2.948
30	1.621	2.033	2.302	2.500	2.652	2.770	2.868	2.951
40	1.688	2.057	2.311	2.500	2.648	2.766	2.866	2.958
50	1.746	2.080	2.319	2.500	2.644	2.763	2.869	2.969
60	1.793	2.100	2.325	2.500	2.642	2.763	2.874	2.984
70	1.826	2.115	2.330	2.500	2.640	2.764	2.880	-----
80	1.846	2.123	2.333	2.500	2.640	2.765	2.886	-----
85	1.852	2.126	2.334	2.500	2.640	2.765	2.886	-----

3. Inhomogeneous Films

Only homogeneous films have been discussed so far. However, the index of refraction of many real films varies in the direction perpendicular to the plane of the films. In many cases, it is not possible to determine the manner in which the index of refraction of the film

TABLE 8. *Calculated values for the real part of the refractive index of a 500 Å film for varying angles of incidence and assumed values from −0.40 to −0.60 for the imaginary part, n_i, of the refractive index of the film*

Angle of incidence	Assumed n_i							
	−0.40	−0.42	−0.44	−0.46	−0.48	−0.50	−0.52	−0.54
deg 10		2.984	2.880	2.767	2.642	2.500	2.320 1.597	
20		2.983	2.879	2.767	2.643	2.500	2.318 1.630	
30		2.981	2.878	2.766	2.643	2.500 1.536	2.316 1.678	
40		2.979	2.876	2.766	2.643	2.500 1.579	2.312 1.733	
50		2.976	2.875	2.765	2.643 1.538	2.500 1.636	2.308 1.785	
60		2.973	2.873	2.764 1.505	2.643 1.580	2.500 1.677	2.303 1.829	
70		2.971	2.872	2.764 1.537	2.643 1.610	2.500 1.707	2.300 1.862	
80		2.970	2.871	2.763 1.556	2.643 1.629	2.500 1.726	2.298 1.882	
85		2.970	2.871 1.502	2.763 1.561	2.643 1.634	2.500 1.730	2.297 1.888	

varies. Therefore, the inhomogeneous film is analyzed as though the film were homogeneous, i.e., the index is regarded as constant throughout the film. Therefore, a thickness,[2] t_{av}, and a refractive index, n_{av}, are obtained.

This refractive index is some kind of average of the variable refractive index of the film, and the thickness is an average of the thickness of the film averaged over the refractive index. A homogeneous film with this average index of refraction and thickness is equivalent to the inhomogeneous film with respect to ellipsometer measurements.

To determine the type of averages represented by t_{av} and n_{av}, the ellipsometer readings were calculated for assumed inhomogeneous films, t_{av} and n_{av} being computed from the ellipsometer readings. Then, various averages over the thickness and refractive index of the inhomogeneous films were computed and compared with the corresponding values of t_{av} and n_{av}. The ellipsometer readings were computed by replacing the inhomogeneous films by a series of homogeneous films and calculating the reflection coefficients by the method of Rouard [2, 6, 7].

The three variations of the refractive index with distance from the substrate shown in figure 8 were assumed. Only non-absorbing films were considered. In all three cases, the refractive index varied from 1.6 at the surface to 1.3, and the index of the surrounding medium

---

[2] The symbol t rather than d is used for film thickness in this section to avoid confusion when derivatives are discussed.

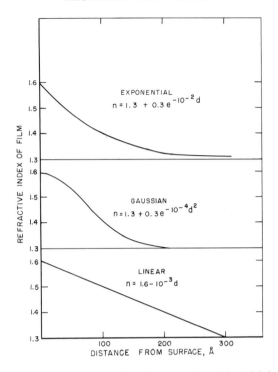

FIGURE 8. *Assumed variations for refractive index of inhomo-geneous films.*

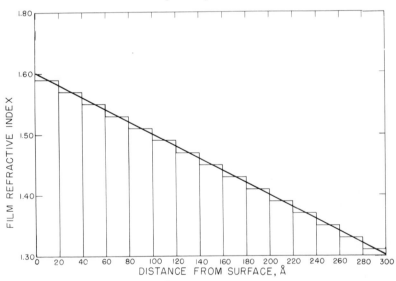

FIGURE 9. *Approximation of an inhomogeneous film by many homogeneous films.*

was 1.3. Exponential, Gaussian, and a linear variation of the refractive index were assumed. These films are expected to be similar to the films of adsorbed polymer discussed by Stromberg et al. [5]. Small differences between the refractive index of these films and the surrounding medium were assumed, so the conclusions that were obtained are probably limited by this condition.

The expected ellipsometer readings that would be measured for these films were then computed as illustrated in figure 9 for the case of the linear film. The inhomogeneous film was approximated by about 15 homogeneous films and the reflection coefficients and ellipsometer readings for these multiple films were computed.

In order to determine if the inhomogeneous film was sufficiently well approximated by the homogeneous films, the inhomogeneous film was more closely approximated by about 30 and about 60 homogeneous films and the ellipsometer readings recomputed. In all cases, the readings computed by using 30 and 60 films agreed within 0.02° of each other, so 30 homogeneous films were considered a sufficiently good approximation for the inhomogeneous films.

From the calculated ellipsometer values for each of these films, an average index of refraction n_{av} and an average thickness t_{av} were computed. The variation of these averages with the angle of incidence of the light is shown in table 9 for the linear and Gaussian films. Both n_{av} and t_{av} are seen to be almost independent of the angle of incidence so the type of average is, for practical purposes, independent of the angle of incidence. For this reason, the variation of ellipsometer readings with angle of incidence cannot determine the type of variation of refractive index in an inhomogeneous film, or even distinguish between a homogeneous and an inhomogeneous film.

TABLE 9. *Variation of* n_{av} *and* t_{av} *with angle of incidence for linear and Gaussian variation of refractive index of film (see fig. 8)*

Angle of incidence	n_1	Linear		Gaussian	
		n_{av}	t_{av}	n_{av}	t_{av}
deg			Å		Å
30	1.3	1.514	213	1.519	123
50	1.3	1.514	213	1.518	123
70	1.3	1.513	215	1.518	123
85	1.3	1.513	215	1.518	123

Values of n_{av} and t_{av} were also computed for distributions with a smaller range of index of refraction. The index, n_1, of the surrounding medium was 1.4268 and the index of the film varied from 1.4268 to 1.4768 at the substrate. The results are shown in table 10.

The types of averages over the distribution of index of refraction of the films that approximate these averages were developed by the following plausible argument. A film of the index n_1 of the surrounding medium has, of course, no effect on the reflection of light or the ellipsometer reading. Therefore, the effect of a film will

TABLE 10. *Average values of the refractive index, n_{av}, and thickness, t_{av}, and total optical effect for inhomogeneous films calculated from ellipsometer readings*

	n_1	n_{av}	t_{av}	$(n_{av}-n_1)t_{av}$	$\int(n-n_1)dt$
Linear					
1.3–1.6	1.3	1.513	214	45.69	45.00
1.4268–1.4768	1.4268	1.462	215	7.49	7.50
Exponential					
1.3–1.6	1.3	1.442	207	29.5	30.0
1.4268–1.4768	1.4268	1.451	206	4.96	5.0
Gaussian					
1.3–1.6	1.3	1.518	123	26.6	26.6
1.4268–1.4768	1.4268	1.466	112	4.44	4.43

TABLE 11. *Averages for the refractive index and thickness of inhomogeneous films compared with the ellipsometer averages*

	n_{av}	n_{cal}	t_{av}	t_{rms}	t_{cal}	t_{av}/t_{rms}
Linear						
1.3–1.6	1.513	1.500	214	122	225	1.75
1.4268–1.4768	1.462	1.460	215	123	227	1.75
Exponential						
1.3–1.6	1.442	1.450	207	141	200	1.47
1.4268–1.4768	1.451	1.452	206	141	200	1.46
Gaussian						
1.3–1.6	1.518	1.512	123	71	126	1.73
1.4268–1.4768	1.466	1.462	112	71	126	1.58

depend on $n-n_1$. Since the effect will also depend on the thickness of the film, the effect of a film of infinitesimal thickness, dt, may be expected to be $(n-n_1)dt$ and the effect of a film of varying index of refraction is obtained by integrating this quantity over the film, i.e.,

$$\int_0^\infty (n-n_1)dt.$$

This integral will be called the optical effect of the film. The value of this integral for the equivalent homogeneous film of index n_{av} and thickness t_{av} is $(n_{av}-n_1)t_{av}$. This integral for the inhomogeneous film and for the equivalent homogeneous film, shown in table 10, are seen to agree closely with each other.

Since the optical effect of a thickness dt of the film is $(n-n_1)dt$, the refractive index was weighted by this quantity to give the average refractive index

$$n_{cal}=\frac{\int_0^\infty n(n-n_1)dt}{\int_0^\infty (n-n_1)dt}.$$

This average is given in table 11 and is in good agreement with the average index n_{av} that would be determined by the ellipsometer.

Various types of average thicknesses for the film were tried. The only average that gave reasonable agreement for these films with t_{av} determined by the ellipsometer was obtained by dividing the total optical effect by $n_{cal}-n_1$:

$$t_{cal}=\frac{\int_0^\infty (n-n_1)dt}{n_{cal}-n_1}=\frac{\left[\int_0^\infty (n-n_1)dt\right]^2}{\int_0^\infty (n-n_1)^2dt}.$$

This average is compared with t_{av} in table 11.

An average for film thickness of special importance is the root mean square thickness given by

$$t_{rms}^2=\frac{\int_0^\infty (n-n_1)t^2dt}{\int_0^\infty (n-n_1)dt}.$$

As may be seen from table 11, the average, t_{av}, by the ellipsometer is from 1.4 to 1.8 times larger than the root mean square average, t_{rms}.

The reflection of light from an inhomogeneous film may therefore be calculated by replacing the inhomogeneous film by a series of homogeneous films. Measurements of an inhomogeneous film by the ellipsometer give rise to averages of the refractive index and thickness of the film. Plausibly defined averages over the refractive index and thickness of the film were found that agree approximately with the averages that would be obtained by ellipsometry for three assumed variations of refractive index in the film.

4. Conclusions

The ellipsometer measures the change of polarization of light produced by reflection from a surface. For a film-free surface, the refractive index of the surface may be computed from ellipsometer readings.

Most applications of the ellipsometer involve measurement of a thin film on a substrate. For a film of known refractive index on a substrate of known refractive index, the thickness of the film may be calculated from ellipsometric measurements. For a nonabsorbing film (real refractive index), both the refractive index and thickness may be calculated from ellipsometric measurements. However, for an absorbing film (complex index of refraction) the refractive index and thickness of the film cannot be determined from a single set of ellipsometric measurements.

Therefore, a method was presented for analyzing sets of ellipsometer readings of absorbing films to determine their refractive indexes and thicknesses. The methods consisted of assuming values for the imaginary part, n_i, of the film refractive index and computing values of the real part, n_R, and the thickness of the film for each assumed value of n_i and each set of ellipsometer readings. Then the value of n_i is chosen that gives a constant value of n_R for the various sets of ellipsometer readings.

This method was tested for computed sets of ellipsometer readings obtained by varying (1) the thickness of the film, (2) the surrounding medium, (3) the substrate, and (4) the angle of incidence of the light. The method worked for sets of readings obtained by varying the film thickness when the film thicknesses were not too thin, but failed, for the assumed conditions, for film thicknesses up to only 100 Å. The method worked for sets of readings obtained by varying the surrounding medium or varying the substrate. However, the method worked only for a particular thickness of film for sets of readings obtained by varying the angle of incidence of the light. Therefore, the refractive index of an absorbing film may be determined from sets of ellipsometer readings obtained in various ways. The method of obtaining the sets of ellipsometer readings will depend on the particular experimental conditions.

The effect of variation of the refractive index in the direction perpendicular to the plane of the film was investigated. Such films are often measured by the ellipsometer and analyzed as though the refractive index of the film was constant. Therefore, average values for the refractive index and thickness of the film are obtained. The type of averaging that is obtained was determined. For this purpose, several films with varying refractive index were assumed and different kinds of averages for the refractive index and thickness of the films were calculated. The ellipsometer readings that would be obtained for these films were calculated and a refractive index and thickness were calculated from the ellipsometer readings. By a comparison of the averages determined by the ellipsometer readings with the directly computed averages, the kind of averaging obtained from the analysis of ellipsometric measurements was determined. Simple averages for refractive index and thickness of a film that agreed closely with those obtained from the ellipsometer readings were found.

5. References

[1] P. Drude, Ann. Physik **272**, 532 (1889); ibid. **272**, 865 (1889); ibid. **275**, 481 (1890).
[2] A. B. Winterbottom, Optical Studies of Metal Surfaces, The Royal Norwegian Scientific Society Report No. 1, 1955, published by F. Bruns, Trondheim, Norway; Trans. Faraday Soc. **42**, 487 (1946).
[3] F. L. McCrackin, E. Passaglia, R. R. Stromberg, and H. L. Steinberg, J. Res. NBS **67A** (Phys. and Chem), 363 (1963).
[4] F. L. McCrackin and J. Colson, A Fortran program for analysis of ellipsometer measurements and calculation of reflection coefficients from thin films, NBS Tech. Note 242 (1964).
[5] R. Stromberg, E. Passaglia, and D. Tutas, this book, p. 281.
[6] P. Rouard, Ann. Phys. **7**, 291 (1937).
[7] O. S. Heavens, Optical Properties of Thin Solid Films, Butterworths Scientific Publications, London (1955).
[8] P. C. S. Hayfield, The Drude-Tronstad polarimeter and its use in corrosion studies, First Intern. Congr. on Metallic Corrosion, Butterworths, London (1962).

Discussion

H. H. Soonpaa (Minneapolis-Honeywell Regulator Co.):
  You assumed the index of refraction was constant for films of varying thickness. In single crystal films, the index is known in at least two cases to vary with the thickness.

F. L. McCrackin:
  Yes, I quite agree. None of the results I presented were real data, except for the barium fluoride data. I assumed constant index. For actual films, the index may vary with the thickness so the method could not be applied. Maybe the index would be constant with thickness for film thicker than 100 Å so the method could be applied for this case.

A. N. Saxena (Fairchild Semiconductor Co.):
  In your presentation, you do not refer to Archer (J. Opt. Soc. Am. 52, 970, 1962), who has already used a program of Miss R. E. Cox, Bell Telephone Labs, and given ψ, Δ values for transparent films of various refractive indices on silicon. Actually it can be used for any film on any opaque substrate having known optical constants. I presume your program is either similar to the one used by Archer or else, is it an advanced version of this program?

F. L. McCrackin:
  The program was developed independently from Dr. Archer's program.

A. N. Saxena:
  Are your $\delta\Delta$ and $\delta\psi$ the differences between the experimentally measured and calculated values for Δ and ψ for a given index for the substrate and for the film?

F. L. McCrackin:
  Yes.

A. N. Saxena:
  The differences $\delta\psi$ and $\delta\Delta$ are rather large. Does that signify changes in the film itself or the error in the theoretical calculation due to inaccurate values of the optical constants of the film-substrate interface?

F. L. McCrackin:
  For the barium-fluoride film, various values of the index of refraction were assumed in order to find the true index. For some values of the refractive index, large values of $\delta\psi$ and $\delta\Delta$ were calculated. This indicated the calculation was inconsistent so these values of the refractive index were eliminated.

A. N. Saxena:
What was the experimental accuracy of Δ and ψ?

F. L. McCrackin:
Several hundredths of a degree.

A. J. Mabis (Procter and Gamble Company):
I would like to ask for which computer and which computer language the program is written and are copies available?

F. L. McCrackin:
The program I discussed is written in Fortran and can be used on an IBM 704, 7090, or 7094 computer, and probably others. A somewhat simplified version of the program has been run on an IBM 1410 computer. I will be happy to give copies of the program to anyone who wants them. The program is available as an NBS technical note. (NBS Tech. Note 242 (May 27, 1964), available from Superintendent of Documents, U. S. Government Printing Office, Washington, D.C. 20402. Price, 30 cents.)

A. Rothen (Rockefeller Institute):
What wavelengths did you use and have you tried different wavelengths?

F. L. McCrackin:
All the results were for the mercury green line. We have not used different wavelengths.

A. Rothen:
When you used different substrates, how thick was the film on the substrate?

F. L. McCrackin:
The films were 100 Å and had an index of 2.5–0.5i.

Factors Influencing the Experimental Sensitivity of the Drude Technique

Richard C. Smith and Michael Hacskaylo

Melpar Inc., Falls Church, Va.

When measuring film thickness with a polarizing spectrometer, the lowest measurable film thickness and the accuracy of the measurement are governed by the limitations of the optical apparatus. In addition, the film thickness calculated using the Drude approximate equations will be in error due to the inherent error in the approximation. The application of the Drude equations requires the measurement of the phase difference Δ and Δ' and the amplitude ratios ψ and ψ' of the uncoated and film-coated surfaces, respectively. The film thickness is then given in terms of the differences in these quantities, $\Delta - \Delta'$ and $\psi - \psi'$. The sensitivity, S, of a film of thickness t is defined as $(\Delta - \Delta')/t$ and $\dfrac{2\psi - 2\psi'}{\sin 2\psi'}\Big/ t$. The remaining experimental parameters or combination of parameters in the Drude equation are chosen so that the sensitivity is maximized, i.e., the maximum difference between the optical properties of the coated and uncoated surface per unit thickness will be realized. Curves and equations are presented to illustrate the dependence of the sensitivity on the experimental parameters and the technique is illustrated by practical cases where the experimental conditions are specified and the corresponding accuracy and limits of thickness determination are discussed.

1. Introduction

The state of polarization of light reflected from a metallic surface is altered when a thin film is introduced on the surface. Drude [1, 2][1] derived exact equations relating the thickness and refractive index of the film in terms of the angle of incidence, the optical constants of the metal surface, and the state of polarization of the reflected light. The exact equations, however, cannot be solved explicitly for the index of refraction and the thickness of the film. Drude therefore expanded the equations and retained only the first-order terms in thickness. The resulting equations are the well-known approximate equations, which are valid if the film thickness is small compared with the wavelength of the incident light. Although the validity of the Drude approximate equations has been confirmed many times [3, 4, 5, 6], their value in determining the refractive index of the film has been the subject of much conjecture [7, 8, 9].

The ellipsometer measures changes in the state of polarization of light reflected from the film-coated and uncoated surfaces, and the Drude equations relate these measurements to the thickness of the film. The purpose of this paper is to give the experimental conditions derived from the Drude approximate equations which will make the ellipsometric measurements most sensitive to film thicknesses. It will then be shown that both the minimum measurable film thickness

---

[1] Figures in brackets indicate the literature references on p. 93.

and the greatest accuracy are achieved under the conditions for which the sensitivity is a maximum.

2. The Drude Technique and the Sensitivity Equations

The "Drude technique" involves the use of an ellipsometer to determine the state of polarization of the light reflected from a bare metal surface and from the same metal surface coated with a thin transparent film. The state of polarization of light reflected from the metal surface is completely described by the two measured parameters,[2] Δ' and ψ', while the state of polarization of the light reflected from the film-coated surface is described by Δ and ψ. To avoid systematic error, the metal surface is only partially coated with the films so that Δ, Δ', ψ, and ψ' can be measured simultaneously. The optical constants can then be calculated from Δ' and ψ' using the equations of Ditchburn [10]. These values are then substituted into the Drude approximate equations from which the thickness and refractive index are calculated. The Drude approximate equations are given in the following form:

$$\Delta-\Delta'=-\frac{4\pi t}{\lambda}\frac{n^2-1}{n^2}\left\{\cos\phi\sin^2\phi\,\frac{\cos^2\phi-a_1}{a_2^2+(\cos^2\phi-a_1)^2}\right\} \tag{1}$$

$$2\psi-2\psi'=\frac{4\pi t}{\lambda}\frac{n^2-1}{n^2}\left\{a_2\cos\phi\sin^2\phi\,\frac{1-n^2\cos^2\phi}{a_2^2+(\cos^2\phi-a_1)^2}\right\}\sin 2\psi' \tag{2}$$

where:

$$a_1=\frac{1-\kappa^2}{\nu^2(1+\kappa^2)^2};\ a_2=\frac{2\kappa}{\nu^2(1+\kappa^2)^2};\ n^*=\nu(1-i\kappa)$$

The terms in the Drude equations can be divided into three groups; the measured parameters, Δ, Δ', ψ, and ψ'; the unknowns, n and t; and the constants of measurement n^*, λ, and ϕ. The constants of measurement can be chosen such that the difference in the measured parameters per unit thickness is a maximum. This difference per unit thickness is defined as the sensitivity.

The Drude approximate equations can be rearranged to yield the following sensitivity equations:

$$S_\Delta\equiv\Delta-\Delta'/t\equiv|-A\sigma_\Delta|;\quad S_\psi\equiv\frac{2\psi-2\psi'}{\sin 2\psi'}\,/t\equiv|A\sigma_\psi|, \tag{3}$$

where

$$\sigma_\Delta=\cos\phi\sin^2\phi\,\frac{\cos^2\phi-a_1}{a_2^2+(\cos^2\phi-a_1)^2} \tag{4}$$

$$\sigma_\psi=a_2\cos\phi\sin^2\phi\,\frac{1-n^2\cos^2\phi}{a_2^2+(\cos^2\phi-a_1)^2} \tag{5}$$

---

[2] See Glossary of Symbols in table 1.

and

$$A = \frac{4\pi}{\lambda} \left(\frac{n^2 - 1}{n^2} \right).$$

The ratios S_Δ and S_ψ, called the Δ- and ψ-sensitivities respectively, are expressed in units of degrees per Ångstrom (when the wavelength is in Ångstroms). Thus the sensitivity of the Drude technique is not uniquely determined by either S_Δ or S_ψ, but by some combination of the two.

3. Constructing the Nomographs

Because of the form of the sensitivity equations, the method of nomographical representation was chosen to display the inter-dependence of the maximum sensitivity, and the conditions for which the maximum sensitivity is derived. The optical constants, the maximum sensitivity, and the angle of incidence for maximum sensitivity are all functions of a_1 and a_2. For this reason a_1 and a_2 are chosen as coordinates for the nomographs. If the sensitivity is plotted as a function of the angle of incidence for fixed values of a_1 and a_2, there will be a maximum in the sensitivity at some characteristic angle of incidence. The nomographs are constructed by plotting the maximum sensitivity and the characteristic angle of incidence corresponding to that sensitivity for every combination of a_1 and a_2.

Each of the $\sigma_{\Delta, \psi}$ equations has terms which will vanish under certain measuring conditions. The factor $(\cos^2 \phi - a_1)$ in the numerator of eq (4) will vanish where a_1 assumes the value of $\cos^2 \phi$. However, if κ assumes only values which are greater than unity, then a_1 will be always negative, thereby precluding the possibility of a vanishing sensitivity. This restriction does not limit the choice of metals appreciably, since most metals which are satisfactory for use as substrates have extinction coefficients larger than unity [11]. The

TABLE 1. *Glossary of symbols*

$\Delta = \delta_p - \delta_s$; the difference in the phase changes of the p-component, δ_p, and the s-component, δ_s, on reflection from the film-coated substrate.

$\Delta' = \Delta$ for the uncoated metal substrate.

$\psi = \arctan \left[\dfrac{R_p/R_s}{E_p/E_s} \right]$ the arctangent of the factor by which the ratio of the p- and s-component reflection coefficients change on reflection from the film-coated substrate.

$\psi' = \psi$ for the uncoated metal substrate.

t = thickness of the film in Ångstroms.

n = index of refraction of the transparent film.

λ = wavelength of the incident light.

n^* = complex index of refraction of the metallic substrate.

ν = real part of the complex index of refraction.

κ = extinction coefficient.

ϕ = angle of incidence.

ϕ_Δ^* = angle of incidence for which the Δ-sensitivity is a maximum.

ϕ_ψ^* = angle of incidence for which the ψ-sensitivity is a maximum.

factor $(1 - n^2 \cos^2 \phi)$ in the numerator of eq (5) cannot be handled in this way, since there is an infinity of combinations of indices and angles of incidence for which the product is unity. Thus, this term must be carried along with no restrictions on the values of the index or angle of incidence. The wavelength appears in the factor A explicitly. At first thought, the sensitivity would be expected to increase for small wavelengths of incident light. But there is a higher order dependence of $\sigma_{\Delta, \psi}$ on the optical constants which in turn exhibit a nonlinear dependence on wavelength, namely dispersion. Thus the wavelength of the incident light should be chosen such that the values of the optical constants at that wavelength will offer the greatest sensitivity. This leaves the angle of incidence as the major experimentally independent variable affecting the Δ- and ψ-sensitivities. For particular values of a_1 and a_2, plots of sensitivity versus angle of incidence result in a peak for each sensitivity equation at some angle of incidence. This angle of incidence is defined as $\phi_{\Delta, \psi}^{*}$.

Curves of the Δ- and ψ-sensitivities as functions of angle of incidence are shown in figure 1. The sensitivities are calculated for the optical constants of chromium which are $\nu = 2.97$ and $\kappa = 1.63$ (see table 2). Under these conditions the Δ-sensitivity reaches a maximum at an angle of incidence, ϕ_{Δ}^{*}, of 76.50. The ψ-sensitivity curves are plotted for three film indices. The maximum values all occur at about the same angle, i.e., near 82.50° with only a slight increase in the characteristic angle of incidence and decrease in sensitivity with increasing film index. These effects are not appreciable. In general each combination of a_1 and a_2 has its characteristic angle of incidence for which maximum sensitivities are achieved.

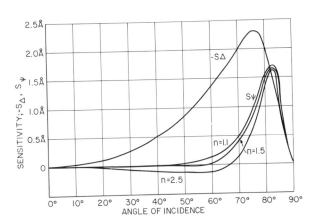

FIGURE 1. Δ-and ψ- sensitivity as a function of the angle of incidence.

These curves are plotted from the σ_{Δ}- and σ_{ψ}-equations (eqs. 4 and 5) using the values for a_1 and a_2 corresponding to a chromium substrate. The values of S_{Δ} and S_{ψ} are given in units of A. The curves for S_{ψ} are given for three indices $n = 1.1$, 1.5, and 2.5.

TABLE 2. *A list of the maximum Δ- and Ψ-sensitivities and related optical properties of various metals*

Metal	λ(Å)	ν	κ	a_1	a_2	ϕ^*_Δ	S_Δ	$n=1.1$		$n=1.5$		$n=2.5$		$\bar{\phi}$	$\bar{\psi}$
								ϕ^*_ψ	S_ψ	ϕ^*_ψ	S_ψ	ϕ^*_ψ	S_ψ		
Ag	5890	a 0.177	a 20.55	−0.0728	0.00703	76.5°	−2.66A	81.5°	0.107A	82.0°	0.110A	82.5°	0.098A	a 75.6°	a 43.8°
Mg	5461	b .57	b 6.14	−.7542	.02524	75.5°	−1.644A	81.0°	0.352A	81.5°	.344A	82.5°	.315A	-----	-----
Cr	5790	b 2.97	b 1.63	−.0203	.03995	76.5°	−2.30A	82.5°	1.68A	82.5°	1.65A	83.0°	1.64A	-----	-----
Hg	5780	c 1.77	c 2.80	−.0279	.02287	78.5°	−2.54A	83.5°	1.16A	83.5°	1.14A	84.0°	1.08A	c 79.8°	c 35.4°
Al	5890	b 1.44	b 3.68	−.0286	.01678	79.5°	−2.66A	83.5°	0.93A	83.5°	.92A	84.5°	0.88A	-----	-----
Cd	5890	b 1.13	b 4.44	−.03416	.01621	79.0°	−2.48A	84.0°	0.73A	84.0°	.72A	84.0°	0.69A	-----	-----
Cu	5000	a 1.10	a 2.13	−.09534	.1148	69.0°	−1.13A	77.5°	0.669A	78.0°	.637A	80.0°	0.542A	a 70.8°	a 33.8°
Au	5890	d .47	d 6.01	−.115	.0395	72.5°	−1.28A	79.5°	0.28A	80.0°	.27A	81.0°	0.24A	d 72.3°	d 41.6°
Stainless steel	5890	e 2.46	e 1.48	−.0193	.0479	74.5°	−2.14A	81.5°	1.70A	81.5°	1.66A	82.5°	1.52A	e 77.5°	e 28.0°

$\bar{\phi}$ ≡ Principal angle of incidence.
$\bar{\psi}$ ≡ Principal azimuth.
a. Minor; Phys. Chem. Tabellen; vol. 1, p. 463, Berlin, 1927.
b. International critical tables; vol. 5 (McGraw-Hill Book Co., Inc.), 1929.
c. Schulz, Wein's Handbook of Experimental Physics.
d. Jenkins and White, Fundamentals of Optics (McGraw-Hill Book Co., Inc.), 1957.
e. Rothen and Hanson, Rev. Sci. Instr.; vol. 20, 66 (1949).

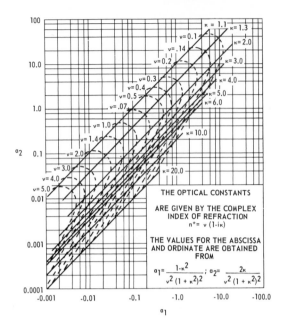

FIGURE 2. *Nomograph giving a_1 and a_2 as a function of the real part of the index of refraction, ν, and the extinction coefficient κ.*

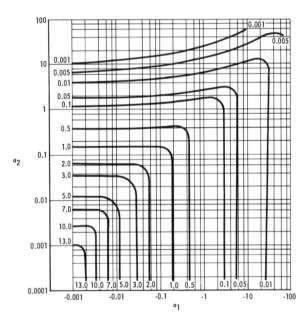

FIGURE 3. *Nomograph giving a_1 and a_2 as a function of the peak Δ sensitivity*

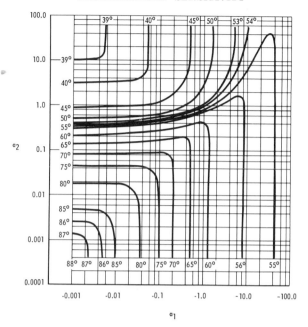

FIGURE 4.   *Nomograph giving a_1 and a_2 as a function of the angle of incidence for maximum Δ-sensitivity*

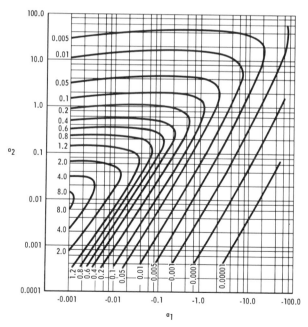

FIGURE 5.   *Nomograph giving a_1 and a_2 as a function of peak ψ-sensitivity*

For the condition where the two sensitivity maxima are not at the same angle of incidence, the optimum angle of incidence lies somewhere between the two maxima. Since both equations are needed to determine the index and thickness of the film, both sensitivities should be as high as possible at the selected angle of incidence. The sensitivity of the Drude technique will be the smaller of the two sensitivities at the chosen angle of incidence. For the case of chromium where the separation in the characteristic angles of incidence is about 6 deg, the optimum angle can be approximately at the value of ϕ_ψ^*. At this angle of incidence the ψ-sensitivity is a maximum and the Δ-sensitivity is very nearly equal to this value.

The nomograph shown in figure 2 gives the variation of a_1 and a_2 for combinations of the optical constants ν and κ. The practical range of values of ν was chosen to be from 0.1 to 5.0 and of κ from 1.1 to 20.0. The corresponding values for a_1 and a_2 can be found on the abscissa and ordinate, respectively.

A plot of the maximum values of σ_Δ as a function of a_1 and a_2 is plotted in figure 3. The values for a_1 and a_2 were selected to encompass the useful and practical range of values of ν and κ given above. The range of a_1 is from -0.001 to -100, and the range of a_2 is from 0.0001 to 100. The highest values of σ_Δ, and consequently the maximum sensitivity, occur at the lower magnitude of a_1 and a_2. The magnitude of the sensitivity is obtained by multiplying the values of σ_Δ of figure 3 by the factor A. From the nomograph in figure 4

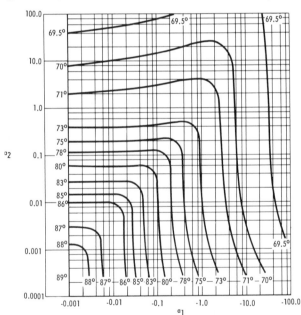

FIGURE 6. *Nomograph giving a_1 and a_2 as a function of the angle of incidence for maximum ψ-sensitivity.*

one can determine the angle of incidence ϕ_Δ^* for which σ_Δ is a maximum. A combination of values of a_1 and a_2 which falls, for example, on the curve marked 70° has a characteristic angle of incidence for maximum sensitivity of 70 deg. Clearly, all combinations of a_1 and a_2 within the limits of the nomograph, which have peak sensitivities at 70°, are included in this curve. The nomograph giving σ_ψ as a function of a_1 and a_2 is shown in figure 5. The values of a_1 and a_2 cover the same ranges as before. The maximum values of σ_ψ are less by an order of magnitude than the σ_Δ values for the same a_1 and a_2 ranges. A plot of the angles of incidence for which maximum values of σ_ψ are obtained at given values of a_1 and a_2 are shown in figure 6. To obtain the magnitude of the ψ-sensitivity the values of σ_ψ in figure 5 must be multiplied by the factor A.

4. Discussion

The metals most suitable for accurate thickness measurements by this technique must afford maximum sensitivities for both sensitivity equations at the same angle of incidence. It is clear that such metals must have optical constants which give values for a_1 and a_2 located in the lower left-hand corner of the nomograph in figure 2. For combinations of lower values of a_1 and a_2 the characteristic angles for maximum Δ- and ψ-sensitivities correspond more closely than for combinations of higher magnitudes. As the magnitudes of a_1 and a_2 increase, the separation of characteristic angles ϕ_Δ^* and ϕ_ψ^* also increases. In general, the larger the real index and the extinction coefficient the closer the values of ϕ_Δ^* and ϕ_ψ^*. However, the choice cannot be strictly limited by coincidence of the angles of incidence.

In table 2 are listed various metals, their optical constants, calculated characteristic angles and sensitivities, and principal angles of incidence. In the visible region of the spectrum, silver has one of the highest extinction coefficients [11] and as a consequence a_2 becomes quite small. Since the ψ-sensitivity is directly proportional to a_2, this sensitivity becomes much smaller than the Δ-sensitivity. Thus, even though the Δ-sensitivity is one of the highest for metals, its relatively low ψ-sensitivity does not make silver particularly useful as a substrate.

The four metals, chromium, mercury, aluminum, and stainless steel, have Δ- and ψ-sensitivities which are of the same order of magnitude. In each case the Δ-sensitivity peaks and the ψ-sensitivity peaks occur at angles of incidence which are separated by about 5° to 7°. Each metal may be treated in the same manner as was previously employed for chromium (fig. 1), and the optimum angle of incidence will be that near ϕ_ψ^*. Thus, for the cases where the sensitivities are comparable in magnitude and the characteristic angles are within 7°, the optimum angles of incidence are those near the ψ-characteristic angle. It has been suggested that an angle of incidence near the principle angle would afford good sensitivity [9]. Note that for the cases where the principal angle of incidence is given, the Δ-characteristic angle is less than the principal angle by about one degree while the ψ-characteristic angle is greater by about 6 deg.

The sensitivity is of interest in extending the minimum measurable film thickness as well as increasing the accuracy of the measurement technique. The Drude technique involves the measurement of the difference in the values of Δ and Δ' and ψ and ψ'. Since in general there is a fixed experimental error involved in the determination of each of these parameters, the error in determining the difference in parameters is also fixed. Thus, the percent error decreases as the difference in the parameters increases.

Consider an ellipsometer which can read the orientation angle of plane polarized light to $P \pm \delta P = 0.01 \pm 0.005$ deg. Thus the difference in two angles, P and P' which can be experimentally determined can be represented as

$$(P - P') \pm (\delta P + \delta P') = 0.01 \pm 0.01 \text{ deg.} \tag{6}$$

This gives an error of 100 percent at the minimum measurable difference in angles. In an effort to determine the minimum measurable thickness one must specify what percent error is permissible. Considering 10 percent as the minimum permissible error, and if the error in determining the difference in these angles is ± 0.01 deg the difference in the angles must not be less than 0.1 deg for the 10 percent maximum error. Thus for 10 percent error the minimum determinable difference in parameters can represented as

$$(P - P') \pm (\delta P + \delta P')_{\text{min}} = 0.1 \pm 0.01 \text{ deg.} \tag{7}$$

Now from the sensitivity equation, the minimum thickness is given in terms of the minimum in the differences in the parameters. For the Δ-equation,

$$t_{\text{min}} = \frac{(\Delta - \Delta') \pm (\delta\Delta + \delta\Delta')_{\text{min}}}{|-A\sigma_\Delta|}. \tag{8}$$

If the Δ-sensitivity, $|-A\sigma_\Delta|$, under optimum experimental conditions is given as 0.1 deg/Å, then

$$t_{\text{min}} = 1 \pm 0.1 \text{ Å.}$$

When the sensitivity increases for films of the same thickness the percent error is decreased by the same factor. This does not hold for films at the minimum measurable thickness. The *percent* error will always remain the same for a film of "minimum thickness" regardless of the sensitivity.

As a practical example consider chromium. At a wavelength of 5790 Å, $\nu = 2.97$, $\kappa = 1.63$, and the angle of incidence for maximum sensitivity is at 76.5°, $\sigma_\Delta = 2.30$, and for a barium stearate film of index 1.5, the value of A is 0.07. This gives the minimum measurable film thickness with 10 percent error as

$$t_{min} = 0.625 \pm 0.0625 \text{ A.}$$

This, of course, does not include the inherent error of this technique due to the theoretical Drude approximations cited before. This error in calculations due to the approximate nature of the Drude equations has been reported to be about 5 percent up to 100 Å in thickness [12].

It is clear that one must choose the optimum experimental conditions, i.e., those conditions for which maximum sensitivity will be afforded, to achieve both high accuracy and minimum measurable thickness. Thus, two methods of choice of conditions are open to the experimenter. He can use the nomographs to determine the optical constants and the corresponding angle of incidence which afford maximum sensitivities and select the metals or form alloys which exhibit these optical constants. Or he may use the nomographs to choose the particular metal substrate of those he has available to him which will afford the highest sensitivity.

The authors acknowledge the assistance of J. C. DeBrie, J. H. Hoskinson, and R. J. Murphy in the preparation of the nomographs.

5. References

[1] P. Drude, Ann. Physik Chemie **36**, 532 (1889).
[2] P. Drude, Ann. Physik Chemie **39**, 481 (1890).
[3] A. Rothen, Rev. Sci. Instr. **16**, 26 (1945).
[4] A. Rothen, Rev. Sci. Instr. **28**, 283 (1957).
[5] J. A. Faucher, G. M. McManus, and H. J. Trurnit, J. Opt. Soc. Am. **48**, 51 (1950).
[6] I. N. Shkylarevskii and N. A. Nosulenko, Opt. i Spektroskopiya **12**, 435 (1962).
[7] A. B. Winterbottom, Kgl. Norske Videnskab. Selskab. **45**, 128 ff (1955)
[8] R. D. Mattuck, Rev. Sci. Instr. **23**, 844 (1957).
[9] F. P. Mertens, P. Theroux, and R. C. Plumb, J. Opt. Soc. Am. **53**, 788 (1963).
[10] R. W. Ditchburn, J. Opt. Soc. Am. **45**, 743 (1955).
[11] See, e.g., Am. Inst. of Physics Handb., sec. 6K (McGraw-Hill Book Co., Inc., New York, 1957).
[12] O. S. Heavens, Optical Properties of Thin Solid Films, p. 143 (Butterworth's Scientific Publications, London, 1955).

Discussion

A. BAIDINS (E. I. duPont deNemours Company):

I noticed that in this symposium practically all the papers deal with ellipsometry on metal substrates and I know in principle that it is possible to determine the thickness of coatings on dielectrics— what are the sensitivities in that case?

R. C. SMITH:

The work which I have done here has only been in terms of metal substrates. This was part of a feasibility study in the use of the ellipsometer to measure the thickness of evaporated films on metal substrates and we did not consider anything on dielectric substrates. One would have to make a study under much the same conditions as this.

E. PASSAGLIA (National Bureau of Standards):

I can comment on that to some extent. We have never done work in our laboratory with direct reflection from a dielectric substrate, nor to my knowledge has anyone else in the Bureau. But we have done work with total reflection. Here, of course, one does not have the problem of low sensitivity because of the low reflection coefficient. On the other hand, one has only one parameter to work with, for tan ψ is always unity. A theoretical calculation shows that for a film with refractive index 1.6 on glass with refractive index 1.838 the whole being immersed in water, a film 250 Å thick causes a change in Δ of about 4°, this is about 60 Å per degree, so there is no problem with sensitivity, provided the refractive index of the film is not too close to that of the substrate or surrounding medium.

A. C. HALL (Socony Mobil Oil Company):

Antonín Vašíček, among others, has used the reflected polarized light method in studying thin films on dielectric substrates. He has contributed two concise analyses of experimental limits; they appear in the Journal of the Optical Society of America **37,** 979 (1947), and **47,** 565 (1957).

D. J. TUTAS (National Bureau of Standards):

I would like to know how you prepared these films? We prepared some films of some of these metals you discussed and also made some tables calculating the sensitivity and find the angles different from what you gave.

R. C. SMITH:

The angles for maximum sensitivity reported in the table are given for optical constants reported by previous workers. The preparation of metallic surfaces and subsequent measurement were not in the scope of this study. The Drude approximate equations were here used to calculate the sensitivity of the parameters by the Drude technique, i.e. Δ, Δ', ψ, and ψ'. The sensitivities and consequently the optimum angle of incidence vary very rapidly with the optical constants and with the wavelength of light. Thus if your metals had the same optical constants as reported here and your definition of "sensitivity" was similar, then I would expect you to obtain the same optimum angle of incidence. If a different set of equations is used to calculate a sensitivity, as for instance the exact Drude equations, one would not expect to obtain exactly the same angle of incidence—even for the same optical constants—because of a different definition of the "sensitivity."

A. K. N. REDDY (University of Pennsylvania):

I am sure that Dr. Archer will agree with me that in connection with photoelectric ellipsometry it would be useful to have tables of maximum Δ sensitivity and minimum ψ sensitivity so that one can throw the whole burden of change of intensity on one of the parameters.

Increased Scope of Ellipsometric Studies of Surface Film Formation

A. B. Winterbottom

Norges Tekniske Högskole (The Norwegian Institute of Technology), Trondheim, Norway

Recent developments in ellipsometric instruments and methods should increase the scope of profitable applications of this technique even though the principles of such applications remain unchanged. The more sensitive photoelectric methods now available will undoubtedly replace classical visual procedures. The development of systems capable of following and registering rapidly changing phenomena would not be expected to involve any specially sophisticated electronics. An experimental photoelectric ellipsometer to explore such possibilities is described.

1. Historical Introduction

Paul Drude [1],[1] with an amazing combination of theoretical insight and experimental skill, derived the basic theory of film optics and demonstrated its validity elegantly by measuring the progressive changes in reflection on cleavage faces of stibnite and tetradymite. Sporadic applications of ellipsometry to the study of film formation were made subsequently by various students of such phenomena. The instruments used were usually adapted spectrometers or so-called crystal ellipsometers, perhaps best suited for simple classroom demonstration but which required the addition of many appurtenances to enable experiments to be conducted under controlled conditions of environment and temperature and even for the reading of scales [2]. Nevertheless, useful results were obtained and these were improved in quality and precision by improvement in the details of the measurement technique and particularly by the preparation of simple, well-defined surfaces free from surface damage and contamination, by the use of single crystal specimens and of electrolytic polishing, etc. [3].

In addition to the desire for higher precision in the quantitative results obtained and a finer discrimination as regards the nature of film substance formed, there was also a need for an automatic recording instrument to make studies of rapid surface changes. The late Professor Bonhoeffer was keenly interested in exploring this aspect and initiated work at Göttingen over ten years ago. A servo-operated ellipsometer was actually built there and this has since been presented to Professor K. Vetter, after Professor Bonhoeffer's death. However, this instrument was apparently much too sluggish to be used to follow rapid changes [4]. Professor J. O'M. Bockris, who is participating in this conference, was also one of those who has long been interested in new and more thorough studies of electrode phenomena with improved ellipsometer technique.

---

[1] Figures in brackets indicate literature references on page 110.

At Norges Tekniske Högskole (NTH), ellipsometric studies of film formation in both liquid and gaseous environments have been made from the late 20's onward by Tronstad [6] and various collaborators, later by the present author [7], and most recently by Marjorie A. Barrett [8]. All these studies have been made with a visual instrument that has previously been described in some detail in various papers [9].

Quite recently a request was made by Norsk Blikkvalseverk for the development of simple ellipsometer equipment to monitor oil film thickness on tin plate. It was decided to undertake this task as, although automatic recording equipment for the purpose could then be purchased in the United States [10], it was felt that it would provide an opportunity to gain experience in photoelectric ellipsometry and at the same time possibly lead to the development of a simpler, cheaper photoelectric ellipsometer suited to this kind of application. This led to studies of the literature on the subject and to the discussion of the problems involved in polarization modulation for simultaneous independent feedback compensation of the two magnitudes involved in ellipsometry with electronic engineer colleagues, both at Norges Tekniske Högskole and at the National Physical Laboratory (NPL).

As a result of these studies and discussions, an experimental ellipsometer with facilities for trial of various modulation and compensation systems is now being built. The design of this instrument will be briefly discussed in the following.

2. Basic Instrument Design

As previously noted, the majority of the ellipsometric studies so far made have been carried out with adapted optical instruments of the classic type to which many auxiliary services have been added. The space for experimental cells or chambers has often been cramped and access to it severely limited. There is also the question whether the plane of incidence shall be horizontal or vertical, or whether the instrument should be adapted to both arrangements. The visual instrument in use at Trondheim can be operated in both ways, but it has been used almost exclusively with the plane of incidence vertical and specimen surface horizontal (figs. 1 and 2).

We know of other workers who have exclusively used the alternative arrangement with plane of incidence horizontal and the experimental surface vertical [11] (fig. 3).

Evidently each arrangement has its advantages and disadvantages. We have chosen to design the new photoelectric instrument for use with plane of incidence primarily horizontal but with facility for adapting to the other arrangement with the plane of incidence vertical.

In view of the desire to experiment with modulation and compensation based on magnetic rotation (Faraday effect), the new instrument construction aims at the minimum use of metal in the

FIGURE 1. *Ellipsometer built by C. Leiss to the specification of Leif Tronstad with quarter-wave plate compensator in incident system and applicable to studies of horizontal or vertical surfaces (1931).*

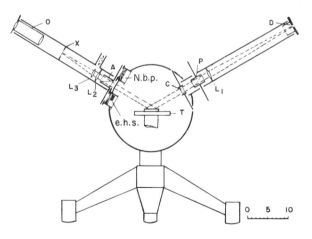

FIGURE 2. *Optical system of Leiss ellipsometer.*

FIGURE 3.   *Ellipsometer designed and used by P. C. S. Hayfield with quarter-wave plate compensator in reflected system and applicable to studies of vertical surfaces (ca. 1950). [11]*

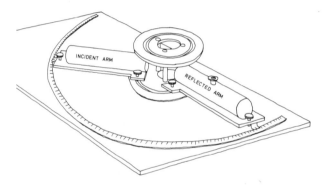

FIGURE 4.   *General arrangement of experimental photoelectric ellipsometer under development at Trondheim (1963).*

vicinity of the optical components and avoidance of magnetic materials entirely. It seems appropriate to enclose the optical systems of the incident beam and the reflected beam, as well as the experimental space, in light-tight chambers so that the instrument can normally be used in a lighted laboratory.

Although it is expected that photoelectric operation will ultimately supersede visual operation entirely, the present experimental arrangement does permit alternative visual operation with halfshades. The instrument table also provides accommodation for the various electronic units and auxiliary service units under the table plate and in the dead quadrant (fig. 4).

3. Basic Ellipsometer Optics

Discussion of the changes in the state of polarization produced on passing the various optical units in an instrument system is of course facilitated by the use of appropriate terminology and mathematical manipulation methods. A specially clear exposition of the analytical treatment of such problems has been given by the late Dr. L. B. Tuckerman of the National Bureau of Standards in a classic paper [12]. The Poincaré method of representation of a general state of polarization as a point on the surface of a sphere has much to commend it for rapid examination of the action of optical systems containing doubly refracting and rotating elements and also reflectors. It has been described in Poincaré's monograph, Théorie Mathematique de la Lumière, and in a series of papers concerned with its utility in various practical cases [13]. A recent monograph on polarized light also discusses and describes this and other methods of treatment [14].

Turning now to the basic optics of the ellipsometer, these aim at determining the two magnitudes characterizing the reflection of a polarized wave, viz, the relative amplitude reduction and the relative phase retardation of the components vibrating parallel and perpendicular to the plane of incidence. It turns out that these magnitudes can be determined for any surface by allowing a monochromatic polarized coherent beam to pass through a system composed of a polarizer, experimental reflecting surface, and an analyser with a quarter-wave plate fixed in a diagonal azimuth either before or after the reflector. It is not necessary that the quarter-wave plate be exactly quarter wave. If the polarizer and analyser settings are found which give perfect extinction, then the two required magnitudes can be computed from these settings and the constants of the quarter-wave plate compensator. The two alternative arrangements with the Poincaré representations of their action are given in figure 5. These

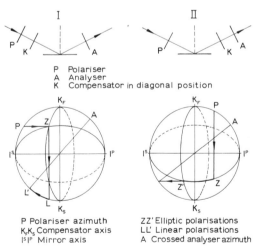

P Polariser
A Analyser
K Compensator in diagonal position

P Polariser azimuth
$K_F K_S$ Compensator axis
$I^S I^P$ Mirror axis

ZZ' Elliptic polarisations
LL' Linear polarisations
A Crossed analyser azimuth

NB. Primed polarisations result from relative
amplitude reduction

FIGURE 5. *Alternative arrangements of ellipsometer optical systems with Poincaré representations of their respective modes of action.*

alternative arrangements each have their advantages and disadvantages, and the choice of one or the other will depend on the relative importance attached to these differences. Since the quarter-wave plate does not occupy much space, it was deemed wise in the present case to provide for easy insertion and removal of plates in both the alternative diagonal positions, together with facilities for fine adjustment of their settings and for changing to alternative diagonal settings quickly with click action as in some types of microscope polarizers

The polarizer and analyser will initially be of the usual polaroid type mounted in circles with manual setting and scales with verniers, but servo-operation may also be tried. The polarizer and analyser may of course be used with fixed settings when some other means is used for varying the polarizer or analyser azimuth, such as magnetic-rotation units.

Elementary considerations of error in such systems reveal that multiple reflection can give rise to systematic effects that are nevertheless difficult to predict and correct [9,13b]. On these grounds there should be the minimum of air/glass (or other transparent solid) surfaces in the system and those surfaces that cannot be avoided should be provided with antireflection coatings or nondeviating prismatic cover glasses. The random error involved in setting the instrument is of the greatest importance for the precision of the measurements and as it is really the essential property of the setting device it is treated in the next section.

4. Ellipsometer Setting Devices: Halfshades or Modulators

Inevitably the precision with which an ellipsometer can measure depends on the precision with which the settings of the adjustable optical units can be made and read. In visual work halfshades are used for increasing the accuracy of setting as in conventional polarimetry. One set of halfshades enables the analyser to be set precisely crossed to the plane of polarization of the final beam and thus to determine the azimuth of the final polarization while the other set must enable another of the optical units, the polarizer, to be set so that the final polarization is precisely plane polarized. The sensitivity with which settings can be made with halfshades depends on the ability of the eye to distinguish intensity differences at various intensity levels, the intensity of the source and the halfshadow angle. This has been treated exhaustively in many papers, monographs, and handbooks [13b,15].

The Poincaré representations in figure 6 show how the amplitudes and accordingly the intensities in the two fields of halfshade systems may be studied. For a symmetrical system it is evident that equality of intensity for the two half fields would be obtained when the points characterizing the polarizations for the two half fields are equidistant from the point representing the polarization crossed by the analyser. To obtain this, the incident polarization or the analyser setting

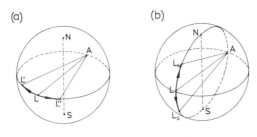

(a) Azimuth (e.g. Nakumara).
(b) Ellipticity.

FIGURE 6. *Poincaré representations of action of halfshade systems or of modulation.*

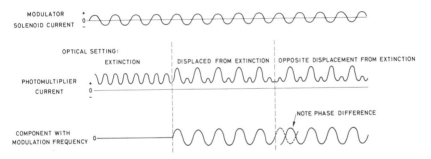

FIGURE 7. *Effect of modulation on photomultiplier output with extinction setting and slight deviations from this in both senses.*

must be altered.   In the case of a biplate with clockwise and anticlockwise rotations of equal magnitude for the two half fields, evidently the system is sensitive solely to azimuth.   Deviation from the truly crossed position leads to differences in intensity for the half fields.   Similarly a symmetrical doubly refracting biplate system would be sensitive only to ellipticity.

Similar Poincaré representations may be used to discuss the effects of periodic modulation of a polarization with suitable periodic alterations in either azimuth or ellipticity.   However, in this case the extreme points represent the extreme alterations produced in the polarization arriving at the analyser at various times.   If the polarization that is modulated would be precisely crossed by the analyser setting, then successive extreme positions of the modulated polarization would be equidistant from the extinguished polarization in the Poincaré representation and the heights of successive peaks in a photomultiplier output would be identical.   It is thus apparent that the output from a photomultiplier analyser combination receiving a polarized beam modulated symmetrically about the truly crossed polarization would only contain a double modulation-frequency component superposed on the dark current.   On the other hand, unsymmetrical modulation or deviation from the true crossed polarization, whether it be in azimuth or in ellipticity, would evidently cause successive peaks in the photomultiplier output to alternate in magnitude. That is, this output would contain a modulation-frequency component in addition to the double-modulation frequency. Furthermore, it turns out that as the deviation alters sense when the polarization passes through the truly crossed azimuth polarization, then the modulation-frequency component of the photomultiplier output would change phase by a half wave (see fig. 7).

Evidently these features of modulation bear in themselves the possibilities not only for sensitive setting of polarizers and the like but also for automatic compensation [16]. This is precisely what is done in the ETL–NPL automatic saccharimeter which is shown in figure 8 and diagrammatically in figure 9 with a block diagram in figure 10. A diagram showing the way in which compensatory feedback is obtained is given in figure 11. This polarimeter is based

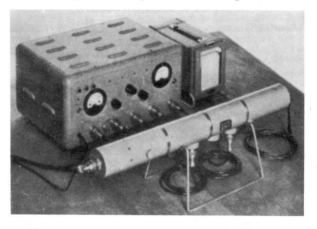

FIGURE 8.   *ETL-NPL automatic saccharimeter.*

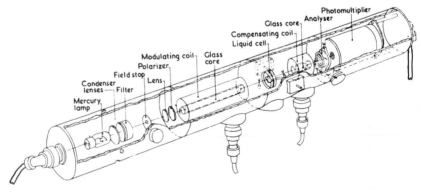

FIGURE 9.   *ETL-NPL automatic saccharimeter (diagrammatic).*

on the utilisation of Faraday magnetic rotation of the plane of polarization with the output feedback. In a commercial version it can measure rotations of up to 0.5° with an accuracy of ±0.0001°.

It is of course feasible to modulate symmetrically by oscillating the polarizer or analyser equally about their settings [17]. This is also done in one type of commercial polarimeter and a sensitive galvanometer used directly in the photomultiplier output. Here the precise crossed position is set with an accuracy of about 0.001° by simply adjusting until the galvanometer spot does not move on on flipping the polarizer. The Faraday rotation is given by the expression:

$$\alpha = vlH \text{ and } H = 1{,}257\ ni,$$

where

α is the instantaneous rotation in minutes of arc,

i is the instantaneous current in amperes,

H intensity of magnetization,

n the number of turns per centimeter length of solenoid,

l the length of solenoid in centimeters,

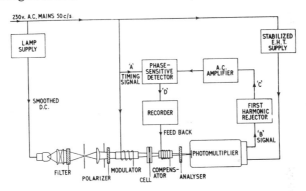

FIGURE 10. *ETL-NPL automatic saccharimeter-diagrammatic section of optics of the saccharimeter and block diagram of the electronic circuit.*

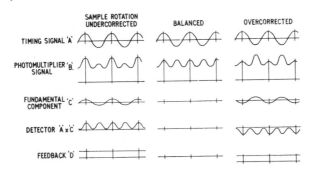

FIGURE 11. *Derivation of feedback signal giving automatic compensation in a photoelectric polarimeter.*

and

   v the Verdet constant in minutes/gauss/centimeter for the core substance.

For a long core extending to negligible fringe field strengths on each side of the solenoid it can be shown that $\alpha = 1{,}257\,vNi$, where N is now the total number of turns. The refractive index and Verdet constant are given in table 1 for a number of transparent materials.

TABLE 1. *Values of Verdet constant for a few transparent solids and liquids at room temperature and for sodium light*

Substance	Refractive index for NaD	Verdet constant minutes of arc/gauss/cm
Carbon disulfide	1.6994	0.04255
Monobromnaphthalene	1.6578	.0519
Chance Pilkington glasses		
EDF 700303	1.70035	.052
DEDF 748278	1.74842	.062
DEDF 801255	1.80120	.074
DEDF 927210	1.92707	.106

TABLE 2. *Specifications of some solenoids used in magnetic rotation experiments*

No	1	2	3	4	5
Name	Perkin	Lowry	Gates	Gillham and King	Gillham and King
Literature references	18	19	16	16	16
Dimension length _mm_	146		115	57	57
diameter int _mm_	76		14	10	10
diameter ext _mm_	476		36		
Winding turns	2000	7620		65000	8
Conductor dimensions	3×2.7 mm			428W G	6 mm bore copper tube
Weight (approx) _kg_	100				
Resistance _ω_		50	1	12500	
Current _A_	12, 5	4	1	0,007	
_V_	50	200	1	87.5	
_W_	625	800	1	0,6	170
Max. field _CGS_	1000				
Core substance	water	CS₂	glass DEDF 930,181		
Max. rotation _deg_	±4.5°	±20°	±3°	±0.1°	±1.8°
Remarks	iron shroud and end plates	iron shroud and end plates			

A group of workers at NPL, England, developing photoelectric polarimeter equipment, have used fused quartz glass or a special double, extra-dense flint glass from Chance Pilkington for both modulators and compensators. The double, extra-dense flint glasses have high refractive indices, as the name implies, and reflected parasite beams, approaching 10 percent per surface, might be expected to be embarrassing. It would therefore be desirable to provide end-cover glasses coated for reduced reflection and possibly to arrange for continuous core rods for each modulator-compensator set if such long rods could be obtained. Alternatively, it might be simpler to use long jacketed polarimeter tubes with a liquid of high refractive index and Verdet constant, such as monobromnaphthalene. The compensators and probably also the modulators should be provided with thermostat-controlled water circulation in order to define the core temperature and hence the Verdet constants.

In table 2 are tabulated the specifications of some Faraday modulator and compensator coils and their performances with specified core material. The coils used by Perkin [18] and Lowry [19] in their classical work on magnetic rotation are also included. Since these were used with steady currents, the materials and design would have to be modified appropriately if modulators or compensators were to be made on similar lines.

4.1. Electro-Optic Effect, Pockels Effect

Other optical effects that might be utilised in automatic ellipsometry are the electro-optic effects: the Kerr effect in liquids and the Pockels effect in crystals. The latter is the converse of the piezoelectric effect, viz., the setting up of anisotropy as a result of an applied electric field. One kind of crystal in which this effect is pronounced is ammonium dihydrogen phosphate (ADP), which is tetragonal, i.e. uniaxial. The properties of this crystal have been studied and reviewed by Billings [20]. A so-called Z-cut slice of ADP is generally mounted between conducting transparent cover glasses (e.g., glass coated with SnO such as NESA) for electro-optic work. On applying a field in the Z direction, the crystal slice becomes

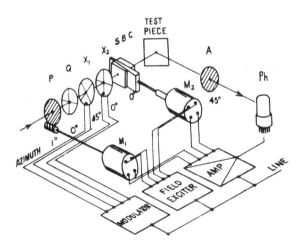

FIGURE 12. *Photoelectric polarimeter after Takasaki (diagrammatic).*

biaxial with induced axes at 45° to the X and Y axes with orientation independent of the field strength. The retardation of such a slice is a linear function of the potential applied and independent of the thickness. A retardation of a halfwave requires a potential of about 9 kv which is near the breakdown voltage for thicknesses less than about 0.2 mm.

It is evidently possible to use ADP to modulate polarizations except linear ones with azimuths identical with those of the induced axes. The modulation will naturally be greatest for polarizations with azimuths diagonal to the induced axes. The modulation will follow small circles having the induced axes as centre in the Poincaré representation.

Takasaki has described a number of applications of such modulators including a photoelectric polarimeter [21[. This utilizes a polarizer and Soleil-Babinet compensator system driven by servomotors (see fig. 12). The elliptic polarization coming from the polarizer quarter-wave plate in zero azimuth is modulated in two directions at right angles on the Poincaré sphere by ADP modulators with induced axes in 45° and 0° azimuths. Thus one modulation is effective only in the azimuth of the ultimate polarization arriving at the analyser, while the other is effective only in the ellipticity. If the final polarization is not exactly crossed to the analyser fixed at 45° in both aximuth and ellipticity, modulation-frequency components appear in the photomultiplier signal. The servos acting as phase-sensitive detectors react only to modulation-frequency components supplied to their control phases derived from modulation by their respective reference phases.

5. Experimental Ellipsometer for Trial of Alternative Modulation-Compensation Systems

It has been seen that automatic compensation can in general be derived from suitable modulation of the polarization in the optical system followed by photoelectric detection, amplification, and feedback. Furthermore it is apparent that various methods of modulation and compensation are feasible, ranging from mechanical movement of components to magnetic or electrical effects. Since the sensitivity and precision of automatic polarimeters based on the use of magnetic rotation for both modulation and compensation have been amply demonstrated, it would be appropriate to try to adapt the same methods to ellipsometry. Evidently, servo-operation with either ADP modulation in the manner of Takasaki or magnetic rotation modulation, could be applied to measurements where the reflecting surface only changes slowly.

The experimental photoelectric ellipsometer now being built at Trondheim provides for manual operation with either visual halfshade systems or with photomultiplier-detector-galvanometer or with various modulator-compensator system combinations (see fig. 13).

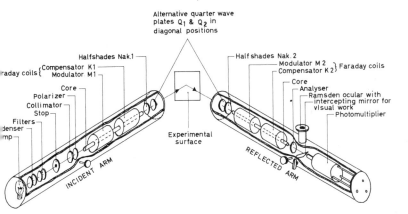

FIGURE 13. *Optical system of experimental photoelectric ellipsometer with arrangements for operation in various ways (diagrammatic).*

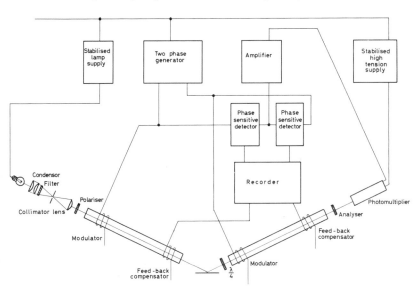

FIGURE 14. *Combined diagram of optical system and block diagram of the electronic circuit for a trial arrangement of the experimental photoelectric ellipsometer.*

One system that seems particularly promising is indicated diagrammatically in figure 14. With this experimental instrument it is hoped that it will be possible to determine the feasibility of a purely electronic ellipsometer with fixed optical units, providing indications and records of the two reflection parameters Δ and ψ, even when changing rapidly. Such an instrument it is felt might find wide applications in both the technological and pure research fields.

This work has been supported with grants from The Royal Norwegian Council for Scientific and Industrial Research over a number of years, which support is gratefully acknowledged. A special grant awarded by Norges Tekniske Högskoles Fond has made the design and construction of the new ellipsometer possible, for which the author expresses his sincere thanks. He is also indebted to the Industrial Research Division (SINTEF) and to many friends and colleagues at the Division of Automatic Control for assistance with electronic problems and to Mr. E. J. Gillham and Dr. King of NPL, Light Division, for stimulating discussions and advice.

6. References

[1] P. Drude, Über Oberflächenschichten I and II, Wiedeman Ann. Phys. **36**, 532, 865 (1899).

[2] A. B. Winterbottom, The study of immersed surfaces based on the reflection of polarized light. Principles and possibilities, Z. Electrochemie **62**, 811 (1958).

[3] F. W. Young, Jr., J. V. Cathcart, and A. T. Gwathmey, Acta Met. **41**, 145 (1956).

[4] K. H. Bonhoeffer, private communication (1957); M. A. Barrett, Norges Tekniske Hogskole, Trondheim, Norway, private communication (1961).

[5] J. O'M. Bockris, Univ. of Pennsylvania, Philadelphia, Pa., private communication (1960).

[6] L. Tronstad, The validity of Drude's optical method of investigating transparent films on metals, Trans. Faraday Soc. **31**, 1151 (1935).

[7] A. B. Winterbottom.

[8] M. A. Barrett, B 173 Report 10, Royal Norwegian Council for Scientific and Industrial Research; M. A. Barrett and A. B. Winterbottom, 1st Intern. Congr. Metallic Corrosion, p. 657, Butterworths, London (1961).

[9] A. B. Winterbottom, (a) A polarization spectrometer for investigation of surface films on metals, J. Sci. Instr. **14**, 203 (1937); (b) Optical studies of metal surfaces, Kgl. Norske Videnskab. Selskabs, Skrifter No. 1, 52 et seq. (1955).

[10] T. P. Murray, Oil film thickness gage, Proc. ISA (Iron and Steel Conf., 1959).

[11] P. C. S. Hayfield, Imperial Metal Industries (Kynoch) Ltd., Birmingham, England, private communication (1960); J. Kruger and W. T. Ambs, J. Opt. Soc. Am. **49**, 1005 (1959).

[12] L. B. Tuckerman, Univ. Nebraska Stud. **IX**, No. 2, 1909.

[13] (a) H. Poincaré, Theorie Mathematique de la Lumière **2**, 275 (1892).
(b) L. Chaumont, Ann. Phys. **4**, 103 (1915).
(c) B. H. Zocher and F. C. Jacoby, Kolloid Chem. Beih. **24**, 395 (1927).
(d) A. F. Turner, J. R. Benford, and W. J. McLean, Econ. Geol. **40**, 18 (1945).

[14] William A. Shurcliff, Polarized Light: Production and Use, London, Oxford. Univ. Press (1962).

[15] G. Bruhat, Traité de Polarimetrie, Paris Dunoyer.

[16] J. W. Gates, An automatic recording saccharimeter, Chem. Ind. (1958), p. 190; E. J. Gillham and R. King, New design of spectropolarimeter, J. Sci. Instr. **38**, 21 (1961).

[17] B. R. Malcolm and A. Elliot, J. Sci. Instr. **34**, 48 (1957).

[18] W. H. Perkin, J. Chem. Soc. **89**, No. I, 608 (1906).

[19] T. M. Lowry, J. Chem. Soc. **103**, No. II, 1322 (1913).

[20] Bruce H. Billings, J. Opt. Soc. Am. **39**, 797, 802 (1949).

[21] H. Takasaki, Photoelectric measurement of polarized light by means of an ADP modulator. II. Photoelectric elliptic polarimeter, J. Opt. Soc. Am. **51**, 463 (1961).

Discussion

A. C. HALL (Socony Mobil Oil Company):

I should like to know how rapidly a servo-controlled ellipsometer might be expected to respond. What time lapse would occur between two readings?

A. B. WINTERBOTTOM:

I feel that this is an electronic problem. The commercial photo-electric polarimeter reacts in a matter of seconds, but it is very heavily decoupled. The type of instrument with servo-operation would also respond in a matter of seconds. However, ADP crystals or Faraday rotators would respond very rapidly similar to Kerr cell which is used for rapid photo shutters, but to realise such possible high speeds, the time constants of the circuits would obviously have to be equally small so far as this is consistent with other requirements, such as noise.

J. KRUGER (National Bureau of Standards):

You mentioned that there are advantages and disadvantages to the two different ways one can arrange the components on the ellipsometer. Would you care to point out the advantages and disadvantages of each of those two arrangements?

A. B. WINTERBOTTOM:

I had thought that the second arrangement enabled Nakamura biplates to be used in different positions in the system as azimuth and ellipticity half shades respectively. However, on further consideration it seems that this applies to both arrangements and we are left with the convenience of placing more components in the incident section or in the reflected section of the instrument as being the decisive factors when choosing one or the other arrangement. Thus if one arm is fixed and the other moved to alter the angle of incidence, it might be convenient to have fewer components on the mobile arm.

M. A. BARRETT (Institutt for Fysikalsk Metallurgi, Norway):

In the case of a technological control instrument in which only variations in Δ were followed, it was convenient to use the second arrangement as then the Nakamura biplate could be used in setting the analyser and determining Δ.

A. N. SAXENA (Fairchild Semiconductor):

Another comment that could be made on the two methods of using the ellipsometer is that in the first case where one uses the quarter-wave plate before reflection, the computations of ψ and Δ from the measured polarizer and analyzer readings is much simpler than in the second case in which one uses the quarter-wave plate after reflection. Also, the disadvantage you have in the second case is that if the reflecting surface introduces a phase retardation such that you get circularly polarized light then you can't analyze with the second arrangement.

A. B. WINTERBOTTOM:

No. With either arrangement the parameters sought are found by solving spherical triangles which incidentally are easily discerned in the Poincaré representations. The error situation can be examined by writing down the partial derivative expressions in the usual way.

M. A. BARRETT:

Although circularly polarized light (or tan $\psi=1$ and $\Delta=90°$) can be analyzed by both arrangements, when tan ψ approaches 0 or ∞, the measurement of Δ becomes increasingly more difficult and of course at these extreme values, Δ is meaningless. Here again the situation appears to be roughly equivalent for the two possible arrangements of the ellipsometer.

R. R. STROMBERG (National Bureau of Standards):

How accurately can Δ and ψ be determined using conventional methods and light sources?

A. B. WINTERBOTTOM:

The accuracy of setting the various circles with half shades depends on the light source, the half shades and the observer. This random error of setting naturally also varies with the quality of the mirror, especially the degree of depolarisation. The further effect of random errors of setting on Δ and ψ will be given by the partial derivative expressions obtained from the relevant formulae for Δ and ψ or from the tables relating instrument readings to these parameters. With the instrument I have used under favorable conditions, polarizer readings were made with settings accuracy of $\pm 0.1°$ corresponding to about $\pm 0.2°$ in Δ and about the same accuracy of setting for analyser corresponding to $\pm 0.1°$ in Δ. However, the commercial photoelectric polarimeter to which reference has been made, measures rotations down to 0.001° and is thus able to work with very small sample thicknesses and samples with high absorption with sufficient accuracy.

M. A. BARRETT:

I would estimate that ideally with half shades you can get to 0.02 centesimal degrees. However, when an actual specimen is involved, the accuracy is somewhat lower.

Electronic Polarimeter Techniques

Jerome M. Weingart and Alan R. Johnston

Jet Propulsion Laboratory, California Institute of Technology, Pasadena, Calif.

A technique for measuring changes in the orientation of linearly polarized light with a precision of a few seconds of arc is described. A Faraday cell and appropriate electronics were added to a standard photoelectric polarimeter. The cell provided an a-c signal at the photomultiplier which was accurately phase-detected to produce a sharp null. A similar technique was used to measure the orientation and ellipticity of elliptically polarized light. Accurate measurement of a-c birefringence into the megacycle region can be made by additional application of an electronic sampling technique.

The instrument described below (fig. 1) was developed to measure electrically induced birefringence in crystals. However, it can be applied whenever precise measurement of optical retardation is desired, and can measure periodically varying retardation into the radio frequency region with a precision approaching that of the static measurements. The collimated, monochromatic light source consists of a PEK 109 high-pressure, mercury-arc lamp in a suitable housing, a collimating lens, and a narrow-band filter centered on one of the prominent lines in the Hg discharge spectrum. With this particular lamp, a collimated beam with ± 8 min of arc divergence is obtained with a collimating lens of 4-in. focal length. Both polarizing and analyzing elements are Glan-Thompson prisms set in rotatable mounts. The analyzer is set in a modified Gurley Unisec divided circle, which will measure rotations to within 2 sec of arc. The polarizer setting can be read to 1 min of arc. The quarter-wave plates are mounted in a holder designed to support them in as strain-free a manner as possible. The holder, in turn, fits in a rotatable mount identical to the polarizer mount.

Previous to 1950, the addition of electronics to a conventional polarimeter generally consisted of substituting a photocell for the eye

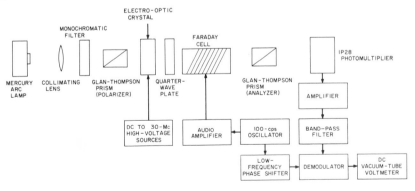

FIGURE 1. *Optical bench and electronics for measurement of optical retardation.*

113

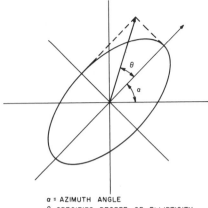

FIGURE 2. *Parameters describing elliptically polarized light.*

α = AZIMUTH ANGLE
θ SPECIFIES DEGREE OF ELLIPTICITY

and adding the appropriate electronics for measuring a minimum in d-c voltage level from the photocell. In 1950, A. C. Hardy [1][1] suggested inserting a Faraday cell (a solenoid containing a transparent material with a large magneto-optical response) in the light path between the analyzer and the rest of the optical elements. A low-frequency current in the coils of the Faraday cell results in a sinusoidal rotation or nutation of the polarized light traversing the cell, thus providing an a-c signal at the photomultiplier which can then be accurately phase-detected using standard demodulator techniques. The Faraday cell contains pure water with a 10-in. pathlength. The polarimeter described here operates on this phase-detection principle and is essentially a refined version of an instrument described by Weingart et al. [2] which is based on the original version by Trageser, Fopiano, and Hardy [3].

A null occurs when the azimuth (fig. 2) of linearly or elliptically polarized light entering the Faraday cell is perpendicular to the transmission axis of the analyzer. The waveform of the intensity $I(t)$ transmitted by the analyzer and detected by the photomultiplier depends on the orientation of the analyzer. In the null position, $I(t)$ contains only even harmonics of the 100-c/s fundamental in the Faraday cell. For positions near null, $I(t)$ contains the fundamental component as well. In passing through the null, the amplitude of the fundamental component passes through zero and changes phase by 180 deg. This behavior around the null position is shown in figure 3.

Phase detection of $I(t)$ is accomplished using the circuits shown in figure 1 providing extremely precise setting of the analyzer to the null position. With linearly polarized light the analyzer setting to null was repeatable to within ± 1 sec of arc. The precision with which the analyzer can be crossed with the major axis of elliptically polarized light depends on the degree of ellipticity of the light entering the Faraday cell. The precision for various degrees of ellipticity is shown in table 1.

---

[1] Figures in brackets indicate the literature references on p. 117.

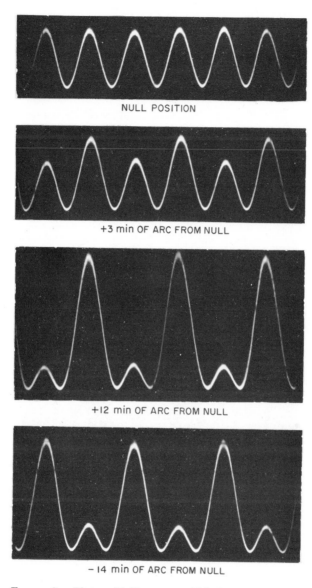

NULL POSITION

+3 min OF ARC FROM NULL

+12 min OF ARC FROM NULL

−14 min OF ARC FROM NULL

FIGURE 3. *Photomultiplier current* $I(t)$ *for different analyzer settings near the null position.*

Measurements of static birefringence are quite straightforward. One method is based on the Sénarmont method [4] and another, which avoids using quarter-wave plates, is described by Robinson [5]. The measurements described below are based on the Sénarmont method.

TABLE 1. *Precision of null setting for varying degrees of ellipticity of light entering the Faraday cell*

θ, deg	Precision of null setting
0	± 1 sec
2	± 2 sec
3	± 5 sec
5	±10 sec
10	±15 sec
15	±30 sec
20	± 3 min
25	± 5 min
30	± 6 min
40	±40 min

The birefringent sample is placed in the optical bench between the crossed analyzer and polarizer (fig. 1) and is then rotated until the principal directions of the sample are alined with the polarizer and analyzer. The sample is properly alined when the polarimeter again indicates a null. Since birefringence and retardation will depend on wavelength, all measurements described here are made in monochromatic light, although alinement of the sample can be made in white light. After rotary alinement, the sample is removed from the optical path by means of a crossfeed attached to the optical bench, which does not disturb the alinement. The analyzer is rotated through an angle of 45 deg, and the polarizer is then recrossed with the analyzer. A quarter-wave plate then inserted in the optical path between the sample and the Faraday cell is alined with the polarizer and analyzer using exactly the same method described for the birefringent sample. The sample is then placed back into position. Linearly polarized light emerging from the polarizer enters the birefringent sample with the plane of polarization making an angle of 45 deg with the principal directions of the sample. The emerging elliptically polarized light enters the quarter-wave plate and emerges linearly polarized, with the plane of polarization now making an angle of 45 + θ deg with the principal directions. The retardation δ of the sample along a given direction is the optical phase shift induced between the ordinary and extraordinary rays as they traverse the sample in that direction. The retardation is related to the birefringence of the sample by $\delta = 2\pi\Delta n d/\lambda$, where Δn is the difference in indices for the ordinary and extraordinary rays, d is the path length through the material, and λ is the free-space wavelength of the monochromatic light. With this alinement of quarter-wave plate and birefringent crystal, $\theta = \delta/2$.

With the sample in place, the analyzer now has to be rotated through an angle θ to reestablish the null condition described above. This readout, therefore, is a direct measure of the birefringence of the sample. It has been shown [2, 6] that first-order errors in either the alinement or the angular retardation of the quarter-wave plate result in second-order errors in measuring θ. The alinement error can be completely eliminated as a result of the sensitivity of the instrument.

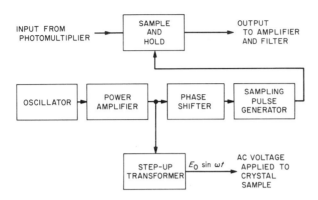

Figure 4. *Polarimeter a-c sampling electronics.*

The actual retardation of the quarter-wave plates available can be accurately measured using the methods described in references [2] and [5], and a correction factor introduced into the measurements if necessary.

Measurements of periodically varying birefringence [7] were made by inserting an electronic sampling network (fig. 4) between the output of the photomultiplier and the input to the phase-detection network used in the steady-state measurements. The sampling network provides a signal which is phase detected and permits using all the techniques available in the steady-state measurements to make measurements into the rf region. Measurements on samples of ADP and KDP indicate that precise, reliable measurements can be made to 120 kc/s with the particular circuitry available. Using the head of a sampling oscilloscope in place of the sampling network, precise measurements to 30 Mc/s are foreseen without much difficulty.

References

[1] A. C. Hardy, private communication.
[2] S. J. Williamson, J. M. Weingart, and R. D. Andrews, Jr., J. Opt. Soc. Am. **54,** 337 (1964).
[3] A. C. Hardy, P. J. Fopiano, and M. B. Trageser, U.S. Patent No. 2 974 561 (1961).
[4] J. R. Partington, An Advanced Treatise on Physical Chemistry, **IV,** p. 156, Longman's Green and Co., New York (1953).
[5] C. C. Robinson, J. Opt. Soc. Am. **53,** 681 (1963).
[6] R. C. Plumb, J. Opt. Soc. Am. **50,** 892 (1960).
[7] Further details are available in the Bimonthly Space Programs Summary No. 37-22, Vol. IV, p. 33, Jet Propulsion Laboratory, California Institute of Technology, Pasadena, Calif.

On Determining Optical Constants of Metals in the Infrared

Shepard Roberts

General Electric Research Laboratory, Schenectady, N.Y.

A review is given of several methods for measuring optical properties of metals in the infrared, starting with simple measurements
of reflectivity and leading to a description of a system employing
three polarizing prisms. The discussion is limited to those methods
which are based on intensity ratios observed at predetermined instrumental settings. The three-prism method is reported to be of comparable precision to the instruments used by Drude in the region of
visible light.

1. Introduction

Optical constants of metals in the infrared are of interest for
several reasons, one of which is that they give information about
the behavior of free electrons, which generally predominate over
other electronic processes in this wavelength range. At any rate,
it is of some importance to know the optical constants in a broad
range of wavelength extending beyond the limits of sensitivity of
photographic film or of the human eye, or even of the photomultiplier.
In this extended range special measuring techniques are required.
The purpose of this paper is to describe several photometric techniques which have been used in the infrared and to point out some
principles according to which high precision may be obtained.

The most effective photometric techniques are those which are
based on Drude's method of determining optical constants from
the relative phase and amplitude of the two reflection coefficients,
R_s and R_p, for perpendicular and parallel components, respectively,
of a beam incident at an angle to the metal surface. In other words,
the quantity to be measured is the complex ratio:

$$R_p/R_s = \tan \psi e^{i\Delta},$$

where $\tan \psi$ is the ratio of the amplitudes of R_p and R_s and Δ is their
relative phase difference.

In order to measure ψ and Δ, Drude used incident light polarized
at an azimuth of 45°. The elliptically polarized light reflected from
the metal was then analyzed by passing it through a compensator
and a second polarizing prism, the latter being called the analyzer.
The values of ψ and Δ could then be related in a simple manner to
the settings of the compensator and analyzer required for extinction.

For infrared work a different method has to be used for determining
the phase and amplitude ratio in the reflected beam. The reason
for this is that the signal intensity from infrared sources is not great
enough, in relation to the minimum level which can be detected, to

119

permit an accurate null setting. For example, if the analyzer is displaced 0.1° from the null position, it will transmit only 3 parts in a million of the incident intensity. This would be several orders of magnitude smaller than the noise level in the detector. However, if the compensator is omitted, one can measure relative intensities for different azimuthal settings of the analyzer. In principle, the shape and orientation of the polarization ellipse may be determined from the measured intensity ratios. The question to be considered is how to do this most expeditiously and accurately.

In Drude's method, the final settings of the compensator and analyzer are arrived at after a certain amount of manipulation involving successive trials and approximations. It is these final settings, then, which make up the raw data from which other information is calculated. In contrast to this, the work to be described here is based on an entirely different philosophy of measurement. It is centered on the idea that the instrumental settings should be entirely prescribed at the beginning of the experiment and that only the indicated intensity ratios should appear in the raw data from which other things are calculated. This principle is emphasized because it is believed to be a prerequisite for the greatest speed and accuracy, though it has not been consistently followed by all workers in this field. The development of appropriate measuring techniques, based on intensity ratio measurements, may be traced through a series of stages in which a number of individuals have made important contributions. The earliest of these did not measure either ψ or Δ, nor make use of Drude's formulas.

2. Earlier Experimental Procedures

The method used by Collins and Bock [1] [1] in 1943 is an example of the application of the principle outlined above. Their method involved a direct measurement of reflectivity of linearly polarized light at various angles of incidence. To do this a mechanical linkage was employed which moved the test surface out of the way of the collimated beam and at the same time moved the receiver into a position to receive the direct beam. The plan of their equipment is shown in figure 1. The polarizing prism which they used is of the square-ended type and operated in a wavelength range from 0.48 to 2.4 μ.

Reflectivities for light polarized parallel to the plane of incidence were measured to an accuracy somewhat better than 1 percent. Optical constants of the metal were obtained from the reflectivities at different angles of incidence by a graphical process. The results were said to be comparable in sensitivity and accuracy with other methods for certain limited ranges of the values of the constants. The method is better adapted to materials having a relatively low reflectivity, since reflectivities close to unity are hard to measure to the required accuracy.

---

[1] Figures in brackets indicate the literature references on p. 126.

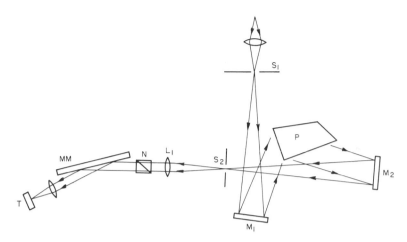

FIGURE 1. *Optical system used by Collins and Bock.*
Exit slit of monochromator—S_2; Polarizer—N; Specimen—MM; Thermopile receiver— T.
(Reproduced from [7].)

In 1952 Avery [2] described a modification of the method of Collins and Bock which avoided the mechanical motions of the test surface and the receiver during a measurement. Avery simply noted the ratio of received intensity when the polarizer was rotated through an angle of 90°. This measurement in effect gave $|R_p/R_s|^2 = \tan^2 \psi$, but it gave no information whatever about Δ. Avery made use of data at different angles of incidence in a manner similar to that used by Collins and Bock and subject to much the same limitations.

Avery noticed that it was necessary to make a correction for the incidental polarization produced by the monochromator and other optical components. For careful work, this incidental polarization is not a trivial matter, and it is not so easy to make a correction for it, because the polarization ratio depends in a complicated manner both on the wavelength and the slit settings of the monochromator.

In 1955 Beattie and Conn [3] pointed out that the limitation on the range of optical constants that can be handled by the foregoing methods is really very serious. A good many metals have high reflectivity, very close to unity, in the infrared, and cannot be measured adequately by these techniques at convenient angles of incidence. They concluded that the most suitable parameter to measure, in addition to the ratio of reflectivities, $\tan^2 \psi$, was the phase difference Δ. These are the parameters which Drude measured in the range of visible light, so that the conclusion of Beattie and Conn really amounts to a reaffirmation of the effectiveness of Drude's technique.

Beattie [4] worked out the experimental procedure for measuring Δ. This fact alone is not significant because Δ had been measured in the infrared by numerous investigators prior to Beattie. However,

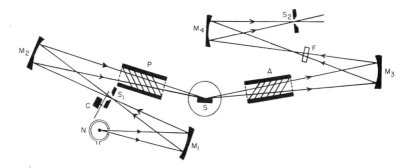

FIGURE 2. *Optical system used by Beattie.*

Source—*N;* Chopper—*C*, Polarizer—*P*, Specimen—*S*, Analyzer—*A*, Entrance slit of monochromator—*S₁*.
(Reproduced from [4].)

Beattie did make a significant advance in that he showed how to determine both ψ and Δ solely from intensity ratio measurements at predetermined instrumental settings and he showed which settings were best.

To do this Beattie used two polarizing units as indicated in figure 2. The polarizing units shown schematically in the figure are selenium film polarizers of the type described by Elliott, Ambrose, and Temple [5] in 1948. These units produce only a very small displacement of the beam and have a high polarizing efficiency in a wavelength range from 2 to 14 μ. With the polarizer set at an azimuth of 45°, Beattie showed that it was only necessary, in principle, to observe the relative transmitted intensity for three positions of the analyzer: 0°, 45°, and 90°. He also added a fourth position, 315°, not because it was necessary but because it served as a useful check.

The equations for transmitted intensity are perfectly symmetrical with respect to the azimuths of polarizer and analyzer. Hence it does not matter, in principle, which polarizing unit is left fixed at the azimuth of 45° and which one is rotated to different positions in determining intensity ratios. In practice it does matter, however, because there is more incidental polarization connected with the monòchromator than there is in the source. For this reason Beattie preferred to rotate the polarizing unit nearest the source, leaving the other unit fixed.

3. The Three-Prism Method

Any partial polarization of the source will result in errors in Beattie's system of measurement. For the highest precision it appears preferable to use a perfectly polarized source, since this is easier to control than a perfectly unpolarized source. For this reason the author [6] introduced a third polarizing prism in work reported in 1959 and 1960. This addition has a slight effect on the method of taking data and calculating results as will be shown.

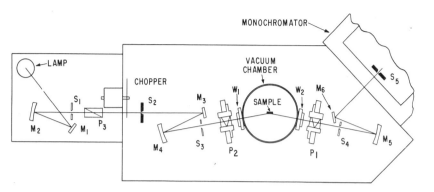

PLANE MIRRORS – M_1, M_3, M_6 POLARIZING PRISMS – P_1, P_2, P_3
SPHERICAL MIRRORS – M_2, M_4, M_5 COLLIMATING SLITS – S_1, S_3, S_4
IMAGE SLITS – S_2, S_5 GLASS WINDOWS – W_1, W_2

FIGURE 3. *Optical system with three prisms.*

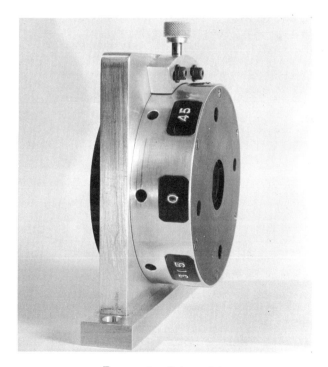

FIGURE 4. *Prism rotator.*

The experimental layout is given in figure 3. This equipment was used in a wavelength range from 0.365 to 2.65 μ and employed prism-type polarizing units. The main polarizing units, P_1 and P_2, are identical and are arranged symmetrically around the sample. Since the beam travels in opposite directions in the two units, the calibration is right-handed for one unit and left-handed for the other, relative to the beam. The third prism, P_3, has just two positions and selects either the parallel or perpendicular polarized component of the source.

One of the main prism rotators is shown in figure 4. The rotator has no graduated scale, but instead eight equally spaced holes, which are used in conjunction with a locating pin to set the azimuth of the prism. This construction permits a precision and reproducibility of settings which exceed those of the usual vernier scale and at the same time permit more rapid shifting of settings. The azimuth calibrations indicate the angle of the electric vector in the transmitted beam relative to the plane of the instrument.

The measurement consists in observing the ratio of two intensities. These intensities are designated by appropriate symbols in table 1, which also shows the azimuth settings of the polarizers corresponding to each intensity value. It should be noted that there are 16 possible combinations when P_1 and P_2 are each set to one of the four positions 45°, 135°, 225°, or 315°. These combinations may be classified as odd or even depending on whether P_1 and P_2 are parallel or at right angles. All of the odd settings are equivalent insofar as the transmitted intensity is concerned and so are the even combinations. The odd settings result in readings of I_{3s} or I_{3p}, for example. However equal readings will not be observed for all equivalent positions if the polarizing prisms are incorrectly oriented in the rotators or if they allow a small displacement or deviation of the beam. A careful study of these effects may be applied to working out a routine which minimizes the systematic errors.

TABLE 1. *Polarizer azimuths for intensity readings*

	P_1	P_2	P_3
I_{1s}	45°	90°	90°
I_{3s}	45°	315°	90° "odd"
I_{4s}	45°	45°	90° "even"
I_{2p}	45°	0	0
I_{3p}	45°	315°	0 "odd"
I_{4p}	45°	45°	0 "even"

Two prerequisites for accurate intensity measurements are a highly stable source and a stable detector connected to an output indicator whose readings are accurately proportional to the intensity being measured. The former is met by a tungsten ribbon-filament lamp with a stable regulated power supply. The detector is a lead sulfide cell connected to a stable a-c amplifier of adjustable gain. The output of the amplifier is converted to d-c by a synchronous rectifier coupled to the light chopper. After filtering, this output is displayed by means of a self-balancing potentiometer indicator. This system gives results which are reproducible to about 0.1 percent of the full scale reading.

The gain of the amplifier may be adjusted so that a reference intensity, say I_{1s}, will read exactly full scale. Then, to read the ratio I_{4s}/I_{1s} directly, it is necessary only to move the polarizer P_2 from azimuth $90°$ to $45°$. This ratio is called e_s. A complete set of measurements includes the following intensity ratios:

$$\frac{I_{4s}}{I_{1s}}=e_s \qquad \frac{I_{3s}}{I_{1s}}=\sigma_s$$

$$\frac{I_{4p}}{I_{2p}}=e_p \qquad \frac{I_{3p}}{I_{2p}}=\sigma_p. \tag{1}$$

If the beam falling on P_3 were perfectly unpolarized, I_{3s} and I_{4s} would be the same as I_{3p} and I_{4p}. In any case these intensities should be in the same proportion so that:

$$\frac{I_{3s}}{I_{4s}}=\frac{I_{3p}}{I_{4p}} \quad . \quad . \quad . \quad . \quad . \tag{2}$$

Consequently,

$$\frac{\sigma_s}{e_s}=\frac{\sigma_p}{e_p}. \tag{3}$$

There must be one more identity between the four measured quantities, because two parameters are sufficient to describe the reflection ratio. Either of the following identities may be chosen for this purpose, since they are equivalent.

$$\frac{1}{\sigma_s+e_s}+\frac{1}{\sigma_p+e_p}=2 \tag{4}$$

$$\frac{(2e_p-1)(2e_s-1)}{(2\sigma_p-1)(2\sigma_s-1)}=1. \tag{5}$$

These identities form a convenient means of checking the self-consistency of the data. When some of the ratios are close to 1/2, the latter identity is a very sensitive check on the linearity of the detector and output indicator.

The final equations for ψ and Δ may be written as follows:

$$\tan^4 \psi=\frac{\sigma_s e_s}{\sigma_p e_p}, \text{ or } \tan \psi=\frac{1}{2}\left(\sqrt{\frac{e_s}{e_p}}+\sqrt{\frac{\sigma_s}{\sigma_p}}\right) \tag{6}$$

and

$$\cos^2 \Delta=(\sigma_s-e_s)(\sigma_p-e_p). \tag{7}$$

The sign of $\cos \Delta$ is the same as that of σ_s-e_s, but this method does not determine the sign of Δ. This is not a severe handicap, however, because it is always clear from the experiment what the sign of Δ ought to be. In addition, this method cannot detect a partial depolarization of light reflected from the sample. Except for these drawbacks, which are not generally very serious, the method and apparatus described here, covering a wide range of wavelength in the infrared, are believed to be comparable in sensitivity and accuracy to the instruments used by Drude in the range of visible light. For example, a change in Δ as small as that attributable to a single molecular layer of water on a copper surface can be detected easily at 1 μ wavelength.

4. References

[1] J. R. Collins and R. O. Bock, Rev. Sci. Instr. **14,** 135 (1943).
[2] D. G. Avery, Proc. Phys. Soc. **B65,** 425 (1952).
[3] J. R. Beattie and G. K. T. Conn, Phil. Mag. **46,** 222 (1955).
[4] J. R. Beattie, Phil. Mag. **46,** 235 (1955).
[5] A. Elliott, E. J. Ambrose, and R. Temple, J. Opt. Soc. Am. **38,** 212 (1948).
[6] S. Roberts, Phys. Rev. **114,** 104 (1959); ibid. **118,** 1509 (1960).
[7] R. O. Bock, Phys. Rev. **68,** 210 (1945).

Discussion

C. E. JONES, JR. (Texas Instruments):
   What type of prisms were you using in your polarizer that allowed you to make measurements at 2.5 μ?

S. ROBERTS:
   The conventional Glan-Thompson prism will work up to and beyond this limit; however, our prisms were somewhat unconventional. If I may, I will describe the prisms used in our work and, also, a second design which we have tested and found to be superior.

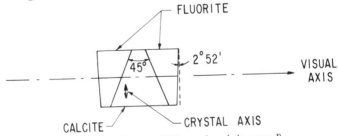

FIGURE 1. *Beam-splitting prism (air spaced).*

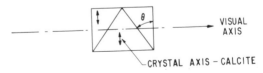

FIGURE 2. *Double Glan prism (air spaced).*

We used beam splitting prisms having a central element of calcite between two fluorite elements as shown in figure 1. These are air spaced. The optic axis of the calcite is perpendicular to the visual axis as shown. The ordinary ray is refracted about 8° in this prism and misses the apertures which follow. The E-ray goes almost straight through, being deviated by less than $\pm 2\frac{1}{2}$ min in a wavelength range from 0.5 to 2.15 μ. Even this small deviation is a nuisance, however, in that it makes it difficult to reproduce readings when the polarizer is rotated 180°.

The second design, developed jointly with D. T. F. Marple early in 1960, might be called a double Glan prism and is shown in figure 2. This consists of three air-spaced calcite elements with optic axis perpendicular to the visual axis as shown. The operation of this prism is similar to the Glan prism except that it has about twice the angular field of view and it has better transmission characteristics. However, it requires only about half as much calcite as a Glan-Thompson prism. The choice of the angle θ depends on the wavelength range to be covered. Our prisms were designed for operation to a maximum of 0.8 μ with $\theta = 37°25'$. These prisms actually gave good results up to 2.2 μ, thereby surpassing the calculated limit. In a prism 25 mm square the transmission of the E-ray was 89 percent at 7000 Å and 38 percent at 2200 Å. These prisms were used in work reported by D. T. F. Marple and H. Ehrenreich in Phys. Rev. Letters 8, 87 (1962).

4. Applications

Use of Ellipsometry for *in Situ* Studies of the Oxidation of Metal Surfaces Immersed in Aqueous Solutions

Jerome Kruger

National Bureau of Standards, Washington, D.C. 20234

Ellipsometry enables one to study *in situ* the formation, dissolution, and optical properties of oxide films on metal surfaces immersed in aqueous solutions while simultaneously measuring or controlling other system parameters, e.g., electrochemical ones. Experimental aspects such as ultra-high-vacuum or electrochemical techniques of surface preparation, effect of changes in the optical properties of the solution and the film, the effect of surface roughness, and the effect of light are discussed. The application of ellipsometry to studies at the metal-solution interface is illustrated by examples from studies of the passivity of iron and the oxidation of copper in water.

1. Introduction

Virtually all processes occurring on metal surfaces immersed in solutions involve at some stage the formation of a very thin film. This film, in the majority of cases an oxide or hydroxide, usually has a vital influence on the course of the process studies. Its existence may be fleeting or its stability tenuous except under the very special conditions existing in solution at the time it is being studied.

Thus in order to study phenomena occurring on metal surfaces immersed in solution one needs to be able to measure these thin films *in situ* while they are forming or disappearing without disturbing the system. Ellipsometry answers these requirements beautifully. This was appreciated in a most effective manner by Tronstad who over 30 years ago carried out a number of pioneering studies on the films that form on metal surfaces immersed in inhibitor solutions or while anodically or cathodically polarized [1,2].[1] It was Tronstad's application of the polarimetric technique of ellipsometry that first yielded meaningful results and pointed the way for further exploitation of this powerful tool. Yet in spite of Tronstad's signposts showing the way and in spite of the great need for a tool to study the initial stages in corrosion processes and electrode kinetics, almost a third of a century passed before ellipsometry was applied to immersed surface studies. A few studies are now appearing in the literature, e.g., the work of Barrett and Winterbottom [3], Kruger [4,5], Hayfield [6], and Andreeva [7] on oxide film formation, of Stromberg et al. [8] on polymer adsorption, and of Reddy et al. [9] on electrochemical studies.

Since the theoretical principles underlying the method are well established, and the ellipsometric technique itself has also been admirably covered elsewhere by Winterbottom [10], the scope of this

---

[1] Figures in brackets indicate the literature references on p. 150.

presentation will be limited to a discussion of the experimental aspects of studying oxide film formation and dissolution with ellipsometry. Further, this discussion will be concerned entirely with the films that form on metal surfaces immersed in aqueous solutions, with most of its attention directed at films thinner than 100 Å, the films that play a very decisive role in corrosion phenomena. For such systems the difficulties associated in achieving meaningful results lie not so much in some of the errors introduced by shortcomings inherent in ellipsometric technique as they do in the problems associated with all surface studies—those of working with a clean, well-characterized surface and solution. In other words, when working with oxide films of less than 100 Å thickness, as will be shown in what follows, the errors introduced by not knowing the optical constants of the film or metal substrate precisely, or by indeed not being able to measure Δ, the relative phase retardation, or ψ, relative amplitude reduction to 0.01°, have much less importance than the introduction of a part per million of impurity. For thicker oxide films, however, where the effects of strains begin to affect Δ and ψ appreciably [11], or for solvent-swollen polymeric films whose optical constants are very close to that of the surrounding solution [8], purely ellipsometric considerations become all-important.

Hence the experimental questions of how to carry out an ellipsometric study of oxide films on immersed metal surfaces will be discussed, mentioning some of the pitfalls, giving techniques we have found useful, and describing examples from our own work which will show some of the information one obtains using ellipsometry. It is probably these experimental considerations that have inhibited others for over 30 years from following Tronstad's brilliant beginnings.

2. Method

This section will be concerned with the apparatus, experimental and computational techniques, and complicating factors. The latter, although they generally limit ellipsometric studies, can sometimes provide valuable information. Four kinds of information can be obtained from studies of metal surfaces immersed in aqueous solutions:

1. Growth of oxide films, i.e., kinetics of growth from thickness measurements.

2. Film breakdown or dissolution.

3. Film formation or dissolution while electrochemically polarizing the surface.

4. Film properties.

The section following this one will give examples of experiments that were concerned with obtaining one or more of these.

2.1. Ellipsometer

No discussion will be given here of the ellipsometer itself, as this is amply and ably covered elsewhere [10]. It will suffice to mention that, in studying processes involving rapid film formation, the photometer method of measuring extinction point offers the possibility of using fast recording techniques. This can prove greatly advantageous, as the work of Reddy et al. [9] has shown. It should also be mentioned that an ellipsometer that can conveniently use a monochromator as its light source may be of considerable help in studying the optical properties of the thin films formed on a metal. When a number of different wavelengths of light are employed, it is not necessary to have a different quarter-wave plate compensator for each wavelength. This was pointed out by Archer [12], who also showed how to take this into account in calculating Δ and ψ values from polarizer and analyzer readings.

2.2. Experimental Cells and Surface Preparation

The types of experimental cells that one can use with an ellipsometer to study immersed surfaces are, of course, limited only by the system under study and the imagination of the experimenter. There are, however, a few general requirements for carrying out ellipsometric measurements on immersed metals that, though they may be obvious, should be listed as follows:

1. Entrance and exit windows set at the proper angle of incidence. If a second angle of incidence is desired, the advantages of which are pointed out by Hayfield [6], a third window is necessary.

2. Means of adjusting specimen surface position. This is not always necessary if the experimental cell is so constructed that the specimen is always positioned accurately. Also, if one is concerned with relative changes that occur on the specimen surface rather than absolute values, as is the case frequently in kinetic studies, precise positioning becomes less important. Sometimes alinement can be achieved by adjusting the position of the ellipsometer rather than that of the specimen.

3. A smoothly polished, strain-free specimen surface.

4. Means for making measurements on a bare specimen surface prior to the introduction of the solution, or a way of producing a film-free surface while the specimen is in the solution. This requirement is especially important since in many studies it is the change in Δ from the bare value $\bar{\Delta}$ that is of prime interest.

5. Means for introducing purified solution.

6. Means, if desired, for making non-ellipsometric measurements, e.g., electrochemical ones, while simultaneously using the ellipsometer.

Three examples of experimental cells and the techniques in using them that more or less conform to the requirements listed above will now be given. They each handle the requirements in a different manner.

The first is shown in figure 1. This apparatus can be used to study film formation on four different crystal orientations simultaneously, illustrating a very important advantage that ellipsometry has in following the kinetics of film growth on single crystal surfaces.

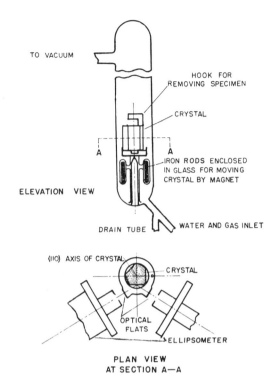

TO VACUUM

HOOK FOR
REMOVING SPECIMEN

CRYSTAL

A   A

IRON RODS ENCLOSED
IN GLASS FOR MOVING
CRYSTAL BY MAGNET

ELEVATION VIEW

DRAIN TUBE   WATER AND GAS INLET

(IIO) AXIS OF CRYSTAL

CRYSTAL

OPTICAL
FLATS

ELLIPSOMETER

PLAN VIEW
AT SECTION A—A

FIGURE 1. *Apparatus for studying by ellipsometry the formation of films on a single crystal immersed in solution.*
(Reproduced from [4].)

The ellipsometer allows one to select areas such as different crystal planes on a specimen to study whereas in using, for example, a microbalance one has to study the whole specimen.

In the study in which this apparatus was used [4], the copper single crystal was machined as a cylinder with its axis in the $\langle 110 \rangle$ direction. Using a crystal of this orientation, it was then possible to cut flat surfaces parallel to the $\{111\}$, $\{110\}$, $\{100\}$, and $\{311\}$ crystallographic planes, these planes being parallel also to the cylinder's axis as shown in figure 1. With such a crystal sealed into this apparatus, the various crystallographic planes can be rotated into position by means of a magnet so that measurements can be made on them with the ellipsometer at various times during the oxidation process.

The method of preparation to be used to render the crystal surface smooth and strain-free and the manner in which high-purity water or solution can be introduced into the apparatus containing no lubricated joints are described elsewhere [13]. The optical parameters of the film-free copper surface are obtained by measurements on the surface after it has been annealed in purified hydrogen at 500 °C. The values for the film-free copper surface in water can be

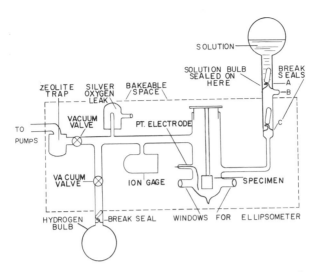

FIGURE 2. *Ultra-high-vacuum apparatus for studying the optical properties of and the electrochemical potential of a metal surface immersed in a solution.*
(Reproduced from [5].)

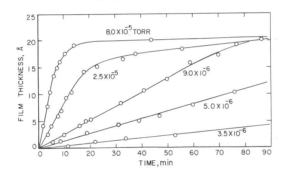

FIGURE 3. *Change of oxide film thickness with time at different oxygen pressures at 300 °K.*
(Reproduced from [14])

calculated from these values. Once these values are obtained, the solution is introduced and the kinetics of film growth are followed.

Such an experimental arrangement as that just described is quite adequate unless one is concerned with the very beginning stages of film formation, where it is necessary to start with a surface that is as bare as is possible using modern ultra-high-vacuum techniques. The apparatus shown in figure 2 was constructed to meet such a requirement in a study [5] whose aim was to determine whether an adsorbed film of oxygen or an oxide film was responsible for the passivity of iron. Figure 3, taken from some recent work of Kruger and Yolken [14], an ellipsometric study of the early stages on the oxidation of iron, shows the film growth that occurs on surfaces prepared in an ultra-high vacuo when they are placed in ordinary vacua. This then emphasizes the necessity for going to ultra-high-vacuum techniques to prepare a metal surface prior to immersion when one wishes to see if a monolayer or two of oxgyen is responsible for a given phenomenon. The apparatus shown in figure 2 is a typical ultra-high-vacuum apparatus capable of attaining pressures of less than 10^{-9} torr. The reaction cell is provided with optically flat 3-mm-thick quartz windows set at a chosen angle of incidence, usually between 60° and 70°. During bakeout the ellipsometer has to be moved, but by putting guide marks on the table upon which it rests it is possible to move it back exactly into its previous position. The specimen is screwed into place in the reaction cell and the bottom of the cell sealed with a hydrogen-oxygen torch. After outgassing in vacuo by induction heating at 800 °C, 85×10^{-3} torr, hydrogen is introduced at the same temperature. At this pressure a glow discharge is obtained in the field of the induction coil. The glow discharge is maintained for a 3-min duration, followed by a pumping-out of the hydrogen. After the system has been baked at 430 °C for 6 to 8 hr, this treatment is repeated a number of times, introducing fresh hydrogen after each 3-min glow discharge. Such a procedure, which bombards the surface with hydrogen atoms and ions, was found to be very effective in reducing the initially present oxide film, as judged by measurements made with the ellipsometer. These are made after each exposure to hydrogen; the values of Δ and ψ will change in a direction that indicates that the surface is becoming cleaner. When further hydrogen treatment produces no changes in the optical parameters, another bakeout is carried out with no change in parameters noted. This will indicate a very low partial pressure of oxygen in the residual gases present during this second bakeout. These readings are taken as the values for the bare surface or, more probably, a surface having a monolayer or less of adsorbed gas. Evaporated metal surfaces can also be used in such an ultra-high-vacuo apparatus if the limitations on their cleanliness mentioned by Hickmott and Ehrlich [15] are borne in mind.

The solutions are prepared so that their dissolved gas content can be controlled. The solution in the bulb shown above break-seal C in figure 2 is degassed in another vacuum system by alternate freezing and thawing a number of times in vacuo and then introducing other assayed reagent grade gases of interest. This bulb, in which the solution is in equilibrium with about 0.5 atm of gas, is then sealed off from the solution preparation system and sealed onto the ultra-high-vacuum system above break-seal C. The space between A and C is then pumped out by a zeolite sorption pump at B, the pump then being removed by sealing off at B. A run is started by breaking break-seal A and then C, the solution covering the specimen in less than 15 sec. Readings can then be made with the ellipsometer. Measurements of the potential between the specimen surface and a platinum electrode provided in the apparatus can also be made if desired.

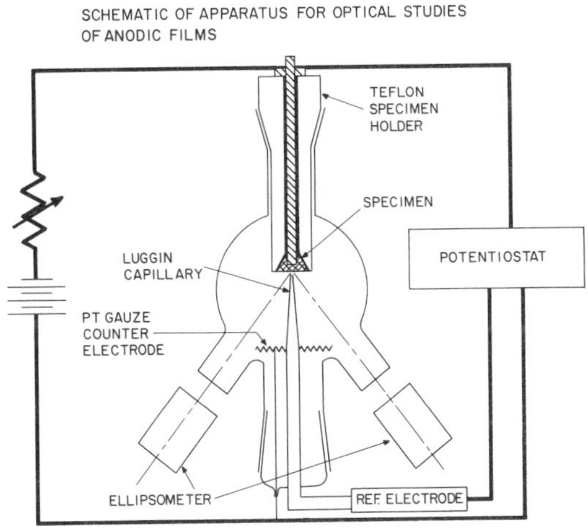

SCHEMATIC OF APPARATUS FOR OPTICAL STUDIES
OF ANODIC FILMS

FIGURE 4. *Cell for studying an electrochemically polarized surface by ellipsometry.*

Another approach to starting with a bare metal surface, which allows one also to control electrochemical parameters while measuring film optical properties and growth, can be carried out by using apparatus similar to that shown in figure 4. This apparatus consists of a means for observing the specimen surface with the ellipsometer, a reference electrode for measuring its potential, and a counter electrode for polarizing the surface at selected potentials by the potentiostat on the right or at selected currents shown on the left in simplified form. With this apparatus one can cathodically or anodically polarize the specimen surface being studied ellipsometrically and control the potential with a potentiostat or control the current galvanostatically. A description of these electrochemical techniques is given by Schuldiner [16]. It is possible to remove any existing oxide films on a number of metals by first making the surface cathodic and thus reducing this oxide film. When the film is so reduced, optical readings can be taken and the surface can then be rapidly brought by the potentiostat to an anodic potential where anodic oxide films start to form. There are a number of difficulties associated with this technique. First, when the surface oxide has been cathodically reduced, in a number of cases, hydrogen evolution takes place and the gas interferes with the optical measurements. Secondly, ions adsorbed from solution, cation concentration gradients, and the electrical double layer may influence the values obtained for bare metal. Finally, metal dissolution may occur in some low pH solutions before the surface is polarized to the proper value. If this occurs while film growth is going on, as it does in some cases, errors in film-thickness measurements are introduced. Besides selecting systems where these effects are minimized, it is possible to obtain a good indication of the bare metal value by cathodically reducing the existing oxide films slowly while continuously taking ellipsometer readings before hydrogen evolution and extrapolating these optical readings to the potential where the metal would be bare. Such a procedure is possible for some metals, e.g., iron in solutions of neutral or alkaline pH.

Obviously, measurements of the optical constants of the bare surface made, if possible, under the ultra-high-vacuum conditions described previously would be the most satisfactory approach. As will be shown in the applications section, very useful information can be obtained, in spite of the limitations mentioned, just from the changes in Δ and ψ observed when electrochemical changes are effected.

2.3. Computation

A number of excellent descriptions of computational methods exist [10, 17, 18]. (See also the paper by McCrackin and Colson in this volume.) This section will be concerned briefly with the aspects of computation associated with the thin films formed on metal surfaces in solution. If one can obtain experimentally a number of Δ and ψ values for different thicknesses of the film on the metal surface and these values are sensitive to changes in the film's complex refractive index $\bar{n}_2$ ($\bar{n}_2 = N_2(1-iK_2)$), then the conventional technique of comparing the experimental curve with one calculated for different values of n_2 by a computer until a good fit is obtained is the recommended approach. There are difficulties in this procedure when $K_2 \neq 0$, as is the case for most oxides (Al_2O_3 is an example of an exception), because there is no unique set of N_2 and K_2 values that can be obtained by this procedure. In other words, good fits may be obtained for a number of $\bar{n}_2$ values. Hayfield [6] suggests that one can determine a unique N_2 by measuring Δ and ψ values at two different angles of incidence

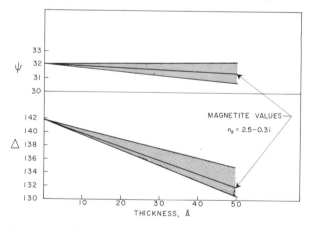

FIGURE 5. *Variation of Δ and ψ with thickness for an n_2 whose N varies from 2 to 3 and whose NK varies from 0.1 to 0.9 for iron immersed in a solution whose refractive index is 1.33.*

$(\phi - 60°, \lambda - 5461\text{Å}, n_1 - 3.06-3.67i)$

thereby overcoming this difficulty. Once this is done K_2 can be determined from the curve fitting technique.

The main factor that should be pointed out here is in connection with the determination of the film thickness of films less than 50 Å thick. Figure 5 shows the sensitivity of the thickness measurement to refractive index. This can be diminished as long as one has a rough idea of the value of $\bar{n}_2$. The bulk value provides a very useful starting point. In this range of film thicknesses Δ is the sensitive parameter so that in studying a system that is changing rapidly only the polarizer readings (from which Δ is obtained) need be followed. Further, the calculation using the exact theory need not be used but instead the simple Drude approximation [1] becomes adequate. For many studies of the phenomenon occurring on immersed metal surfaces, such thin films (< 50 Å) play an all-important role in controlling the process.

2.4. Complicating Factors

A description has been given of the technique of the use of elliptically polarized light in the study of film growth. Some of the complicating factors that must be borne in mind by anyone using the technique should now be pointed out. This is done for two reasons: (1) To show some of the limitations of the method and (2) to point out that some of these complications actually give information that adds to its power. The first group of items are of lesser importance and are the difficulties connected with the technique.

a. Rough Metal Surface

This can arise from difficulty in properly polishing a surface or from dissolution taking place in the solution in which the metal is immersed. Drude and later Tronstad [1] have found as long as the roughness is small as compared to the wavelength of the light its effect is negligible, especially on Δ. If it is larger it can have a marked effect on the readings.

b. Strains in Viewing Windows

These can affect the readings drastically and hence precautions to minimize thermal strains such as using quartz windows or avoiding uneven heating during bakeout are necessary. Strain introduced when readings are taken in vacuo is best eliminated by using thick windows or obtaining bare metal readings in a H_2 or inert gas atmosphere.

c. Change of the Refractive Index of the Solution

This can occur if the process under study introduces ions continuously into the solution or some sort of decomposition of the solution is taking place. One good way to take care of this is to introduce a gold mirror into the solution from which readings can be made from time to time. These readings then allow one to compute the changes in n_2, if they occur, assuming that nothing is happening to the gold.

d. Difficulty in Using Constant-Temperature Baths

Two difficulties exist here: (1) There is not enough room in commercially available ellipsometers to provide for the use of a constant temperature bath. (2) Windows have to be provided in the bath and stirring introduces alinement problems and variations in light intensity. This latter difficulty can perhaps be overcome by using an air thermostat.

e. Absorption by the Solution

In this case the refractive index of the solution is complex complicating the calculations. This is best overcome by choosing a different wavelength for the light source than the conventional 5461 Å Hg line when it is absorbed by the solution.

f. Influence of Light on Process Being Studied

Figure 6, from some work by Kruger and Calvert [19], shows how light can affect the oxidation of copper in water. The light used was

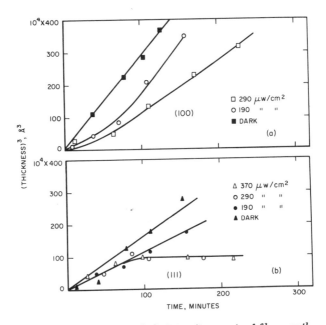

FIGURE 6.   *The effect of light intensity on rate of film growth on copper immersed in water in equilibrium with an inert atmosphere containing 1% O₂.*
(Reproduced from [19].)

white radiation of different intensities. Because of this effect of light on some oxidation processes in solution, Cu, Fe, Zn being some of the metals affected, one must bear this effect in mind in studying oxidation using light. Thus it is necessary to expose the specimen to the light from the ellipsometer as little as possible (shielding it when a measurement is not being made). If this is done the effect is negligible.

The next group of items arises because of the oxidation process itself. In this case the ellipsometric technique becomes less precise in that one cannot always determine film thickness or optical constants precisely, but on the other hand it reveals events happening at the metal surface and in the film just as they occur—an extremely valuable aspect of the technique.

g. Two Phase Films

When a film consisting of two components with different refractive indices forms on a metal surface in solution, the situation becomes considerably more complicated than that for the one-component case. This is so because three new unknown parameters are introduced: the thickness of the new phase, its refractive index, and absorption coefficient. However, the very fact that the ellipsometer reveals the formation of a second phase at the time it happens is of great value, as will be shown in the section on applications.

h. Nonuniformity of the Films

By this is meant variations in oxide thickness over the metal surface. Winterbottom [10] points out that what one actually measures according to theory is the average amount of matter in the film equivalent to that of a thin uniform film of the measured thickness. However, the refractive index measured is probably made up of an average index that includes empty spaces between oxide nuclei.

i. Anisotropy of Film and/or Substrate

Here there is a variation in the refractive index with direction in the plane of the surface studied. This serves to introduce another variable, the orientation of the specimen with respect to the light beam, and the different refractive indices for the different crystal directions. Winterbottom [10] has treated this theoretically, but all of the extra parameters make the task of computation formidable indeed. Cathcart [11] has recently shown that a normally optically isotropic oxide can become optically anisotropic when strain is present in the oxide for epitaxial reasons. Thus a study of the anisotropy of the oxide film may throw some light on the important question of strain in the oxide film.

3. Applications

In this section examples are given from four different studies which illustrate in a specific way the use of the techniques described earlier to obtain varied types of information about the films that form on immersed surfaces.

3.1. Kinetics of Film Growth or Dissolution

This is the most frequent and obvious application of ellipsometry. Here the ellipsometer is used to measure the change of film thickness with time. It can, as is shown in figure 7, relate the kinetics of growth to another simultaneously measured parameter (e.g., potential). The results in figure 7 obtained for iron immersed in $0.1\ N$ $NaNO_2$ solution [5] are plotted logarithmically showing that the film growth kinetics follow a logarithmic law. Similarly, film dissolution could be followed.

3.2. The Formation of a Second Phase

Using the apparatus shown in figure 1, it was found in a study of the oxidation of copper single crystal surfaces [4] that when the copper was oxidized in pure water in equilibrium with 1 atm of oxygen that very rapid oxidation took place initially, followed by a leveling off at 65 to 95 A (fig. 8). The {111} face exhibited a smaller limiting film thickness than the other three faces studied. During the formation of these initial films the value of Δ decreased with time until the limi ing film thickness was reached. The fact that $\Delta-\overline{\Delta}$ (with an increase in film thickness) was negative is what one would expect when cuprous oxide forms on copper immersed in water.

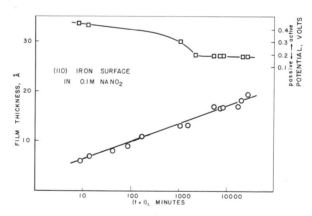

FIGURE 7.   *Growth of a passive film on a (110) iron surface in an air-saturated 0.1 N NaNO₂ solution.*
Logarithmic plot.   (Reproduced from [5].)

However, the value of Δ reached a minimum after from 90 to 120 min and then began to increase. This is shown in figure 9, where Δ is plotted versus time. It can be seen that the greatest change in Δ occurred for the $\{100\}$ and the $\{111\}$ faces. This change in the sign of $\Delta-\overline{\Delta}$ was probably associated with the formation of a new component or layer in the oxide film. X-ray diffraction studies made after removal of the crystal from the solution bear this out by showing the presence of CuO. Also if one uses a reasonable approximation

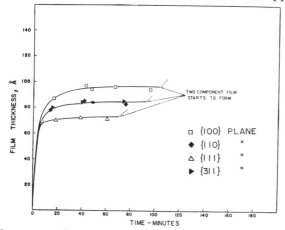

FIGURE 8. *Growth of oxide film on copper in unstirred water in equilibrium with 1 atm of O_2.*
(Reproduced from [4].)

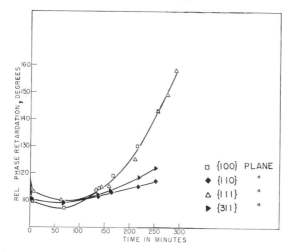

FIGURE 9. *Change in relative phase retardation for film growing on copper in unstirred water in equilibrium with 1 atm of O_2.*
(Reproduced from [4].)

for the refractive index for CuO (2.7–9i) based on the few bulk values available in the literature [20] such a behavior can be reproduced by computer calculations using a program for double films. The reasonableness of this assumption, i.e., that a new component starts to form, is also made clear by considering figure 10. In this figure are plotted the two optical parameters, Δ and tan ψ, determined by the ellipsometer for films of different thicknesses both for the all-Cu_2O film, and for the two-layer film found experimentally. If the Cu_2O film had continued to thicken, the optical parameters would have moved to the right on the solid curve. Instead, after a film of 65 to 95 Å had formed on the copper surface after 90 to 120 min, the parameters suddenly followed the dashed curve. It is also known from previous work on the system that the introduction of CO_2 will convert the CuO to Cu_2O. When this was done, after the parameters measured were those found on the two component curve, subsequent measurements of Δ and tan ψ always lay on the solid curve that was calculated for a film made up of Cu_2O only. If the sudden change in optical parameters was associated with changes in structure or the introduction of strain, as is sometimes the case, it is highly unlikely that introduction of CO_2 would have brought the values of the optical parameters back to the curve calculated for Cu_2O. Hence it seems reasonable to say that the change in the sign of $\Delta-\bar{\Delta}$ from negative to positive was associated with the formation of CuO.

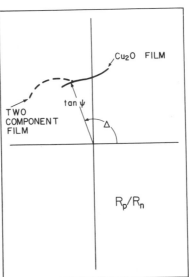

FIGURE 10.   *A comparison between the polar plot of relative phase retardation, Δ, and relative amplitude reduction, tan ψ, calculated for a Cu_2O film growing on copper and obtained experimentally for a film starting out as Cu_2O and then starting to form a second component.*
(Reproduced from [4].)

One observation made when a crystal was removed after being immersed for 18 hr should be mentioned. The CuO formed was loosely held and could be partially wiped off. Beneath it a film was observed showing interference colors, presumably Cu_2O. These interference colors indicated thicknesses greater than the limiting thickness of the Cu_2O, 65 to 95 Å, observed before the formation of CuO. Thus it appeared that, as the CuO formed, the Cu_2O layer underneath was also increasing in thickness. Therefore, since both CuO and Cu_2O were growing simultaneously and at different rates, the values of Δ plotted in figure 9 were related in a complicated manner to the thickness of the combined film. Hence one cannot say from looking at this plot that the {100} and {111} planes have thicker films on them than the {311} and {110}.

The value of the observations is that for the particular situation described here ellipsometry could detect the formation of second phase in the oxide film forming on the copper—a valuable piece of information even though this complication of a second phase makes determination of film thickness most difficult.

3.3. Distinguishing Between Adsorbed Oxygen and an Oxide Film

As pointed out earlier in describing the ultra-high-vacuum apparatus in figure 2 there exist two theories of the origin of the passivity of iron. Experiments using this apparatus and the technique described earlier [5] were aimed at fulfilling the need for a positive way for distinguishing between the adsorption and solid film theories of passivation. By using ellipsometry it is possible to determine whether the passivation process involves the adsorption of an oxygen film, the growth of a three-dimensional oxide, or a combination of both, a transformation of an adsorbed film into an oxide. The theoretically derived variation of Δ with thickness for each of these three models is shown in figure 11.

When the iron surface was immersed in an inhibitor solution (0.1 N $NaNO_2$) saturated with air the Δ at the beginning of the passivation process increased rather than decreased with time. Such initial increases in Δ were found occasionally by Tronstad and Borgmann [21] for films formed in concentrated HNO_3. This is shown in figure 12, along with a simultaneous plot of the potential of the iron surface versus platinum for an air-saturated 0.1 N $NaNO_2$ solution.

Because the growth of iron oxide films is accompanied by a decrease in Δ, the increase found indicates that at the beginning of the passivation process something else was occurring. Figure 11(a) points to one possible reason for the increases. It implies that a rise in Δ could indicate that a film is forming with a refractive index, n_2, less than 1.3349, the refractive index of 0.1 N $NaNO_2$ solution, n_1, for the wavelength of the light used in all of the studies reported here, 5461 Å. None of the oxides of iron whose refractive indices are known or indeed any of the possible solids whose values are known, which could constitute the film, have a refractive index lower than that of the

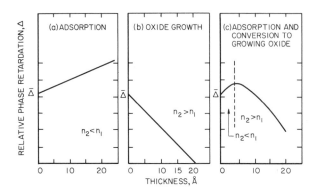

FIGURE 11.   *Theoretically derived curves for the variation of the phase retardation with film thickness for: (A) a film whose refractive index is less than the solution $(n_2 < n_1)$; (B) a film whos refractive index is greater than the solution $(n_2 < n_1)$ (C) a film where initially $n_2 < n_1$, but later n_2 becomes greater than n_1.*

(Reproduced from [5].)

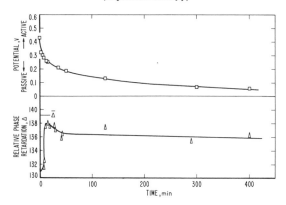

FIGURE 12.   *Change in phase retardation with time for an iron surface immersed in air-saturated 0.1 N NaNO$_2$ solution.*

(Reproduced from [5].)

nitrite solution.   On the other hand, an oxygen film [22] or an adsorbed nitrite film would probably have a refractive index lower than that of the solution.

This interpretation does not apply in this case, however, because although a rise in Δ-values was initially observed, Δ was always less than $\bar{\Delta}$, the value of the relative phase retardation for the film-free surface. This quantity (shown in fig. 12) was obtained from a calculation of its value in nitrite solution based on the all-important measurements made in ultra-high vacuo. During the time when the solution was introduced into the cell containing the specimen, and a reading was made (in some cases less than 0.5 min), Δ had decreased 4°. This corresponds roughly to the formation of a 20 Å film,[2] whose refractive index was higher than that of the solution, during the time of solution introduction. Thus the rise in Δ-values was due either to the adsorption of a low index film ($n_2 < n_1$) on top of the film formed almost instantaneously at the beginning of the process, or to the dissolution of this initial film, where decreasing film thickness values cause an increase in Δ-values. The fact that Δ_{max} always approached Δ closely, but never exceeded it, argues for the film dissolution interpretation. This interpretation is also bolstered by thermodynamic considerations [23] for an air-saturated solution (pH 5.8).

In order to see if initial film dissolution was occurring because of the low pH of the air-saturated solution due to the CO_2 present in it, outgassed solutions in equilibrium with 0.5 atm of high-purity oxygen were used. As can be seen from figure 13, the initial rise in Δ is completely absent, the instantaneously formed film instead continuing to increase (Δ decreasing) with time. Thus it appears that the initial rise in Δ for air-saturated solutions was due to film dissolution rather than to the adsorption of a low-index film on top of the instantaneously formed film. The condition for the latter possibility still existed when oxygen was the only gas present. This experiment

[2] These were based on the approximation, used by Tronstad and Borgmann [21], for films less than 100 Å that the mean thickness is proportional to the difference in the phase retardation values of the "film-free" and film-covered surface ($\bar{\Delta}-\Delta$), 1° corresponding approximately to 5 Å.

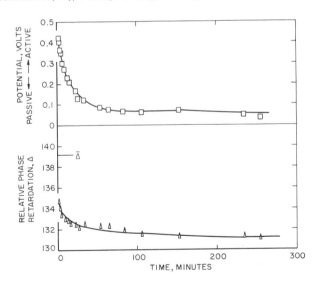

FIGURE 13. *Change in phase retardation with time for an iron surface immersed in 0.1 N NaNO₂ solution in equilibrium with 0.5 atm of pure oxygen.*
(Reproduced from [5].)

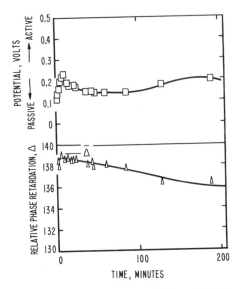

FIGURE 14.   *Change in phase retardation with time for an iron surface immersed in a deaerated 0.1 N NaNO₂ solution.*
(Reproduced from [5].)

with the pure oxygen also casts doubt on the very remote possibility that the initial rise in Δ was due to the formation of a second film with a very high adsorption coefficient (a situation analogous to that described earlier in the oxidation of copper). This is so because it is not likely that raising the pH by using pure oxygen would have done anything but enhance the formation of the second phase layer, and if this had the proper optical constants, a rise in Δ would have again been noted.

To ascertain whether the instantaneously formed film was produced during the solution introduction interval by interaction with oxygen and water vapor, experiments were carried out using de-aerated solutions and high-purity argon as the gas for pushing the solution in rapidly. As figure 14 shows, an extremely thin film (<5 Å) formed in the almost completely deoxygenated solution. An initial adsorption on top of or dissolution of this film appeared to take place; it then started to grow.

Thus by the use of ellipsometry, ultra-high-vacuum techniques, and a control of the atmosphere in equilibrium with the solution covering the metal surface studied, it is possible in some cases to distinguish between adsorbed and three dimensional oxide films.

3.4. Study of Electrochemically Polarized Surfaces

The same arguments used to distinguish between an adsorbed oxygen film and a three-dimensional film can be used in studies carried out on polarized surfaces using the apparatus shown in figure 4

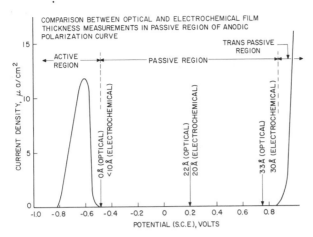

FIGURE 15. *Anodic polarization curve for iron in 0.15 N sodium borate–0.15 N boric acid solution with a comparison between film thicknesses obtained by coulometric measurements (from Nagayama and Cohen [22]) and those obtained by ellipsometry.*

and described in section 2, Method. It is very important wherever possible to supplement ellipsometric results with those obtained from other techniques. By combining ellipsometry with an apparatus capable of polarizing a metal surface it is possible to intercompare the optical with electrochemical measurements of film thickness. This is done in figure 15 on a typical anodic polarization curve obtained from the work of Nagayama and Cohen [24] for iron in a boric acid-sodium borate solution. In the passive region of this curve are shown values of film thickness measured at three different potentials by the ellipsometer and by measurement of total coulombs passed to form the film made by Nagayama and Cohen. The first value listed for the ellipsometer was taken as zero thickness, since good $\overline{\Delta}$ and $\overline{\psi}$ values could not be obtained from cathodically reduced surfaces, as mentioned in the previous section, because of the presence of hydrogen bubbles. At this point on the polarization curve this assumption of a very thin film (thickness ≈ 0) is reasonable. The electrochemical measurements indicate a thickness of <10 Å. Using such an assumption, the values obtained optically and electrochemically compare quite well. If the film thickness was not zero at -0.6 V, the optical values would then be somewhat higher than those obtained by coulombic measurement.

Such an optical-electrochemical approach was applied to a system where the nature of the film formed in the passive region of the anodic polarization curve is a subject of controversy. This system is iron in $1\ M\ H_2SO_4$. When the iron is polarized to a potential of around 1 V and kept at this potential by a potentiostat, the flow of current is markedly reduced and the iron is said to be passive even though dis-

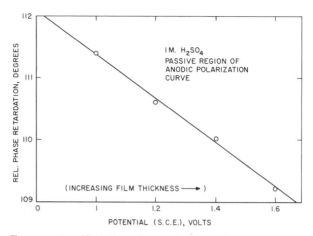

FIGURE 16. *Variation of Δ with potential in the passive region of the anodic polarization curve of iron in 1 M H₂SO₄.*

solution continues, albeit at a diminished rate. Figure 16 shows how the argument applied in the case of inhibitor formed films may be applied to this system. It is known that film thickness increases with increasing potential in the passive region of the polarization curve [25]. Figure 16 shows that with this increase in potential and film thickness a decrease in Δ is obtained. On the basis of what was said before this indicates the formation of a film of greater refractive index than the solution, thus arguing against the formation of an adsorbed oxygen film. Further work has to be done in this difficult system (surface roughening occurs if the experiment is carried out for times greater than a few minutes) to establish the optical constant of the film and its thickness. Similar electrochemical-ellipsometry experiments have been carried out by Hayfield [6].

These examples of applications of ellipsometry to the study of immersed metal surfaces are just a small sampling of the sort of studies that wait to be carried out in the future. Although the difficulties of preparing clean, well-characterized surfaces and solutions, of determining accurate film optical constants, and understanding the effects of the double layer and cation concentration gradients near the metal surface remain, the prospect of obtaining many valuable insights into processes at the metal solution interface is, as Tronstad believed 30 years ago, promising.

4. References

[1] L. Tronstad, Optische Untersuchungen zur Frage der Passivität des Eisens und Stahls, Kgl. Norske Videnskab. Selskabs Skrifter 1931, **1**, F. Bruns Bokhandel, Trondheim (1931).
[2] L. Tronstad, Trans. Faraday Soc. **29**, 502 (1933).
[3] M. A. Barrett and A. B. Winterbottom, First Intern. Congr. on Metallic Corrosion, London, Apr. 1961, p. 657 (Butterworths, London, 1962).

[4] J. Kruger, J. Electrochem. Soc. **108,** 504 (1961).
[5] J. Kruger, ibid. **110,** 654 (1963).
[6] P. C. S. Hayfield, First Intern. Congr. on Metallic Corrosion, London, Apr. 1961, p. 663 (Butterworths, London, 1962).
[7] V. V. Andreeva, Corrosion 20, 35t (1964).
[8] R. R. Stromberg, E. Passaglia, and D. J. Tutas, J. Res. NBS **67A,** 431 (1963).
[9] A. K. N. Reddy, M. A. V. Devanathan, and J. O'M. Bockris, J. Electroanal. Chem. **6,** 61 (1963).
[10] A. B. Winterbottom, Optical studies of metal surfaces, Kgl. Norske Videnskab. Selskabs Skrifter 1955, **1,** F. Bruns Bokhandel, Trondheim (1955).
[11] J. V. Cathcart, J. E. Epperson, and G. F. Peterson, Acta Met. **10,** 699 (1962).
[12] R. J. Archer, Phys. Rev. **110,** 354 (1958).
[13] J. Kruger, J. Electrochem. Soc. **106,** 847 (1959).
[14] J. Kruger and H. T. Yolken, Corrosion **20,** 29t (1964).
[15] T. W. Hickmott and G. Ehrlich, J. Phys. Chem. Solids **5,** 57 (1958).
[16] S. Schuldiner, Naval Research Laboratory Report 5775 (1962).
[17] F. L. McCrackin, E. Passaglia, R. R. Stromberg, and H. L. Steinberg, J. Res. NBS. **67A,** 363 (1963).
[18] R. J. Archer, J. Opt. Soc. Am. **52,** 970 (1962).
[19] J. Kruger and J. P. Calvert, accepted for publication in J. Electrochem. Soc.
[20] Gmelins Handbuch der Anorganischen Chemie, System-Nummer 60B1, p. 76, Verlag Chemie, Weinheim (1958).
[21] L. Tronstad and C. W. Borgmann, Trans. Faraday Soc. **30,** 349 (1934).
[22] J. Kruger and W. J. Ambs, J. Opt. Soc. Am. **49,** 1195 (1959).
[23] M. Pourbaix, Z. Elektrochem. **62,** 670 (1958).
[24] M. Nagayama and M. Cohen, J. Electrochem. Soc. **109,** 781 (1962).
[25] K. G. Weil, Z. Elektrochem. **62,** 638 (1958).

Discussion

A. N. Saxena (Fairchild Semiconductor):
Whenever you quote the thickness of a film in your results what value of the optical constants do you use for the substrate? Are these for the clean bulk surface?

J. Kruger:
Yes.

A. N. Saxena:
Would you agree or disagree that the biggest source of error in interpreting the ellipsometer measurements to give thickness and refractive index of thin films on metallic (or opaque) substrates comes from the fact that the optical constants of the film-substrate interface are not really that of the true surface? The true bulk surface could be obtained when we cleave the specimen in ultra-high vacuum.

J. Kruger:
I agree with you very strongly. In fact, that is the whole point in using an ultra-high-vacuum system. I am not saying that we have achieved this completely but we have reasons for believing that we have come fairly close. The whole point in that experiment was to determine carefully the optical constants of bare surfaces.

A. N. SAXENA:

You may start with a bare surface whose optical constants you know. However, as soon as you start growing a film or when you have grown a film (for example an oxide layer) on top of the original "bare" surface, the film-substrate interface has no longer exactly the same optical constants as the original "bare" surface. The difference between the two sets of optical constants depends on a number of factors, e.g., ambient temperature, type of film growth, etc. The optical properties of the film-substrate interface can be studied by using non-ellipsometric techniques to measure film thickness (like multiple beam interferometry which does not depend on the optical constants of the interface) and combine this with the ellipsometer measurement which does depend on the optical constants of the interface. This procedure is quite tedious but I am not aware of other methods by which one can study the optical properties of the interface. The agreement between the multiple beam interferometer and ellipsometer measurements of thickness of a film will be good if we use the correct optical constants of the interface in the ellipsometer calculations.

J. KRUGER:

Perhaps we are not talking about the same thing. I never refer to the optical constants of the interface itself. I refer to the optical constants of the substrate, the bare metal, and the optical constants of the film. The combination will from ellipsometric measurements give a value for Δ and tan ψ which depends on the thickness of the film, its optical constants and optical constants of the substrate. One needs to know accurately the optical constants of both the substrate and the film to determine the thickness. I don't know what you mean by "the optical constants of the interface" itself unless you mean the Δ and tan ψ of the film-substrate combination.

A. N. SAXENA:

By optical properties of the interface I mean its optical constants. Let me give you an example to explain this. Archer (J. Op. Soc. Am. **52**, 970, 1962) quotes for the optical constants of Si, $n\text{-}ik$, as $4.050-0.028\ i$. He estimates k from the transmission measurements of the absorption coefficient of Si and using the standard formulas for n and k and measured ψ, he estimates n. To relate the (ψ, Δ) (which you measure with an ellipsometer), for a specimen of a transparent film of refractive index n_1 on Si, with the thickness d of the film and n_1, the exact ellipsometer equation is used in which the optical constants of the substrate used are that of Si, viz. $4.050-0.028\ i$. If $n_1 \lesssim 1.49$ or $\gtrsim 3.5$, a family of closed contours is obtained for ψ, Δ each corresponding to a particular n_1 and the thickness of the film is marked off in terms of path difference in the film σ. In a set of experiments, we obtained SiO_2 films on a batch of identical Si wafers in which n_1 was the same, 1.46, but d was different. The measured (ψ, Δ) points for each sample did not coincide with the theoretical curve for $n_1 = 1.46$ which was obtained using 4.050–0.028 i for the Si substrate. I am attempting to analyze this experimental curve to assign more accurately the optical constants for SiO_2-Si interface obtained during thermal oxidation in steam at 1200 °C. I am also trying to investigate the SiO_2-Si interface for the case of anodic oxidation where I feel the optical constants should be closer to the bulk value.

J. KRUGER:
    I feel that the changes that you measure are due to the changes in the optical properties of the film and not changes in the interface.

A. N. SAXENA:
    The changes in the optical properties of the film will show up in the refractive index measurement as you etch the film gradually to smaller thicknesses. In the refractive index measurements on our films performed by Dr. A. E. Lewis of our laboratory, we found that the refractive index n_1 was 1.45 ± 0.003 as we etched the SiO_2 films from 9000 Å down to 600 Å. So the discrepancy between experimental (ψ, Δ) and theoretical (ψ, Δ) is not due to changes in the optical properties of the film but due to the difference in the optical constants of the SiO_2-Si interface. Regarding what Dr. Plumb said about charge transfer at the interface which changes the potential barrier seen by electrons on either side, I think it will be very interesting to compare the measured tunneling currents across a thin insulator film with a theoretical calculation of the tunneling current in which the thickness of film used is that determined by ellipsometer.

J. KRUGER:
    One thing I agree very strongly with is that one should not rely on one technique to get things like film thickness. If possible an independent and different technique should be employed. For instance, interferometry is still optical, one might use electrical techniques or something of this sort.

A. N. SAXENA:
    I must emphasize that when the film thickness gets < 100 Å, other techniques like interferometry fail to retain any useful accuracy. This thin film region, however, is of interest to those who want to look at tunneling currents.

JEAN BENNETT (Michelson Laboratory):
    There has been some discussion about the use of multiple-beam interferometry for film thickness measurements. I may be able to clarify this point somewhat. In the method we use at Michelson Laboratory, we evaporate the film whose thickness is desired on part of the surface of an optical flat. We then overcoat the whole surface of the flat with an opaque material, such as silver, and form a Fabry-Perot interferometer using this overcoated flat as one of the plates.

The other plate would be coated with a semi-transparent material, such as a 90 percent reflectivity silver film. We then photograph the fringes of equal chromatic order which are formed in reflection in white light. From the measured wavelengths of these interference fringes the desired film thicknesses may be obtained. Using proper care, film thicknesses may be determined with an accuracy of ± 2 Å. Although we normally measure film thicknesses in the range 100 Å to 10,000 Å this method should be able to be used for thicknesses from 25 Å up to several microns. The limitation of the method is that part of the surface has to be free of the film, so that there is a sharp step at the edge of the film. I don't know of any way to remove part of an oxide film from a metal surface. I think this is a major limitation of the interferometric method.

A. N. SAXENA:
In reference to Mrs. Bennett's statement, I do not disagree that theoretically you could measure film thicknesses from 10 Å up to several thousand Å, and if one is careful, one may achieve an accuracy of ± 10 Å with multiple-beam (Fizeau) interferometry (monochromatic light, measure shift of fringes at the step), and an accuracy of ± 5 Å or maybe even ± 2 Å with multiple-beam (fringes of equal chromatic order) interferometry (white light, measure wavelength of fringes). To achieve this in practice is not very easy. Problems are encountered due to incomplete removal of the film at the step (typically for the case of SiO_2 on Si, after etching and rinsing, the thickness of the film which grows again on the so-called clean Si is about 50 Å), uneven metallization of the step and surface roughness of the substrate. I must point out that this method is a measurement of the physical height of the film above the substrate at the step, and this method is independent of the optical constants of the interface and the film.

WILLIAM PRIMAK (Argonne National Laboratory) (communicated):
Measurements of birefringence of vitreous silica have been in progress in our laboratory for a number of years under the auspices of the U.S. Atomic Energy Commission. Some of the technical information may be of value to those seeking strain-free vitreous silica windows.

Several commercial grades of vitreous silica were tested about 1960, mostly optical blank stock purchased about that time; some from purchases dating back perhaps up to a decade are labeled "old." Since manufacturing procedures change from time to time, present stock may be different. Some of our birefringence retardation results obtained in ½ to 1 in. thick sections follow.

General Electric: grade 101, even in thin sections, patches about
50 mμ
grade 103, patches about 6 mμ
grade 104, fine patchwork about 5 mμ.

Corning High Purity, optical and schlieren grades, $<\frac{1}{2}$ mμ; all Corning blanks we have examined showed small bubbles observed as stars in our polarimeter and our schlieren apparatus.

Engelhard Industries, Amersil: one Amersil grade (old) spiral patterns ~ 50 mμ; Optosil very fine patchwork about $1\frac{1}{2}$ mμ; Homosil $<\frac{1}{2}$ mμ, no refractive index variations; Suprasil $<\frac{1}{2}$ mμ, variation in refractive index in sixth decimal from center to edge of a 2-in. section found in one block. Faint patterns are seen in Homosil and Suprasil as described in literature from Engelhard Industries and taken from work published by Mohne. These are more distinct in our polarimeter than in our schlieren equipment. They are more distinct in one direction in the stock, and if they are of concern, the stock should be cut accordingly. A specimen of selected Dynasil supplied for test showed some bubbles, edge strain from sawing, and a rectangular pattern birefringent patchwork much like that of GE 104, but with lower birefringence, about $\frac{1}{2}$ mμ. In our past work we have preferred Homosil or Suprasil, depending on whether radiation-induced coloration (occurs in Homosil) is of concern. We have heard a rumor there has been some alteration in Suprasil manufacture to reduce its relatively large OH$^-$ content but we have not yet seen this stock.

Cutting stock is a severe problem in working strain-free silica. Our diamond saws readily introduce 15 mμ retardation along edges, 30 to 50 at corners. In our most careful work, a rubber-bonded carborundum wheel with copious coolant was used, and 1-mil-deep cuts were taken in a surface grinder so that many hours were spent cutting a $\frac{5}{8}$-in.-thick slab of Herasil I. The birefringence near the edge was doubled by this operation to about 2 mμ. We have been told mud saws (copper disk dipping in carborundum slurry) make relatively strain free cuts but have not had the opportunity to examine such work. We have found that wet grinding and polishing, as practiced by opticians, if done on all faces of a piece, will remove most of the birefringence introduced by cutting if the work had not been pushed through the saw. If the piece is sawed after a pair of faces have been finished, it is necessary to refinish these as well as finish the other faces. The ordinary edging machines introduce birefringence, but if small cuts are taken and care is taken not to chip the corner at the edge of the work, the birefringence introduced is rather less than by a saw cut. We have been told that etching will remove birefringence introduced by cutting, but we have not tested this ourselves.

Waxing or cementing plates will usually introduce considerable birefringence. Even with the soft wax, Cenco Tackiwax, it is easy to introduce a retardation of 15 mμ/cm in a small piece. It is virtually impossible to cement silica to another material with a cement which requires melting or thermal curing and obtain a strain-free piece. The problem for other glasses has become severe in optical manufacture as thermally cured polymers have supplanted balsam as a cement. If silica pieces are waxed to other silica pieces, a reasonably strain-free joint can be obtained by placing the waxed piece into the oven, turning off the heater, and letting the work cool slowly overnight to anneal the wax.

Our polarimeter for the above tests consists of a lantern with a 100-W projection bulb focussed at a distance, polarizer and analyzer of Polaroid sheet crossed at 45° azimuth, plastic sheet quarter-wave material parallel to the analyzer between it and the specimen which is mounted at 0° or 90° azimuth. A 15 to 30 cm lens is used either as a magnifier or the objective of a telescope for viewing. It is important to use a large aperture (3 to 4 in. recommended) so that a large field outside of the specimen is viewed. The angular rotation of the analyzer to secure extinction is proportional to the retardation, about 3 mμ/deg. At high light intensities it is easy to detect 0.3 mμ retardation.

An Assessment of the Suitability of the Drude-Tronstad Polarised Light Method for the Study of Film Growth on Polycrystalline Metals

P. C. S. Hayfield and G. W. T. White

Imperial Metal Industries (Kynoch) Limited, Birmingham, England

Theoretically derived changes in ellipticity resulting from reflection of polarised light from different film-covered metals are considered. The examples illustrated include single layer and two layer films, and films varying in thickness laterally across the surface under examination. On the basis of this information, interpretation is made of Drude-Tronstad experimental data recorded during a study of several gaseous and aqueous oxidation reactions on polycrystalline metals, as well as aqueous corrosion reactions. The significance of changes both in film thickness and film absorptivity is briefly discussed.

1. Introduction

The reflection and transmission of polarised radiation at interfaces has been understood mathematically in terms of Maxwell's electromagnetic theory for many years. One of the practical implications of this theory in the field of optics is the measurement of the optical properties of metal surfaces, in which determination is made of the ellipticity, after reflection at a flat surface, of incident plane polarised light. As shown by Drude [1] [1] and later Tronstad [2], the reflected component of light is greatly changed by the presence of contaminating film. Indeed, the change in ellipticity produced by films 10 to 1000 Å is so great that the phenomenon forms the physical basis of one of the most powerful techniques presently available for measurement of thickness of thin tarnish films. The title Drude-Tronstad was chosen for the technique in order to distinguish it from saccharimeters and similar instruments, but the name ellipsometer seems to have been chosen very largely by other contributors to this symposium when describing the same technique.

In this paper emphasis is given to the suitability of the technique to measurement of the thickness of tarnish films formed on polycrystalline metals during corrosion. Because films formed under these conditions are frequently non-uniform in thickness and optically inhomogeneous, section 2 of the paper is devoted to development of equations describing reflection of polarised light by various types of non-uniform film. The equations are used in the remaining sections of the paper as a basis for the interpretation of experimentally determined data.

---

[1] Figures in brackets indicate the literature references on p. 198.

2. Theoretical Principles

The object of this section is to present the physical and mathematical principles underlying the theoretical calculations needed for the interpretation of the experimental work presented in the following sections of this paper. For this purpose two models will be considered in detail, namely,

(i) a surface covered by two or more homogeneous films of uniform thickness, and

(ii) a surface covered by a single homogeneous film of non-uniform thickness.

As a necessary introduction to the theoretical treatment of these models, an outline is first given of the traditional treatment of the single, uniform layer.

2.1. The Optical Properties of a Plane Boundary

In order to understand the properties of a thin film, it is first necessary to evaluate the reflection and transmission coefficients of a plane boundary between two media, simply because the thin film comprises two such boundaries in close proximity. The problem is to determine the amplitude and phase of the electric vector of the reflected and transmitted beams when a plane polarised beam having an electric vector E_{1+} is incident at an angle ϕ_1 on a plane boundary between media 1 and 2 of refractive index n_1 and n_2 (see fig. 1). The solution to this problem is most conveniently expressed by representing amplitude and phase as a single complex number denoted by a boldface symbol, say E, such that E equals $(a+ib)$, where a and b are real numbers, and i is the square root of -1. In this notation the amplitude is taken as the modulus of E, viz, $(a^2+b^2)^{\frac{1}{2}}$; the phase of E relative to some arbitrary standard, such as the phase of the incident beam at the point of incidence, is taken as the argument of E, viz,

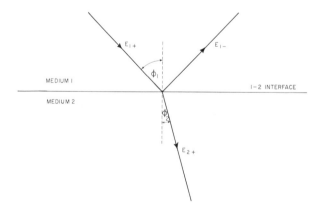

FIGURE 1. *Reflection and transmission at a plane interface.*

arg $(\mathbf{E}) = \tan^{-1} (b/a)$. With this notation the reflected and transmitted beams can be formally related directly to the incident beam by the equations

$$\mathbf{E}_{1-} = r\mathbf{E}_{1+} \tag{1}$$

$$\mathbf{E}_{2+} = t\mathbf{E}_{1+} \tag{2}$$

where r and t are the complex reflection and transmission coefficients. It is shown in standard textbooks (Heavens [3] and Vašíček [4]) that when the incident beam is polarised parallel to the plane of incidence, r and t have the values

$$r_p = \frac{n_1 \cos \phi_2 - n_2 \cos \phi_1}{n_1 \cos \phi_2 + n_2 \cos \phi_1} \tag{3}$$

$$t_p = \frac{2n_1 \cos \phi_1}{n_1 \cos \phi_2 + n_2 \cos \phi_1} \tag{4}$$

and when the incident beam is polarised normally to the plane of incidence, r and t assume the values

$$r_s = \frac{n_1 \cos \phi_1 - n_2 \cos \phi_2}{n_1 \cos \phi_1 + n_2 \cos \phi_2} \tag{5}$$

$$t_s = \frac{2n_1 \cos \phi_1}{n_1 \cos \phi_1 + n_2 \cos \phi_2}. \tag{6}$$

These reflection and transmission coefficients are known as the Fresnel coefficients. If either one or both of the media are absorbing, the corresponding refractive indices n are complex, and the Fresnel coefficients are similarly complex: in the following work the assumption is made that this is so. In all cases ϕ_2 is obtained from Snell's law

$$n_1 \sin \phi_1 = n_2 \sin \phi_2. \tag{7}$$

It should be noted that if the direction of incidence is reversed, the transmission or reflection coefficients are changed. By interchanging n_1 and n_2 in eqs (3) to (6) it can be seen that the Fresnel coefficients r' and t for the reflection and transmission of light travelling in the reverse direction to that shown in figure 1, are related to r and t by the equations

$$r' = -r, \tag{8}$$

$$tt' = 1 - r^2. \tag{9}$$

These equations are required in the following subsections.

2.2. The Optical Properties of Thin Film

At this stage the properties of a uniform thin film can be discussed. Suppose the film is of thickness d_1, and that a plane polarised beam of unit amplitude is incident upon the 0–1 boundary, as shown in figure 2. The light will suffer multiple reflection within the film and upon each reflection at the 0–1 interface, a fraction t_1' will be transmitted and a fraction r_1' (equal to $-r_1$) will be reflected. Likewise, at the 1–2 boundary, a fraction t_2 will be transmitted and r_2 reflected. Thus, the amplitudes of the successive beams from C, E, G, etc., decline in geometric progression. However, in order to calculate the total amplitude reflected into medium O, it is not sufficient to sum these intensities, for in travelling through the film from A to B to C, the beam acquires a phase lag of

$$2\delta = (2\pi/\lambda) n_1 d_1 \cos \phi$$

with respect to the incident beam at the point A, and on each successive double reflection an additional lag of 2δ is introduced. Consequently, the amplitudes at C, E, G, etc., must be multiplied by the factors $\exp(-2i\delta)$, $\exp(-4i\delta)$, $\exp(-6i\delta)$, etc. Thus, the phase and amplitude of the total reflected beam are represented by the sum

$$R = r_1 + t_1 t_1' r_2 \exp(-2i\delta)\{1 - r_1 r_2 \exp(-2i\delta) + r_1^2 r_2^2 \exp(-4i\delta) - \ldots\}$$

$$= r_1 + \frac{t_1 t_1' r_2 \exp(-2i\delta)}{1 + r_1 r_2 \exp(-2i\delta)}.$$

Finally, eliminating $t_1 t_1'$ by use of eq (9),

$$R = \frac{r_1 + r_2 \exp(-2i\delta)}{1 + r_1 r_2 \exp(-2i\delta)}. \tag{10}$$

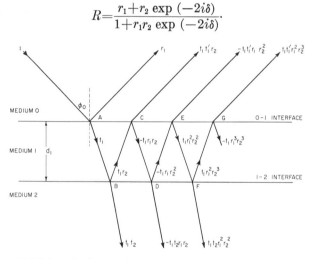

FIGURE 2. *Multiple reflections and transmissions of a light beam incident on a thin film.*

The Fresnel reflection coefficients, r_1 and r_2 in this equation, must be those appropriate to the direction of polarisation. Thus the reflection coefficient, Rp, defining reflection when the incident beam is polarised parallel to the plane of incidence, will be obtained by substituting into eq (10) values of r_1 and r_2 derived by use of equations of the type (3). Similarly, for polarisation in the normal direction, the reflection coefficient Rs is obtained by substituting into (10) the Fresnel reflection coefficients obtained from equations of type (5).

At this point, in preparation for discussion in subsection 2.4, it is worth paying attention to the following aspects of eq (10). Firstly, the derivation of (10) by use of figure 2 makes no assumption concerning the coherence of the incident light over the region of film illuminated. The phases of the reflected beams are all related to the phase of the light arriving at A. Reflection of light incident at some other point can be described by the same reflection coefficient provided, in this case, phases are all referred to the new point of incidence. If these two light beams are not coherent, then the resultant reflection cannot be described, a priori, by an expression such as (10), because it is then not possible to define uniquely the phases of the incident and of the reflected beams.

In the Drude-Tronstad technique as normally practised, this difficulty is overcome by illuminating the sample with light polarised at approximately $45°$ to the plane of incidence. In this situation the p and s waves incident at any point must be coherent with each other because they are resolved components of the same incident wave. Thus, the ratio $Z=R_p/R_s$, which involves only the difference in phase between the reflected p and s components, is uniquely determined. Moreover, this phase difference is independent of the absolute phase of the incident light, and thus it is unaffected by coherence of the incident light over the region of film illuminated. The Drude-Tronstad polarimeter is therefore designed to measure solely this phase difference—a feature which is extremely important to the discussion in section 2 describing reflection from non-uniform films.

2.3. A Matrix Approach to Multilayer Films

This next theoretical section is concerned with a detailed consideration of reflection from multilayer films. Unfortunately, the method of summing the contributions from individual multiple reflections, as given in section 2.2, is not suitable for calculating the properties of multilayer films. A more practical approach is provided by the use of matrix algebra more commonly associated with the theory of four-pole electrical networks or with the theory of periodic heat flow [5]: this approach has been used for calculating the properties of optical filters [6] and its pertinency to calculations for the Drude-Tronstad polarimeter has been mentioned by Winterbottom [7].

As a starting point consider an optical system involving, perhaps, many layers of various materials; in general the light at any point in the system can be resolved into two components—a forward travelling wave, $\mathbf{E}_{1+}$, say, and a backward travelling wave, $\mathbf{E}_{1-}$, say. It is worth emphasising, at this point, that $\mathbf{E}_{1+}$ is not the complex amplitude of a *single* light beam subject to multiple reflection as in the previous section, but is the *resultant* total beam, observed, as it were, after all the multiple reflections have taken place; likewise, $\mathbf{E}_{1-}$ represents the whole resultant wave. At some other point in the system the light may again be resolved into forward and backward travelling waves, say $\mathbf{E}_{2+}$ and $\mathbf{E}_{2-}$ (see fig. 3). Because the equations governing the propagation of light are linear, the relationships between $\mathbf{E}_{1+}$, $\mathbf{E}_{1-}$ and $\mathbf{E}_{2+}$, $\mathbf{E}_{2-}$ must be of the form

$$\mathbf{E}_{1+} = A\mathbf{E}_{2+} + B\mathbf{E}_{2-}$$

$$\mathbf{E}_{1-} = C\mathbf{E}_{2+} + D\mathbf{E}_{2-} \tag{11}$$

or, in the matrix form,

$$\begin{pmatrix} \mathbf{E}_{1+} \\ \mathbf{E}_{1-} \end{pmatrix} = \begin{pmatrix} A & B \\ C & D \end{pmatrix} \begin{pmatrix} \mathbf{E}_{2+} \\ \mathbf{E}_{2-} \end{pmatrix}, \tag{12}$$

but the relationship between $\mathbf{E}_{1+}$, $\mathbf{E}_{1-}$ and $\mathbf{E}_{2+}$, $\mathbf{E}_{2-}$ must necessarily be governed by the properties of that part of the optical system which lies between the two points at which $\mathbf{E}_{1+}$, $\mathbf{E}_{1-}$, etc., are defined: These properties enter eq (12) in the form of the matrix of coefficients A, B, C, D—indeed, the matrix $ABCD$ may be completely identified with

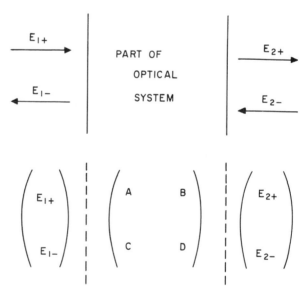

FIGURE 3. *Illustration of relationship between an optical system and the matrices used to describe it.*

the optical properties of the system, as is shown diagrammatically in figure 3.

This representation of optical properties by a matrix is made clearer by study of the situation shown in figure 4 where two optical systems are placed in series. The matrix equation relating the amplitudes of the light entering and leaving the first system may be taken as that given by eq (12) and the corresponding equations for the second system may be written

$$\begin{pmatrix} \mathbf{E}_{2+} \\ \mathbf{E}_{2-} \end{pmatrix} = \begin{pmatrix} E & F \\ G & H \end{pmatrix} \begin{pmatrix} \mathbf{E}_{3+} \\ \mathbf{E}_{3-} \end{pmatrix}. \tag{13}$$

The intermediate amplitudes $\mathbf{E}_{2+}$, $\mathbf{E}_{2-}$ may now be eliminated between eqs (12) and (13) to give

$$\begin{pmatrix} \mathbf{E}_{1+} \\ \mathbf{E}_{1-} \end{pmatrix} = \begin{pmatrix} A & B \\ C & D \end{pmatrix} \begin{pmatrix} E & F \\ G & H \end{pmatrix} \begin{pmatrix} \mathbf{E}_{3+} \\ \mathbf{E}_{3-} \end{pmatrix} \tag{14}$$

but, since the two juxtaposed optical systems may be regarded as a single system, $\mathbf{E}_{1+}$, $\mathbf{E}_{1-}$ may be related to $\mathbf{E}_{3+}$, $\mathbf{E}_{3-}$ by an equation analogous to (12), namely

$$\begin{pmatrix} \mathbf{E}_{1+} \\ \mathbf{E}_{1-} \end{pmatrix} = \begin{pmatrix} P & Q \\ R & S \end{pmatrix} \begin{pmatrix} \mathbf{E}_{3+} \\ \mathbf{E}_{3-} \end{pmatrix} \tag{15}$$

where the matrix $PQRS$ represents the properties of the composite system. Comparison of (14) and (15) shows that

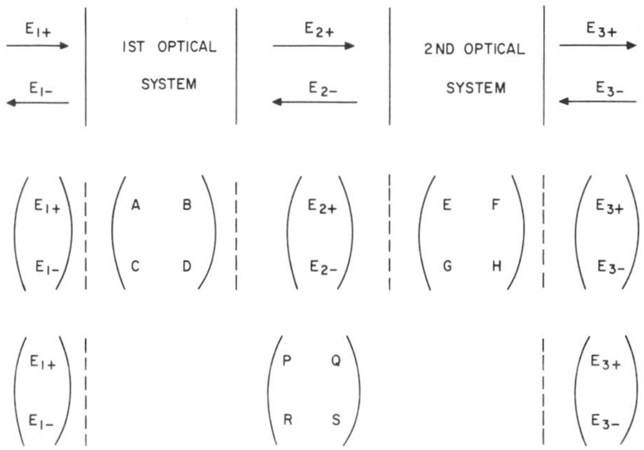

FIGURE 4. *Illustration of matrix representation of duplex optical system.*

$$\begin{pmatrix} P & Q \\ R & S \end{pmatrix} = \begin{pmatrix} A & B \\ C & D \end{pmatrix} \begin{pmatrix} E & F \\ G & H \end{pmatrix} = \begin{pmatrix} (AE+BG) & (AF+BH) \\ (CE+DG) & (CF+DH) \end{pmatrix}.$$

That is to say the matrix representing the properties of a composite system is obtained simply by multiplying together the matrices representing the individual components of the system taken in order. This rule is clearly applicable to any number of components, and herein lies the great usefulness of this approach in the study of multilayer problems, for matrix multiplication is a simple, systematic operation.

At this stage it is informative to evaluate the precise values taken by the coefficients $ABCD$, etc., when the optical system is particularly simple. As a first case, the matrix elements for a plane interface will be determined. To do this, $\mathbf{E}_{1+}$, $\mathbf{E}_{1-}$ are defined as the amplitudes in medium 1 immediately adjacent to the interface, and $\mathbf{E}_{2+}$, $\mathbf{E}_{2-}$ as the corresponding amplitudes in medium 2. In the special case of a beam incident from medium 1, as shown in figure 1, $\mathbf{E}_{2+} = t\mathbf{E}_{1+}$; $\mathbf{E}_{1-} = r\mathbf{E}_{1+}$ and $\mathbf{E}_{2-} = 0$, where r and t are the Fresnel coefficients appropriate to the direction of polarization. Substitution into (12) now gives

$$\mathbf{E}_{1+} = At\mathbf{E}_{1+}$$

$$\mathbf{E}_{1-} = Ct\mathbf{E}_{1+} = r\mathbf{E}_{1+} \qquad (16)$$

or

$$A = 1/t; \ C = r/t.$$

Similarly, when light is incident from medium 2 only,

$$\mathbf{E}_{1-} = t'\mathbf{E}_{2-}$$

$$\mathbf{E}_{2+} = r'\mathbf{E}_{2-}$$

and

$$\mathbf{E}_{1+} = 0$$

which, in conjunction with (12) leads to the equations

$$B = r'/t$$

$$D = (tt' - rr')/t. \qquad (17)$$

The reverse Fresnel coefficients r' and t' can be eliminated by use of the eqs (8) and (9) leading to the simpler relations

$$B = r/t$$

$$D = 1/t. \qquad (18)$$

Thus, the matrix representing the properties of a plane interface is

$$\begin{pmatrix} 1/t & r/t \\ r/t & 1/t \end{pmatrix} = 1/t \begin{pmatrix} 1 & r \\ r & 1 \end{pmatrix}. \qquad (19)$$

The second elementary optical system that it is necessary to consider is a simple homogeneous slab. The objective is to determine the matrix relating the amplitudes of the forward and reverse travelling light, $\mathbf{E}_{1+}$, $\mathbf{E}_{1-}$ at one point in a homogeneous medium, say at $x = x_1$, to the corresponding quantities $\mathbf{E}_{2+}$, $\mathbf{E}_{2-}$ at another point, say $x = x_2$. In a medium of refractive index n the electric vector $\mathbf{E}_+(x)$ of a plane wave of wavelength λ propagating in the forward x direction is given by the equation

$$\mathbf{E}_+(x) = \mathbf{E}_0 \exp\ (i\omega t - ikx)$$

where $\mathbf{E}_0$ is the amplitude at the point $x = 0$ and

$$k = \frac{2\pi n}{\lambda} \cdot \cos\ \phi,$$

whence it follows that

$$\mathbf{E}_{1+} = \mathbf{E}_{0+} \exp\ (i\omega t - ikx_1) \qquad (20)$$

and

$$\mathbf{E}_{2+} = \mathbf{E}_{0+} \exp\ (i\omega t - ikx_2). \qquad (21)$$

Now for the special case of a forward travelling wave in a homogeneous medium, $\mathbf{E}_{2-} = 0$, and there is no reflected wave, i.e., $\mathbf{E}_{1-} = 0$; taking this in conjunction with (20) and (21) and substituting into (12) at once reveals that

$$A = \mathbf{E}_{1+}/\mathbf{E}_{2+} = \exp\ (i\delta)\ \text{ and } C = 0$$

where

$$\delta = k(x_2 - x_1)$$

$$= \frac{2\pi nd}{\lambda} \cos\ \phi.$$

Similarly, consideration of a backward travelling wave shows that

$$B = 0 \text{ and } D = \exp\ (-i\delta).$$

In other words, the matrix of a homogeneous slab is

$$\begin{pmatrix} e^{i\delta} & 0 \\ 0 & e^{-i\delta} \end{pmatrix} = e^{i\delta} \begin{pmatrix} 1 & 0 \\ 0 & e^{-2i\delta} \end{pmatrix}.$$

On the basis of principles already discussed, the matrix representing the properties of a thin film is simply the product of the matrices representing the properties of the 0–1 interface, the homogeneous film of thickness d, and the 1–2 interface, taken in order, viz,

$$\begin{pmatrix} 1/t_1 & r_1/t_1 \\ r_1/t_1 & 1/t_1 \end{pmatrix} \begin{pmatrix} e^{i\delta} & 0 \\ 0 & e^{-i\delta} \end{pmatrix} \begin{pmatrix} 1/t_2 & r_2/t_2 \\ r_2/t_2 & 1/t_2 \end{pmatrix}$$

$$= e^{i\delta}/t_1 t_2 \begin{pmatrix} 1+r_1 r_2 e^{-2i\delta} & r_2+r_1 e^{-2i\delta} \\ r_1+r_2 e^{-2i\delta} & r_1 r_2+e^{-2i\delta} \end{pmatrix}. \quad (22)$$

Equations (16) show that the reflection coefficient for a plane interface is given by the ratio C/A; by analogy with this result it follows that the reflection coefficient of a thin film is the ratio of the second to the first elements of the first column of the matrix (22), i.e.,

$$R = \frac{r_1+r_2 e^{-2i\delta}}{1+r_1 r_2 e^{-2i\delta}}.$$

This result agrees with that previously obtained by detailed analysis of multiple reflections.

The advantage of the matrix approach is the ease with which it can be extended to deal with multilayer cases. In order to calculate the properties of two-layer films, it is necessary only to multiply (22) by the matrices

$$e^{i\delta_2}/t_3 \begin{pmatrix} 1 & 0 \\ 0 & e^{-2i\delta_2} \end{pmatrix} \begin{pmatrix} 1 & r_3 \\ r_3 & 1 \end{pmatrix}$$

and compute the ratio of elements of the first column of the resulting matrix product. Because the reflection coefficient is calculated as a ratio, the calculation may be further simplified by ignoring the common terms $e^{i\delta}/t$ which are factored out of the individual matrices. Moreover, this approach is well-suited for programming on a digital computer, because it provides a routine for calculating the reflection coefficient of a composite system comprising any number of films, as opposed to providing an explicit expression which, of course, varies according to the number of films in the multilayer.

The calculations of the reflection coefficients for light polarised parallel and normal to the plane of incidence proceed along exactly similar lines, except that in the first case, the Fresnel reflection coefficients, r_p, are computed from eq (3), whereas in the second case the coefficients, r_s, are calculated from eq (5). Z is then calculated from the ratio R_p/R_s in the usual way.

For the present work this matrix procedure was programmed for a Ferranti Mercury computer which enabled Z for approximately 100 double layer cases to be computed in about 1 min. The use of these Z curves is discussed in subsequent sections.

2.4. Films of Non-uniform Thickness

For practical work with specimens which are optically imperfect by reason of roughness or uneven film growth, it is essential to be able to assess, at least in a qualitative way, how far such departures from perfection will affect Drude-Tronstad measurements. Unfortunately, an accurate theoretical treatment of non-uniform films is difficult to devise, and the following brief account describing one of the more plausible lines of approach serves only to illustrate some of the difficulties of constructing a satisfactory theory.

The oversimplified model chosen to represent a non-uniform film sample is one in which the film is laid down on a plane substrate in such a way that it comprises finely divided and intermixed areas of distinct thicknesses d_1 and d_2 (see fig. 11). The aggregate area of thickness d_1, represented as a fraction of the whole area illuminated, is α, and the corresponding fractional area of thickness d_2 is $(1-\alpha)$. Apart from this discrete difference in thickness the film is assumed to have uniform properties.

The reflection coefficients of such a uniform film will be given as usual by eq (10) wherein the value of δ is that appropriate to the thickness d_1 or d_2. These reflection coefficients can be denoted by R_{1p}, R_{1s} for that part of the film which is of thickness d_1, and by R_{2p} and R_{2s} for that part of the film which is of thickness d_2: the corresponding ellipticities can be Z_1 and Z_2.

The assumption is now made that in the experimental determinations of ellipticity the relative importance of reflections from the two areas is proportional to the aggregate relative areas, α and $(1-\alpha)$; in the expression for the ellipticity of the whole film the reflection coefficients must therefore be weighed accordingly. Because this assumption is independent of the orientation of the plane of polarisation, it follows that

$$Z = \frac{\alpha R_{1p} + (1-\alpha) R_{2p}}{\alpha R_{1s} + (1-\alpha) R_{2s}}. \tag{23}$$

In general this equation will not describe experimental observations because the derivation just given tacitly assumes total coherence of the incident light, in addition to optical perfection of the film and substrate—conditions which are not satisfied in the conventional Drude-Tronstad setup. In an attempt to understand the effects of incoherence it is necessary to recall the discussion given at the end of section 2.2, where it was suggested that provided the Drude-Tronstad apparatus was arranged to detect solely the phase *difference* between the reflected p and s components of the same incident plane polarised beam, coherence was not essential to the validity of eq (10). Thus, if there exists an arbitrarily changing phase difference ϕ between reflections from different points on the sample given by the reflection coefficient R_{1p} and R_{2p} the same phase difference must exist between components polarised normally to the plane of incidence, e.g., between R_{1s} and R_{2s}. Accordingly, eq (23) is modified to

$$Z=\frac{\alpha R_{1p}+(1-\alpha)R_{2p}e^{i\phi}}{\alpha R_{1s}+(1-\alpha)R_{2s}e^{i\phi}}$$

The observed value of Z will be the average $\bar{Z}$ given by

$$\bar{Z}=\frac{1}{2\pi}\int_0^{2\pi}Zd\phi=\frac{1}{2\pi}\int_0^{2\pi}\left\{\frac{\alpha R_{1p}+(1-\alpha)R_{2p}e^{i\phi}}{\alpha R_{1s}+(1-\alpha)R_{2s}e^{i\phi}}\right\}d\phi. \tag{24}$$

Direct integration of this expression shows that if

$$\alpha R_{1s}>(1-\alpha)R_{2s}$$

then

$$\bar{Z}=R_{1p}/R_{1s}=\bar{Z}_1$$

and if

$$\alpha R_{1s}<(1-\alpha)R_{2s}$$

then

$$\bar{Z}=R_{2p}/R_{2s}=\bar{Z}_2.$$

As intimated at the beginning of this section this result is not entirely satisfactory: it indicates that the presence of small areas of a different thickness in a film which is otherwise uniform, has no influence on the measured ellipticity, and implies that Z changes abruptly from Z_1 to Z_2 and vice versa according to the relative magnitudes of αR_{1s} and $(1-\alpha)R_{2s}$. In section 3 it is pointed out that these conclusions are not verified by experiments, and the assumptions leading to eqs (23) and (24) are therefore suspect.

Accordingly, at present we cannot satisfactorily account for the phenomenological conclusions given in the following section, that the ellipticity of a non-uniform film is the same as that of a film having a uniform thickness equal to the mean thickness of the non-uniform film, nor can we justify the empirical equation

$$Z=\alpha Z_1+(1-\alpha)Z_2, \tag{25}$$

which is briefly discussed in the next section, and which appears to describe the formation of oxide on uranium (see section 4.2a) and the corrosion of aluminium in demineralized water (see section 4.2f), but does not describe non-uniform films of calcium fluoride on aluminium see section 3).

3. Experimental Verification of Formulae Derived in Section 2

Before making use of formulae derived in section 2 to interpret the thickness of films formed during corrosion processes, experimental evidence for their validity is essential. In the past, strong circumstantial evidence has existed for eq (10), in the close correspondence between ellipticity changes predicted on the basis of this formula, and experimental results relating to the growth of film of constant chemical composition. This is most conveniently seen in the polar plots of ellipticity with increasing thickness of film, as practised by Winterbottom [8]. These curves trace out distinctive shapes, but it transpires that mere correspondence of shapes is not in itself a sufficient criterion to define absolutely the parameters in eq 10 [9]. Other evidence takes the form of comparison between film thicknesses determined optically and by other techniques. Thus Winterbottom has shown close correspondence of data obtained optically and by electrometric reduction for oxidised copper [10]. However, in order to be able to obtain more direct proof of eq (10), and other equations relating to more complicated film configurations, some attempt has been made to reproduce films of known thickness and uniformity. The deposition of barium stearate monolayers, as practised by Rothen [11] and Mertens et al. [12], was rejected on the grounds of optical anisotropy within each layer deposited, and the experimental difficulty of putting down thick films. As an alternative, experiments were carried out using controlled vacuum evaporations, the evaporated material being most usually calcium fluoride, and the substrate electro-polished aluminium. This condition was chosen because the polar plot of the reflection characteristics of aluminium covered with transparent film (frequently referred to as the Z curve) is a very distinctive crescent-shaped curve. This shape of curve is known to be very sensitive to change in film absorptivity and thickness. Also, calcium fluoride is readily evaporated without decomposing, and as a consequence the deposited film has a composition close to stoichiometric. Greater sensitivity would have been obtained using a film material of higher refractive index, such as zinc sulfide, but against this advantage it is considerably more difficult to deposit films of stoichiometric composition.

The amount of calcium fluoride deposited was estimated entirely from the weight of sample evaporated, using a V-shaped molybdenum boat, and assuming uniform evaporation over a solid cone of angle 60°. The accuracy of measurement can be considerably improved by multiple beam interferometry on evaporated deposits, but this is time-consuming and it was not adopted for the investigation now reported. A polar graph illustrating the experimentally determined ellipticity values is shown in figure 5, and these data are to be compared with a corresponding theoretically derived curve using eq (10) (heavy line in fig. 5). There are differences in detail in the shape of the two curves. First, the width of the crescent formed by experiment is smaller than that of the theoretical curve, and also the azimuth at which the end point of the crescent turns is approximately 310°, whereas that for the theoretical curve is 272°. Contained in figures 6 and 7 are additional theoretically computed curves in which different optical constants have been employed for the aluminium substrate as well as changes in angle of incidence. The former changes do not provide a reason for the changed angle of the turning point of the curve,

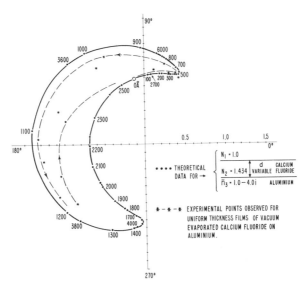

FIGURE 5.   *Comparison between theoretical and experimental Z curves for uniform thickness films of calcium fluoride on aluminium.*

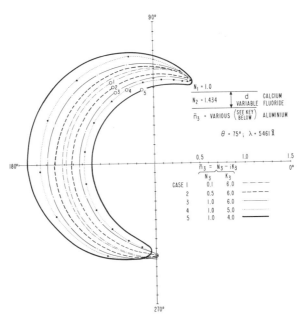

FIGURE 6.   *Theoretically derived Z curves indicating the influence of substrate optical constants upon ellipticity of light reflected from calcium fluoride films.*

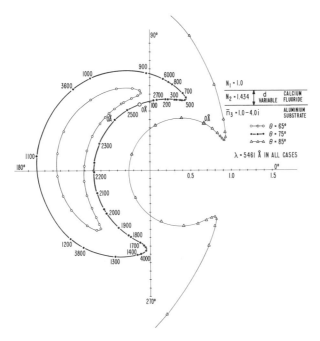

FIGURE 7. *Theoretically derived Z curves indicating the influence of angle of incidence upon ellipticity of light reflected from aluminium covered with calcium fluoride film.*

whereas the latter do. Examination of the surface for possible faceting that might have resulted in a component of light reflected at a smaller angle of incidence than that measured using the plane of the specimen revealed there was none, and this could not therefore be the explanation. Similarly, calculations on films of different refractive index revealed that a fall in refractive index (as might be produced by a non-stoichiometric, possibly partially hydrated film) would not account for the observed shape of the Z curve. This discrepancy between theory and practice is still unexplained by us. Comparison between estimated thickness of evaporated material, and values computed from optical data on the basis of a film refractive index of 1.434 are given in table 1. Bearing in mind the possible large error in evaporation, the agreement to a first order is satisfactory.

3.1. Two-Layer Film

To test the applicability of a two-layer model, a condition was required that would give some change in shape of the Z curve in order to compensate for the relatively poor accuracy available in ascertaining the thickness of evaporated deposits. Merely to change the refractive index of transparent film would not appreciably change the shape of

TABLE 1. *Comparison between apparent computed film thickness of nonhomogeneous calcium fluoride on aluminium and mean estimated thickness from vacuum evaporation data*

9 percent coverage of surface

	Film thickness, angstroms						
Estimated thickness evaporated through mask	250	1250	2250	2500	3000	------	------
Estimated mean thickness of overall film	22	112	180	225	270	------	------
Apparent film thickness computed from comparison with theoretical Z curve for uniform film growth	20	90	120	180	180	------	------

25 percent coverage of surface

Estimated thickness evaporated through mask	250	1250	1750	2000	2500	------	3500
Estimated mean thickness of overall film	62	312	437	500	625	------	875
Apparent film thickness computed from comparison with theoretical Z curve for uniform film growth	50	325	420	380	690	------	820

39 percent coverage of surface

Estimated thickness evaporated through mask	250	750	1250	1750	2000	------	2500
Estimated mean thickness of overall film	98	293	488	682	780	------	970
Apparent film thickness computed from comparison with theoretical Z curve for uniform film growth	75	400	380	950	980	------	1010

100 percent coverage of surface

Estimated thickness evaporated through mask	250	750	1250	1750	2000	3000	3500
Estimated mean thickness of overall film	250	750	1250	1750	2000	3000	3500
Apparent film thickness computed from comparison with theoretical Z curve for uniform film growth	160	640	1140	2100	2260	3000	3500

the crescent-shaped curve; calculations for the systems air/ZnS/CaF$_2$/ aluminium and air/CaF$_2$/ZnS/aluminium confirmed this point. Some advantage would be obtained by using water as an environment in place of air, but although this would produce change in curve shape more readily, the film thickness dispersion along the curves is considerably reduced and in any case it was feared it would create problems of film dissolution, hydration, etc. The condition finally selected was to deposit vacuum evaporated calcium fluoride upon absorbing metallic oxide films. For this purpose copper samples were oxidised to thickness levels of 209, 350, 490, and 625 Å by heating them to 120 °C in 30 mm O$_2$ for different periods; the cuprous oxide thus produced had an absorptivity lying between 0.2 and 0.25. Onto this was evaporated calcium fluoride in successive layers up to 2500 Å, optical readings being taken at each stage. Comparison between theoretical and experimental data is shown in figures 8 to 10. Results for the cuprous oxide film 490 Å thick are very similar to those of the 625 Å film shown in figure 10, and are therefore not included. To a first order the expected shape of Z curve is reproduced experimentally, and this is true also for the expected thickness of

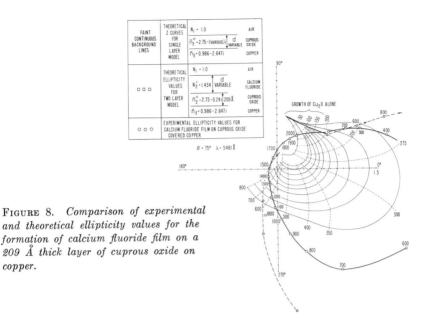

FIGURE 8. *Comparison of experimental and theoretical ellipticity values for the formation of calcium fluoride film on a 209 Å thick layer of cuprous oxide on copper.*

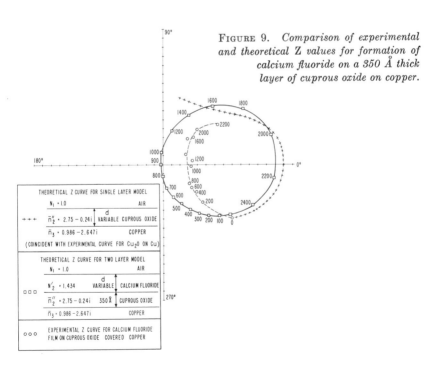

FIGURE 9. *Comparison of experimental and theoretical Z values for formation of calcium fluoride on a 350 Å thick layer of cuprous oxide on copper.*

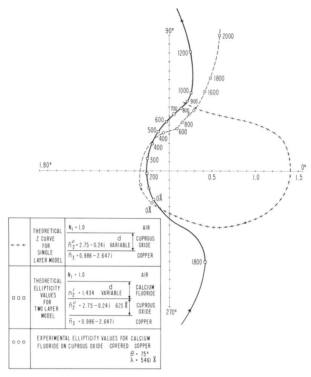

FIGURE 10. *Comparison of experimental and theoretical ellipticity values for the formation of calcium fluoride on a 625 Å thick layer of cuprous oxide on copper.*

calcium fluoride on the thicker deposits of cuprous oxide. The significance of the large discrepancy in film thickness values for the case of cuprous oxide 209 Å is unknown, more especially because the calcium fluoride evaporations were always made onto the four specimens at the same time. The conclusion is reached, however, that the formula relating to the two-layer model can be used to predict experimental results.

3.2. Non-Uniform Thickness Films

To study the influence of non-uniform films of the type illustrated in figure 11, calcium fluoride was vacuum evaporated in the form of small islands or cells upon electropolished aluminium surfaces. Three variables were studied:

    (i) the relative area of surface covered by the cells—9.5, 25, 39, and 100 percent;

    (ii) the relative thickness of film present over each cell compared with surrounding surface;

    (iii) the influence of such a cellular structure as provided by (i) and (ii) upon surfaces already covered with uniform thickness film.

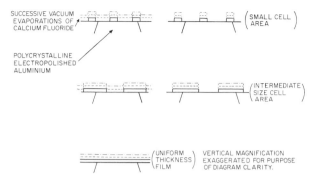

FIGURE 11.   *Diagram illustrating sections through various types of non-uniform thickness calcium fluoride films deposited upon electropolished aluminium.*

TABLE 2.   *Details of masks employed for the preparation of non-uniform thickness films*

Description of grid	Shape of cells	Distance between cells	No. of cells per cm²	Transmission through cells as determined spectrophoto-metrically
		cm		*percent*
Copper plated Monel grid_____	Square_____	0.034	500	9.5
Image of grid system reduced photographically onto sensitised copper sheet. Holes prepared by etching.	Circular_____	.018	1600	25
Chemically thinned stainless steel mesh_____	Square_____	.013	330	39

Area of sample illuminated when using the Drude-Tronstad technique 0.56 cm² ± 0.02.

The cellular structure was obtained by evaporating through grids having dimensions as given in table 2.   The grids were affixed horizontally to a framework such that the aluminium samples could be rested on top of them during the period of vacuum evaporation from a source located vertically underneath.   The distance between specimen and source was 20 cm in order to ensure that the edge of the film transmitted through the mask was quite sharp.   This point was confirmed microscopically when the calcium fluoride deposits were sufficiently thick to show temper colours, but no multiple beam interferometric traces were taken to confirm the actual profile.

Prepared samples were examined by the Drude-Tronstad method, data being recorded in figures 12 and 13.   The first figure shows results from samples representing all the different types of film thickness configurations tested, and all the points follow fairly closely to the Z curve for uniform thickness film.   Figure 13 provides rather more detail of the example where film over only 9.5 percent of the surface was increased, while the remainder was zero or at some fixed level

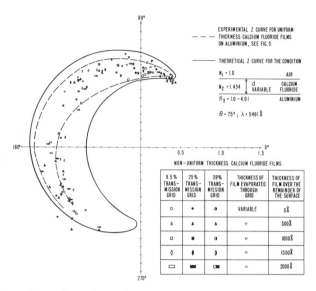

FIGURE 12. *Comparison of experimental ellipticity values from aluminium covered with non-uniform thickness calcium fluoride films, with experimental and theoretical Z curves for uniform thickness films.*

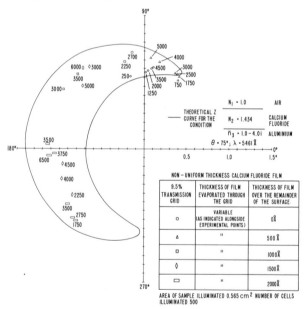

FIGURE 13. *Experimental ellipticity values from non-uniform thickness calcium fluoride films on aluminium.*

such as 500, 1000, and 1500 Å. For the thinner films sufficient results were obtained to show that the Z curve traced was in the same
direction as the one for uniform film growth, and the variation of
ellipticity with film change appeared to follow the average thickness
of film existing over the whole surface. Interpolation of apparent
film thicknesses for all three nonhomogeneous film cases studied, i.e.,
cell areas covering 9.5, 25, and 39 percent of the surface, are given in
table 1; and to a first approximation the apparent thickness levels
recorded are an average for the surfaces examined, in spite of widely
ranging configurations.

In section 2 consideration was given to the expected ellipticity of
light reflected from non-uniform thickness films. Data contained
in figure 14a represent ellipticity values calculated on the basis of
eq (23), derived on the assumption of a coherent light source, while
the curves in figure 14b are computed from eq (25). Data in the
first of these figures take the form of closed loops, with increasing
thickness of film producing movement in a clockwise direction.
Further, the increase in thickness to produce a complete rotation is
considerably less than that necessary to give a complete cycle of the
uniform film example (see fig. 5) and is completely contrary to observed experimental results. The method adopted for calculating
data given in figure 14b produces miniaturised forms of the Z curve
for uniform film growth, and as the area of surface being covered
with film increases, so the resultant size of Z curve increases, and
finally for 100 percent becomes identical with that for a uniform thickness film. Although there is some correspondence with observed
experimental results in that the movement around the Z curve with
increase in film thickness is the same, and also the basic shape of the
Z curve is the same, there is no correspondence in the positioning of
the curve on the polar plot, and also the increase in film thickness to
give a rotation of the miniaturised Z curve is the same as necessary
to give a complete rotation from a uniform thickness film. One of the
results of the experimental work carried out with non-uniform thickness films was that movement along the Z curve not only follows the
curve for a uniform film, but moved at a rate equal to the average
thickness of film, i.e., if 10 percent of the surface only was being
covered, then these areas would need to increase 25,000 Å in thickness before a complete rotation of the Z curve was made. It is clear,
therefore, that the empirical eq (25) does not represent the conditions
encountered experimentally.

Experiments with absorbing films are less easy to contrive on
account of the difficulty in depositing films of controlled absorptivity,
but a naturally occurring example exists which goes some way towards
providing an illustration. Previously [13] it has been reported that
prior vacuum annealing of copper changes the subsequent oxidation
rate at temperatures up to 120 °C very considerably (see the lower
part of fig. 15), this effect being produced by impurity atoms spreading
from grain boundary sites which effectively prevents the surface
covered from reacting with oxygen at temperatures up to 120 °C.

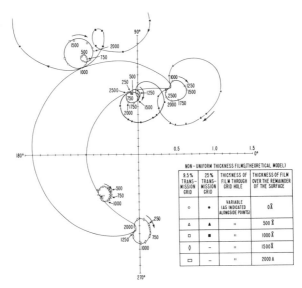

FIGURE 14a.   *Theoretical Z curves for non-uniform thickness films of calcium fluoride on aluminium, calculated using eq (23).*

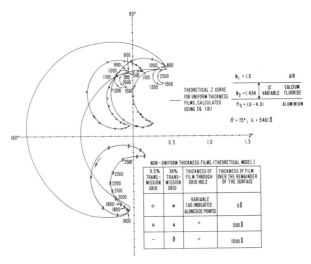

FIGURE 14b.   *Theoretical Z curves for non-uniform thickness films of calcium fluoride on aluminium, calculated using eq (25).*

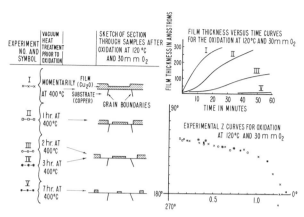

FIGURE 15. *Formation of non-uniform thickness optically absorbing films of cuprous oxide on copper and its effect upon experimentally determined Z curves.*

Such samples provide some naturally occurring examples of extreme non-uniformity of oxide film thickness, and it is interesting to note that the polar plots of optical readings all follow the same course, in confirmation of the data already described in this section for transparent non-uniform films on aluminium. Furthermore, although the observed optical changes for film growth on samples vacuum annealed prior to oxidation represent only short sections along the polar plot (see fig. 15) the islands of oxide exhibit first- and second-order temper colours, indicating that the apparent optical readings displayed in the graph are average film thickness values only.

On the basis of the experimental work carried out on non-uniform thickness films, the conclusion is reached that even under extreme conditions of non-uniformity, the shape of the recorded Z curve is not appreciably altered, and the interpolated apparent film thicknesses correspond to the mean thickness of film.

3.3. Anisotropy of Film and Substrate Optical Constants

The problems implicit in the study of systems involving optically anisotropic media have been outlined in the work of Mallemann and Suhner [14] and Blodgett and Langmuir [15]. The number of variables to be considered becomes so great that it is doubtful whether much progress can be made in interpreting results, save those from single crystals where precise orientation details are available. For polycrystalline materials the exact interpretation of waves reflected from film and metal which are made anisotropic by strain, or which are inherently anisotropic, would seem to pose insuperable difficulties. There is some possibility, however, that provided both films and substrate are fine grained and randomly oriented, the effects of anisotropy are likely to be cancelled out. A practical test for the presence of anisotropy consists of taking optical readings at different orientations of the sample, any anisotropy being detected by a periodic change every $180°$ in analyser reading Δ, where $Z=\rho e^{i\Delta}$. As an illustration of the absence of overall anisotropy on samples where substrate and film are known to be optically anisotropic, listed in table 3 are readings taken from film-covered titanium surfaces.

TABLE 3. *Drude-Tronstad optical readings from chemically polished and anodised polycrystalline titanium samples*

Method of preparation	Angle of rotation of specimen	Annealed ρ	Annealed Δ deg	Annealed Δ min	76 percent cold rolled ρ	76 percent cold rolled Δ deg	76 percent cold rolled Δ min
	deg						
Polished with alumina + 10% oxalic acid, bright dipped 20 secs in warm mixture of 40% HNO_3, 30% H_2SO_4, and 30% HF.	0	0.466	93	56	0.490	94	48
		.462	93	44	.490	94	08
	45	.462	94	00	.496	95	36
		.466	93	44	.499	95	08
	90	.477	93	44	.494	94	12
		.483	94	08	.494	93	24
	135	.490	93	20	.499	94	44
		.488	92	44	.492	94	32
	180	.466	93	12	.496	93	24
		.471	93	08	.499	93	12
Prepared as above, anodised in 0.005% wt/wt H_3PO_4/water at 100 V for 5 min.	0	0.445	−99	24	0.262	−117	04
		.433	−99	48	.261	−118	36
	45	.420	−104	00	.259	−114	08
		.424	−102	56	.253	−112	20
	90	.464	−105	32	.300	−118	32
		.462	−105	08	.294	−116	40
	135	.422	−99	48	.264	−113	16
		.431	−100	16	.287	−112	20
	180	.431	−101	16	.264	−116	24
		.433	−99	56	.261	−116	24

Under a polarising microscope, film overlying individual substrate crystals of such samples can readily be shown to have optical anisotropy.

The influence of oxide nuclei upon reflected ellipticity has been briefly mentioned elsewhere [9]. Nuclei which contribute largely to diffuse reflectivity are undetected by the Drude-Tronstad method. This means that measurements taken during early stages of some reactions, where the nuclei form an appreciable fraction of the total reaction product, may be very misleading. Such conditions exist during the early stages of thermal oxidation when metals are subjected to high temperature and low partial pressure of oxygen, e.g., during bright annealing processes. Under these conditions the electrometric or manometric techniques provide a more reliable result than the optical technique. In order to assess how accurate the interpretation of Drude-Tronstad measurements is likely to be, there must clearly be electron microscope inspection, or direct comparison from other techniques.

For nuclei shapes which take part in determining specular reflectivity, it can be assumed that the contents will be included in the average film thickness computed, provided the dimensions are such as to allow the requisite number of multiple reflections within the film as necessary for the derivation of eq (10). To a first approximation the width of nuclei must be the same order as the height, and known examples of nuclei which contribute to specular reflection are covered by this criterion.

4. Application of the Drude-Tronstad Method to the Study of Film Growth on Metals During Oxidation and Corrosion

In section 3 of this paper it has been established that ellipticity changes produced during reflection of polarised light from film-covered surface are a function of average film thickness and of the optical constants of the media concerned. It follows that in applications of the method to oxidation and corrosion studies, interpretation will be most straightforward for those conditions where optically homogeneous films of uniform thickness are formed. In general, these conditions of film formation are most frequently encountered on polycrystalline metals during anodic aqueous oxidation: the film profile becomes progressively more complicated in conditions promoting gaseous oxidation and corrosion respectively. Each reaction condition, however, presents its own special characteristics, and because of this it is now proposed to describe a number of specific examples.

4.1. Aqueous Anodic Oxidation

a. Aluminium

Commercial purity polycrystalline aluminium, having surfaces prepared either by mechanical or chemical processing methods, was anodised in ammonium borate solution at a range of voltages up to 120 V, the samples being periodically removed, washed and dried, and then examined optically. The shape of the Z curve produced by plotting ellipticity values on a polar plot can be matched very closely by theoretical data, on the assumption of a single uniform thickness film of transparent and isotropic oxide. The results are not reported here in detail because of the similarity of the data to that reported by Barrett for anodic oxide film growth on single crystals of high purity aluminium in a similar electrolyte [16, 17]. It is noteworthy that the shape of the curve is very similar to the example illustrated in figure 5, and in particular that the lower turning point of the crescent-shaped curve occurs at the theoretically determined value between 270 and 280°. Film thickness data has been studied up to one complete cycle of the Z curve, i.e., up to a thickness of about 2500 Å. Metallographic examination confirms qualitatively the uniformity of film thickness, even although temper colours are only weakly developed.

b. Uranium

Data for the anodic oxidation of polycrystalline uranium in ethylene glycol/ammonia/water mixtures at constant current density are shown in figures 16 a and b.   The temper colours exhibited are uniform over the surface, and up to film thickness of 1800 Å there is a close similarity between theory and experiment.

c. Titanium

A wide range of titanium samples, varying in purity and metallurgical condition, have been examined during anodisation in both 40 percent sulfuric acid and 0.005 percent phosphoric acid electrolytes. Temper colour formation was found to be uniform only on substrates produced by vacuum evaporation; in all other instances the colour, and therefore anodic film thickness, showed a marked dependency upon substrate orientation.   The wide differences in shape of observed Z curves can best be attributed to differences in film composition, a fact already briefly reported [9].

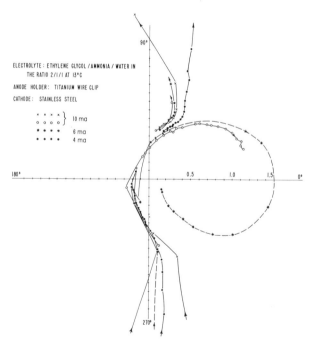

FIGURE 16a.   Z curves recorded for the anodization of uranium in ethylene glycol/ammonia/water mixture at constant current.

4.2. Gaseous Oxidation

a. Uranium in Carbon Dioxide

Gaseous oxidation of single crystal and polycrystalline uranium in carbon dioxide of various purities has been studied up to 550 °C. Data for reaction in very pure gas [<0.1 ppm H_2O; <1.0 ppm O_2] at 300 °C is represented in the Z curves of figures 17 a and b. Uniform film formation, as judged metallographically, is observed on single crystal material whether the surface preparation is made by chemical or mechanical methods, but large differences are observed with polycrystalline material; with the latter, marked differential oxidation rates with substrate crystal orientation are observed for electropolished surfaces, but not for those prepared by mechanical polishing on selvyt impregnated with $\frac{1}{4}$ μ diamond dust paste. The single crystal specimens (of considerably better purity than the polycrystalline material), both electropolished and mechanically polished, exhibited identically shaped Z curve plots (fig. 17a) even though the oxidation rates derived from the results were markedly different (see fig. 18a).

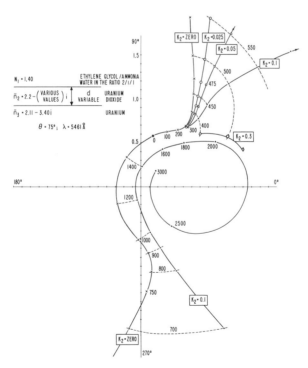

FIGURE 16b.   *Theoretical curves for growth of oxide on uranium during anodization in ethylene glycol/ammonia/water mixture at 13 °C.*

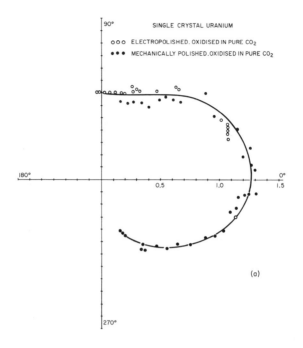

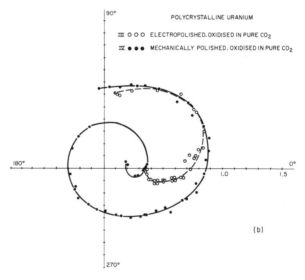

FIGURE 17 a and b. *Experimental Z curves obtained from the oxidation of single and polycrystalline uranium at 300 °C in carbon dioxide.*

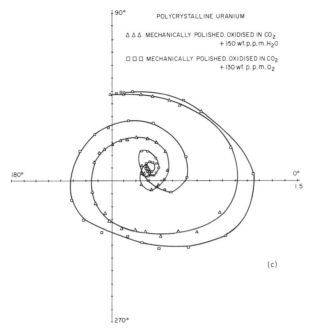

FIGURE 17c. *Experimental Z curves obtained from the oxidation of polycrystalline uranium at 300 °C in carbon dioxide.*

By comparison, although a similar difference in oxidation rate is exhibited by polycrystalline samples (fig. 18b), the Z curve for the samples displaying differential oxidation rates is now drawn in towards the origin (fig. 17b). However, although theoretical curves of the Z curve shape resulting from oxidation of electropolished polycrystalline material can be derived on the basis of eq 25, the conclusions reached in section 3 suggest this cannot be a valid explanation, and make it necessary to attribute the change in shape to a true increase in oxide film absorptivity. Similar relatively high film absorptivity is detected on electropolished surfaces oxidised over a range of temperatures, and also for dilute uranium-molybdenum alloys. The tentative explanation must be advanced that such films differ either in structure or composition from film built up on mechanically polished surfaces of the same material, but the nature of the differences is not known.

Additional information yielded during optical examination of polycrystalline uranium is illustrated in figures 18b and 19. Data in the first of these diagrams show the influence of gaseous impurities in carbon dioxide upon the rate of growth of uniform thickness film on mechanically polished samples, leaving no doubt that separate additions of oxygen and water vapour are responsible for considerable

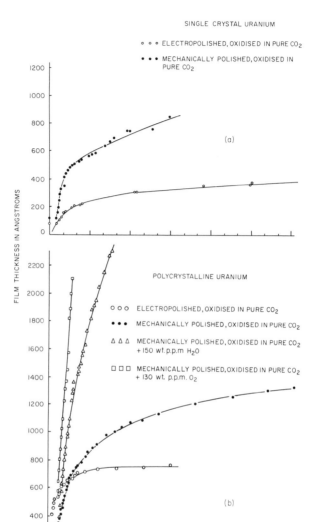

FIGURE 18 a and b.   *Oxidation of single and polycrystalline uranium at 300 °C in carbon dioxide.*

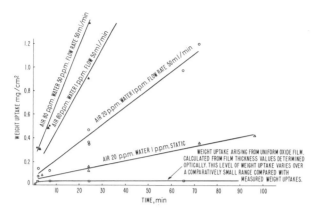

FIGURE 19. *Weight uptake of polycrystalline uranium heated at 400 °C in carbon dioxide of various impurity contents.*
(Published by permission of the Institute of Metals.)

increases in growth of film over the surface. Identical conclusions are drawn from examination of single crystal material.

In figure 19 comparison is made between optical and gravimetric results taken on samples subjected to the same reaction conditions. The fact that the two sets of results are quite different is attributable to the growth of irregularly shaped mounds of reaction product not contributing significantly to specular reflection, and yet containing the greatest percentage of oxygen. The point in time when the two sets of results begin to differ defines the stage at which the overall film is weakening sufficiently to allow a "breakaway" type of oxidation to begin, and the subsequent divergence between the results becomes a measure of the severity of the localised, as opposed to general, oxidation.

b. Beryllium

Oxidation of polycrystalline beryllium at temperatures up to 700 °C in carbon dioxide of varying pressure and purity has been examined. A comparison between optical and gravimetric results is instanced in figure 20, the overall result showing similarities to the example already quoted for uranium. The divergence between the two sets of results when the film reached 1000 Å in thickness indicates that at this point, localised oxidation, which with beryllium takes the form of intergranular oxidation, is becoming the dominant cause of oxygen uptake. Qualitative confirmation of this point is provided by metallographic examination of samples so severely internally oxidised to be grossly swollen and distorted, whilst the outer grain surfaces still remain locally flat and covered with second order temper colours.

Figures 21a and b illustrate *Z* curves obtained from oxidation under different conditions of humidity and pressure of the carbon dioxide. Three observations of particular interest are:—

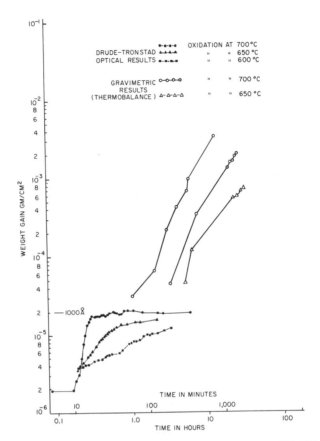

FIGURE 20.   *Oxidation of beryllium over the temperature range 600–700 °C in wet carbon dioxide.*

(i) the "hump" in the Z curve produced by very thin films formed in wet carbon dioxide (fig. 21a).   This change in shape of the Z curve at such an early stage must result from a marked change in optical properties of the film.   Under these conditions the only variable capable of producing the desired change in a theoretical model is a sharp fall in film refractive index, suggesting the formation of an hydrated oxide or hydroxide.

(ii) the increase in optical absorptivity of film formed in wet as opposed to dry carbon dioxide.

(iii) the large increase in absorptivity of oxide formed at 300 psi compared with carbon dioxide at atmospheric pressure.

The differences in film absorptivities noted in (ii) and (iii) are thought to arise from defects in the oxide, producing absorption peaks

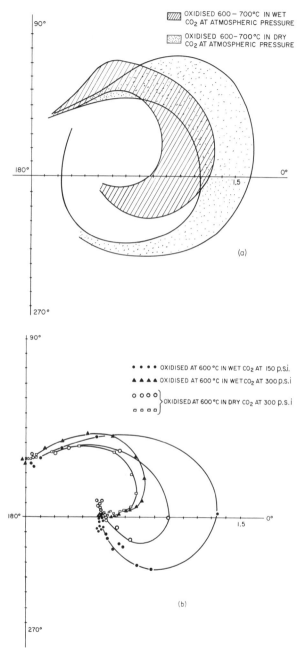

FIGURE 21 a and b. *Experimental Z curves for oxidation of polycrystalline beryllium.*

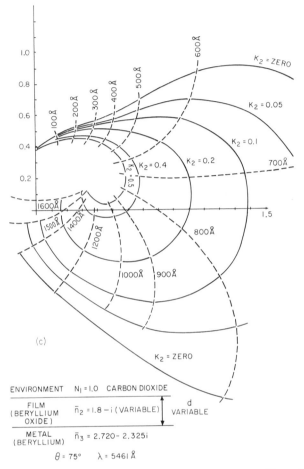

FIGURE 21c.   *Theoretical Z curves for growth of beryllium oxide on beryllium.*

in the visible spectrum. Some metallographic confirmation of this point is provided by the appearance of oxide overlying grain boundaries. Examination of specimens in the very early stages of reaction in wet gas, before localised oxidation of grain boundaries has been initiated, shows a discolouration effect over grain boundaries which serves to highlight the grain structure. Covering such surfaces with vacuum evaporated aluminium causes this network to disappear, suggesting that the observed appearance of dark lines is associated with a colouration effect in the oxide as opposed to a topography variation. The evidence is consistent with the film covering grain boundaries becoming highly non-stoichiometric prior to breakdown. On

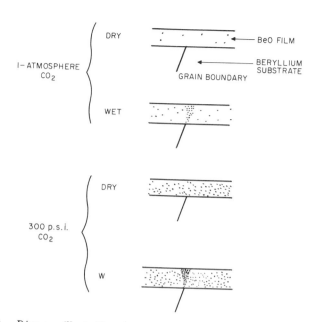

FIGURE 22. *Diagram illustrating the probable degree of disorder existing in beryllium oxide formed under different conditions of oxidation in carbon dioxide.* Density of spots is a measure of disorder in the beryllium oxide film as deduced from micro-discolouration effects and Drude-Tronstad optical measurements.

the basis of this and Drude-Tronstad measurements of average film absorptivities, the lattice disorder in beryllium oxide formed under different conditions can be represented by the model shown in figure 22.

c. Copper

Optical data obtained during the oxidation of copper over the temperature range room temperature to 200 °C in pure oxygen has been reported elsewhere [18]. The observed changes in film absorptivity with conditions of formation are attributed to variations in cupric ion content of cuprous oxide. These results are confirmed by Wieder and Czanderna [19], who have reported, on the basis of additional techniques, including electrometric reduction of oxide and microchemical analysis, that film forming at the temperature under consideration has an overall composition of $CuO_{0.67}$ which changes to CuO at temperatures above 300 °C.

4.3. Aqueous Corrosion

a. Brass in Seawater

Polycrystalline aluminium brass, 76/22/2, polished on $\frac{1}{4}$ μ diamond dust, has been exposed to circulating seawater at room temperature

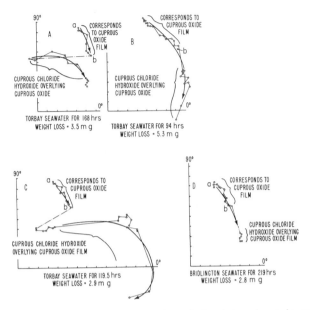

FIGURE 23a.   *Z curves recorded for corrosion of aluminium brass in various sea waters.*

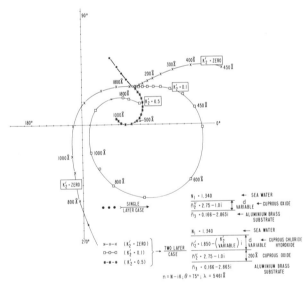

FIGURE 23b.   *Theoretical Z curves describing growth of cuprous oxide and cupric chloride hydroxide films on aluminium brass immersed in sea water.*

for periods of several weeks, and subjected to intermittent optical observations without removal from the solution. Film formed during the first 24 hr on test, i.e., the portion ab of the Z curves illustrated in figure 23a, corresponds to the growth of a highly absorbing form of cuprous oxide. This film attains a limiting value even though the metal oxide interface is receding at a rate considerably faster than film growth. After a further period of immersion, the length of time varying with batch of seawater and other variables, a second film, this one of cupric chloride hydroxide, begins to form rapidly on top of the first film layer, producing a range of Z curve shapes as illustrated. The direction of this second portion of curve is variable, and some possible explanations for the courses taken can be gaged from the theoretically derived Z curves in figure 23b, derived on the basis of a two-film model. On this interpretation the overlying film varies widely in absorptivity and therefore composition, and may reach thicknesses considerably in excess of the initial cuprous oxide.

b. 70/30 Cupro-Nickel in Seawater

In a similar manner to that just described for aluminium brass, samples of 70/30 cupro-nickel were prepared by mechanical polishing and then exposed to natural seawater for periods of several weeks. Z curves describing optical observations recorded during the first 30 hr of immersion are illustrated in figure 24a. Electron diffraction examination revealed the presence of a layer with crystal size too small for identification, but some deductions about its properties can be made from trying to prepare theoretical models capable of reproducing the Z curves obtained (fig. 24 b and c). To produce crescent-shaped curves of the type illustrated, rather than the spiral-type growth observed for brass, it is necessary to postulate a film which is not only of low refractive index but which is also transparent. These findings preclude the possibility of cuprous oxide being formed, and suggest a corrosion product containing principally salts precipitated from the seawater. X-ray microanalysis of reaction products indicates the existence of magnesium and sulfur, suggesting that the reaction product contains magnesium sulfate.

c. Aluminium in Demineralised Water at 80 °C

Specimens of polycrystalline commercial purity aluminium were polished on $\frac{1}{4}$ μ diamond dust and exposed to demineralised water at 80 °C for periods of a few days. At frequent intervals samples were removed from the solution for optical examination; the surfaces dried off quickly and naturally with no visible staining. Examples of the types of Z curve produced are shown in figure 25, other variable loop-type shapes being observed. These curves show a habit that is very different from the theoretical curves illustrated in figure 5, or the Z curves produced by anodisation of the same material in ammonium borate solution. Similar differences have been reported by Tronstad [20] and Barrett [16, 17] under slightly different conditions.

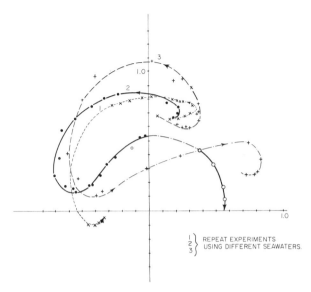

FIGURE 24a.   *Experimental Z curves describing the corrosion of 70/30 copper/nickel*
(+ 1% iron and 1% manganese) in various natural sea waters.

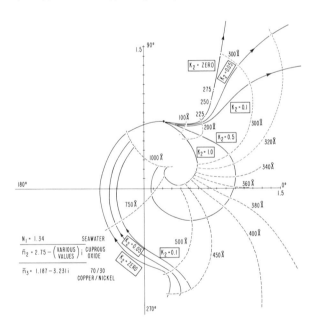

FIGURE 24b.   *Theoretical curves for growth, on 70/30 copper/nickel, of film having*
refractive index 2.75 and various optical absorbtivity.

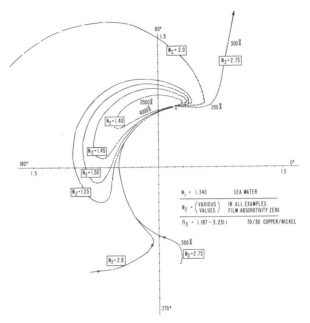

FIGURE 24c.   *Theoretical Z curves for growth of film on 70/30 copper/nickel in-dicating the change of ellipticity produced by transparent films of various refractive indices.*

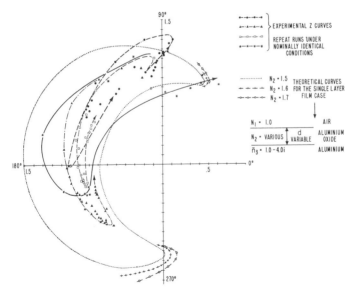

FIGURE 25.   *Experimental Z curves for the formation of Bohmite film on mechanically polished aluminium exposed to deionized water at 80 °C.*

Examination of samples corroded in the present experiments revealed Bohmite formation ($Al_2O_3H_2O$) only, but metallographically the film was found to be very non-uniform in thickness. This latter effect arises from the presence of pits which are each surrounded by an annulus of thick reaction product.

In order to interpret the observed Z curve, the ellipticity to be derived from a wide range of theoretical models has been computed. Uniform thickness single layer films of a wide range of refractive index produce crescent-shaped curves in which the lower turning point is always near 270°. Other models, based upon a high refractive index "barrier" layer adjacent to the film, and with an outer lower refractive index film, also produce similar shaped Z curves, which differ only in the dispersion of film thickness values around the curve and in the total thickness necessary to give a complete rotation. Neither do models, based on a large number of films in which the refractive index is made to decrease from metal to the air interface in a more uniform manner, produce any major change in Z curve shape. Introduction of absorbing film at either of the interfaces, using either two or three layer models, fails to reproduce in any way the shape of the experimental curves illustrated in figure 25. Theoretical curves derived on the basis of eq (25) can be made to reproduce the desired curve but, as described in sections 2 and 3, there is no theoretical justification for doing so. Interpretation of optical data in this instance remains unsolved.

5. Discussion

Examples illustrated in the foregoing section show that where reaction conditions give rise to formation of uniformly thick optically homogeneous film, whether the substrate is a single crystal or polycrystalline, there is close correspondence between experimental Drude-Tronstad observations and theoretical data derived from eq (10). Under these conditions optical observations may be interpreted with the full accuracy inherent in the technique. Although this will vary widely with the optical constants of the particular media concerned, with film thickness levels, etc., it generally means that absolute film thickness measurements can be made accurate to a few angstrom units.

There are, however, few conditions encountered during oxidation and corrosion of metals where such ideal filming conditions exist, the principal reason being non-uniformity of composition caused by concentration gradients, these being responsible for influencing optical properties. The closest approach to simple optical properties results from such conditions as are met in aqueous anodic oxidation, more especially on single crystal as opposed to polycrystalline material. However, even under apparently uniform film thickness conditions, Heavens and Kelly [21] have shown that, for the anodisation of tantalum in N/10 sodium sulfate, the average film refractive index varies linearly from 1.95 to 2.15 with increasing thickness. Although the advent of computers has made possible calculations which take account of constantly changing refractive index, such changes are not readily detected experimentally except by the special means employed by Heavens and Kelly, a procedure not always possible to apply during corrosion studies.

As the conditions of film formation become more complicated, e.g. by the formation of non-uniform thickness oxide, layered oxide structures, mixed oxides, stressed oxides, oxide nucleaton etc., the expectancy of providing a perfect interpretation of observed optical changes becomes smaller. Interpretation cannot be made without recourse to examination by a wide range of additional techniques. For data reported in section 4 it was found mandatory to obtain reflection electron diffraction examination of samples both before and at the end of a reaction, and also to assess qualitatively the homogeneity of film by reference to optical and electron microscopy. By this means an interpretation may be attached to optical observations which is sufficiently unequivocal to be of scientific value. The failure to achieve maximum sensitivity of absolute film thickness determinations does not mean that the method becomes generally inapplicable. Indeed, because of the considerable sensitivity still achievable, it remains under many conditions the most sensitive technique still available for measurements of film thickness in the 10 to 1000 Å range.

6. Future Developments

In the U.K. there are no instruments available with electronic recording, and a method utilised by Hodgson [22] would appear to offer considerable advantages. With such an improved method of recording, the logical extension of the technique to the measurement of optical changes over a wide range of wavelengths would become possible. Up to this stage in its development the technique has been employed almost exclusively for measurement of film thickness, but in future the detection of absorption peaks corresponding to various lattice imperfections may be of equal or greater value. For most semiconducting materials the spectrum of the visible and ultraviolet wavelength radiations is dominated by the fundamental lattice absorption, and consequently is a field not greatly investigated because crystals cannot be thinned sufficiently for conventional examination by transmission. Using the optical reflection technique described in this paper, and by utilisation of computing aids now available, the derivation of absorption data in this wavelength range is entirely practical, and it should now be possible to study absorption peaks arising from lattice imperfections in this wavelength range, a subject only occasionally mentioned in the literature. On the high wavelength side of the fundamental absorption band for semiconductors, and more especially in the infrared, the correlation between lattice imperfections and associated optical transitions has been widely reported for germanium and silicon, and to a considerably smaller extent for metallic oxides. Drude-Tronstad observations in this wavelength range represent a method of detecting the presence of absorption peaks in thin films, and offers the means of classifying the type and average concentration of impurities present, necessary data for the confirmation of theoretical models describing thin film growth of the type proposed by Uhlig [23].

General experience on corrosion of metals and alloys in service promotes the idea that microfailures in thin films are more important than macrofilm properties of the type described in the present paper. The development of a micro-optical technique would seem to merit consideration, but it is unlikely that the minimum area illuminated could be made sufficiently small to be of practical value. This is because the area for illumination must be a few microns, i.e., close to the resolving power of microscopes using visible wavelength radiation, and manifestly too small for measurements with infrared radiation.

7. Conclusions

Equations have been derived describing reflection of plane polarised light from surfaces covered with various film structures, and some experiments designed to check their validity have shown that although the theory of two layer films is in broad agreement with experimental observations, the theory of films of non-uniform thickness is still inadequate. Subsequently, a survey has been given of the applicability of the Drude-Tronstad polarised light method to the study of film growth on polycrystalline materials under different corrosion conditions, and it is concluded that results may be obtained which are helpful for understanding the mechanism of the processes under examination.

The authors gratefully acknowledge the sanction of the Directors of Imperial Metal Industries (Kynoch) Limited to publish this paper. In addition, sections 4.3(a) and 4.3(b) are included by permission of Yorkshire Imperial Metals Limited, sections 4.2(a) and 4.2(b) by permission of U.K.A.E.A., and figure 19 by permission of The Institute of Metals.

8. References

[1] P. Drude, Ann. Phys. **32,** 584 (1887); **34,** 489 (1888); **36,** 532, 865 (1889); **39,** 481 (1890).
[2] L. Tronstad, Trans. Faraday Soc. **29,** 502 (1933).
[3] O. S. Heavens, Optical Properties of Thin Solid Films, Butterworths, London (1955).
[4] A. Vašiček, Optics of Thin Films, North Holland Publ. Co., Amsterdam (1960).
[5] G. W. T. White, J. Appl. Sci. Res. **6A,** 433 (1957).
[6] F. Abelès, Ann. d. Physique **3,** 504 (1948).
[7] A. B. Winterbottom, Norske Videnskabers Selskab **45,** 1 (1955).
[8] A. B. Winterbottom, J. Opt. Soc. Am. **38,** 1074 (1948).
[9] P. C. S. Hayfield, First Intern. Congr. Metallic Corrosion, p. 663, Butterworths, London (1962).

[10] A. B. Winterbottom, J. Electrochem. Soc. **76**, 327 (1939).
[11] A. Rothen, Ann. N.Y. Acad. Sci. **53**, 1054 (1951).
[12] F. P. Mertens, P. Theroux, and R. C. Plumb, J. Opt. Soc. Am. **53**, 788 (1963).
[13] E. C. Williams and P. C. S. Hayfield, Institute of Metals Monograph No. 23, p. 131 (1957).
[14] R. Mallemann and F. Suhner, Rev. D'Opt. **23**, 20 (1940).
[15] K. B. Blodgett and I. Langmuir, Phys. Rev. **51**, 964 (1937).
[16] M. A. Barrett and A. B. Winterbottom, First Intern. Congr. Metallic Corrosion, p. 657, Butterworths, London (1962).
[17] M. A. Barrett, p. 213 in this volume.
[18] P. C. S. Hayfield, First Intern. Congr. Metallic Corrosion, p. 670, Butterworths, London (1962).
[19] H. Wieder and A. W. Czanderna, J. Phys. Chem. **66**, 816 (1962).
[20] L. Tronstad and T. Høverstad, Trans. Faraday Soc. **30**, 362 (1934).
[21] O. S. Heavens and J. C. Kelly, Proc. Phys. Soc. **122**, 906 (1958).
[22] J. N. Hodgson, Phil. Mag. **4**, 183 (1959).
[23] H. H. Uhlig, Acta Met. **4**, 541 (1956).

Studies of Thin Oxide Films on Copper Crystals With an Ellipsometer

J. V. Cathcart and G. F. Petersen

Metals and Ceramics Division, Oak Ridge National Laboratory [1]

The problems encountered in the use of an ellipsometer to study the oxidation of copper single crystals are described. Thin Cu_2O films are crystalline, highly oriented, and subject to large epitaxial stresses. The resulting strains, investigated by both optical and x-ray techniques, cause the films generally to be optically anisotropic. In addition the average index of refraction varies with film thickness, and a gradient in the refractive index exists across the films.

Modifications of the classical equations for reflection from a film-covered interface are suggested in an effort to provide a more realistic optical model for the films. A description is given of the construction of a thickness calibration curve for the ellipsometer using these equations in conjunction with a series of thickness values obtained from x-ray measurements.

One of the uses for which the ellipsometer is in principle admirably suited is the investigation of the kinetics of the early stages of oxidation of metal single crystals. Various advantages afforded by the ellipsometer, such as (1) the nondestructive nature of the measurements, (2) the possibility of making essentially continuous measurements at a distance, and (3) the extreme sensitivity of the method, have all been mentioned in previous papers. In practice, however, serious complications may arise from the fact that oxide formed on such metal specimens is frequently a highly oriented, crystalline material [1].[2] The existence of epitaxial forces between oxide and metal may lead to an inhomogeneous distortion of the oxide and possibly of the metal substrate as well. In general, films will not only be optically anisotropic, but a gradient in their index of refraction will also exist.

This paper reports on the problems encountered in the use of an ellipsometer in the study of the oxidation of copper single crystals in which both ellipsometry and x-ray measurements were used to characterize the oxide films.

1. Optical Anisotropy in Cu_2O Films

The initial indication of the existence of anomalous optical effects in Cu_2O films came in the course of a study of oxide films formed on the (100), (111), (110), and (311) faces of copper [2]. At that time an ellipsometer, which had been calibrated in terms of a literature value for the index of refraction of Cu_2O on the assumption that the Cu_2O

---

[1] Operated for the U.S. Atomic Energy Commission by Union Carbide Corporation.
[2] Figures in brackets indicate the literature references on page 210.

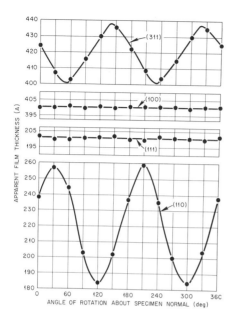

FIGURE 1. *Variation of the apparent oxide film thickness on four crystallographic planes of copper as a function of the angle of rotation about the film normal.*
After Cathcart, Epperson, and Petersen [2].

films were optically isotropic, was being used to measure the thicknesses of the oxide films. It was discovered, however, that the rotation of the (110) and (311) specimens about their surface normals led to periodic changes in the ellipsometer readings. Such optical anisotropy obviously invalidated the previously used calibration scale for the ellipsometer, but it was felt that the anisotropy of the films might still be usefully characterized qualitatively in terms of changes in "apparent film thicknesses" obtained from this calibration curve.

Typical sets of data for the four crystallographic planes of copper investigated are shown in figure 1. For the (311) and (110) specimens, maxima and minima in the thickness values occurred at 90° intervals during rotation. No such variation in apparent film thickness was observed for oxide films formed on the (111) and (100) faces of copper, nor did these films exhibit optical anisotropy when examined with a polarizing microscope.

These effects may be rationalized through a consideration of the epitaxial relationships between the oxide and metal and of the resulting strains in the oxide. As is well known, thin oxide films on copper single crystals are highly oriented and may be regarded as pseudo single crystals; the epitaxial relationships are summarized in table 1.

When a cuprous oxide film is viewed symmetrically with respect to the film normal, as is the case for ellipsometer measurements, the observation of optical anisotropy requires that the crystal lattice in the plane of the oxide film be strained in such a way as to have lost the elements of cubic symmetry. It is to be expected that this condition is fulfilled for the oxide formed on both the (110) and (311)

TABLE 1. *Epitaxial relationship between* Cu_2O *and copper after Lawless and Gwathmey* [1]

Plane of copper	Plane of oxide parallel to copper surface	Direction in surface of oxide parallel to [110] in surface of metal
(100)	(111)	[110]
(111)	(111)	[110]
(110)	(110)	[110]
(311)	(110)	[110]

faces of copper, either because the ratio of the elastic constants for the principal directions in the oxide is different from that for the metal, or because of differences in orientation of oxide and metal which lead to a variation in misfit as a function of direction in the plane of the film.

The situation for the (111) faces of copper is different. Not only are the lattices of the oxide and metal completely parallel to one another, but the threefold symmetry exhibited by both requires circular symmetry for the stresses developed in the (111) plane. Thus a distortion of the oxide lattice should be circularly symmetrical about the surface normal, and the film should exhibit no optical anisotropy.

A similar argument, based also on the high degree of symmetry of both oxide and metal, may be used to explain the lack of anisotropy of the (100) films. In general, however, it would appear that epitaxially induced strains in oriented oxide films will lead to an anisotropic distortion of the films except in special cases.

An attempt was made to determine the change in the degree of anisotropy of the oxide as a function of average apparent film thickness. The "degree of anisotropy" for a given film was defined in terms of its maximum and minimum apparent thickness values:

$$\text{Degree of anisotropy} = \left(\frac{d_{\max} - d_{\min}}{d_{\max}} \right) 100.$$

A plot of the degree of anisotropy versus the average apparent film thickness is shown in figure 2 for oxide films on the (110) face of copper. A similar curve was obtained for films on the (311) face. The most striking feature of the figure is the large peak in the degree of anisotropy which occurs at an average apparent thickness of about 200 to 300 A.

Given the association of optical anistropy with anisotropic strains in the oxide film, it is logical to relate a change in the degree of optical anisotropy with a corresponding change in the degree of strain anisotropy. It appears that the existence of the pronounced peak in the degree of anisotropy curve reflects a more rapid change in the strain in one principal direction of the oxide than another, although the nature of such a change is still not fully understood. In any event,

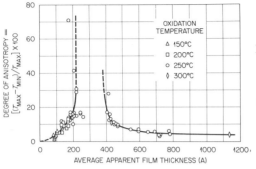

the data illustrate a sensitive, although qualitative, method for studying structural changes in growing oxide films with an ellipsometer.

2. Strain Model for Oxide Films Deduced From X-Ray Diffraction Data

The optical studies just described illustrate the dangers of considering the oxide as a uniform, homogeneous film and emphasize the need
for the development of a more realistic optical model for the films if
the full potential of the ellipsometer is to be realized.   Fortunately,
the existence of an x-ray technique, recently developed at the Oak
Ridge National Laboratory by B. S. Borie and C. J. Sparks [3, 4],
has permitted them to make useful measurements of lattice strain,
strain gradients, and oxide film thicknesses for Cu_2O films with average thicknesses as small as 20 Å, and the data thus obtained provide
considerable insight into the detailed structure of the oxide films.

Lattice parameter measurements for films on the ($\bar{1}$10) face of
copper [5] showed the existence of a lattice expansion of 1 to 2 percent
in a direction normal to the surface of the oxide, and preliminary
results for films on the (111) [6] and (311) [7] faces suggest the presence of comparable strains in these films as well.   The strain appears
to be of epitaxial origin, and oxide on the (110) is compressed in the
plane of the film.   These lateral strains are themselves anisotropic,
the oxide being compressed to a maximum degree in the direction
parallel to the [001] direction in the surface of the metal.   In the [$\bar{1}$10]
direction, on the other hand, the average lattice parameter of the oxide
is equal to that for bulk oxide.   The average unit cell volume of the
oxide is also that of the bulk material.

An analysis of the line shapes of the diffraction maxima for the
films indicates the existence of a strain gradient in the oxide on the
(110) face of copper.   At the oxide/gas interface the oxide has bulk
lattice parameters, and the strain varies approximately linearly as a
function of position in the film, reaching a maximum at the oxide/
metal interface.   It has been suggested that this strain gradient in
the oxide may be described in terms of an array of edge dislocations
in the oxide [5].

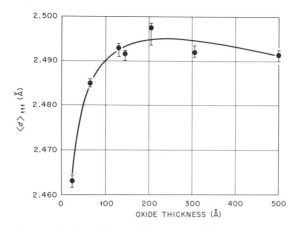

FIGURE 3. *Variation of the average lattice parameter measured along film normal as a function of film thickness* [6].

Finally the average lattice parameter of the oxide changes as a function of film thickness. In figure 3 the average lattice parameter, measured normal to the surface of the film on a (111) of copper, is plotted against film thickness. For extremely thin films, the oxide has bulk lattice parameters, but d_{111} then increases rapidly and passes through a maximum. Similar measurements on oxide films on the (110) face of copper also demonstrated the existence of variations of d_{110} as a function of film thickness.

The observation that a 25-Å-thick Cu_2O film has bulk lattice parameters was a surprising one, since epitaxially induced strains would be expected to be at a maximum in the thinnest oxide films. This result may be rationalized in terms of a discontinuous oxide film and lattice distortions in the substrate metal [6], but the possible consequence for the optical properties of the system occasioned by changes in the index of refraction of the substrate with film thickness has not been investigated.

The physical picture of the oxide as indicated by the x-ray data may be summarized as follows: In general the oxide film is subject to epitaxial forces in the plane of the surface, causing the oxide to be compressed in a lateral direction; normal to the surface there is a corresponding expansion of the lattice. A strain gradient exists in the film, which implies the existence of a corresponding gradient in the index of refraction of the oxide. Likewise, the average lattice parameter of the film varies with film thickness, implying that the average index of refraction of the oxide is also a function of film thickness.

3. The "Gradient" Optical Model for the Oxide

An attempt was made to formulate an optical model (hereafter referred to as the "gradient model") for the oxide films which takes

into account these findings.   The film was considered as consisting of
m layers, each of which was treated as a homogeneous, isotropic
medium.   Reflection from this "composite film" was described in
terms of the standard Drude equations [8], making use of the recursions
formulas developed by Wolter [9] for reflection from multiple films.
The only modification made in the equations was that suggested by
Vašíček [10] to take into account the effect of the optical absorbancy
of the Cu_2O films.

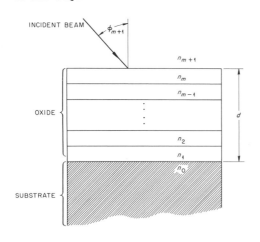

FIGURE 4. *Schematic representation of an m-layered
oxide film with refractive indices* n_1, n_2, *...* n_m *on a
substrate with refractive index
n_0 immersed in a transparent
medium with refractive index
n_{m+1}.*

Reflection from a layered system consisting of $m+1$ interfaces may
be described in terms of the ratio of the Fresnel reflection coefficients:

$$\frac{R^p_{m+1}}{R^s_{m+1}} = \tan \psi \, \exp i\Delta$$

where R^p_{m+1} and R^s_{m+1} are the reflection coefficients for respectively,
the parallel and the perpendicular components of the electric vector of
the incident light.   The experimentally determined quantities, $\tan \psi$
and Δ, represent the relative amplitude reduction and the phase
retardation, respectively, suffered by the two components on reflection.   Values of R^α_{m+1} are given by

$$R^\alpha_{m+1} = \frac{r^\alpha_{m+1} + r^\alpha_m \exp (-2\rho_m d_m)}{1 + (r^\alpha_{m+1})^* r^\alpha_m \exp (-2\rho_m d_m)}$$

where $\alpha = p$ or s, $(r^\alpha_{m+1})^*$ represents the complex conjugate of r^α_{m+1},
and r^α_m and r^α_{m+1}, the reflection coefficients for the mth and $(m+1)$th
interfaces, are obtained from the recursion formulas given below.

$$r^\alpha_1 = \frac{g_1 - g_0}{g_1 + g_0} \equiv Z_1 / N_1$$

$$r_2^\alpha = \frac{(g_2-g_1)N_1 \exp{(\rho_1 d_1)} + (g_2+g_1)Z_1 \exp{(-\rho_1 d_1)}}{(g_2+g_1)N_1 \exp{(\rho_1 d_1)} + (g_2-g_1)Z_1 \exp{(-\rho_1 d_1)}} \equiv \frac{Z_2}{N_2}$$

$$r_m^\alpha \equiv \frac{Z_m}{N_m}$$

$$r_{m+1}^\alpha = \frac{(g_{m+1}-g_m)N_m \exp{(\rho_m d_m)} + (g_{m+1}+g_m)Z_m \exp{(-\rho_m d_m)}}{(g_{m+1}+g_m)N_m \exp{(\rho_m d_m)} + (g_{m+1}+g_m)Z_m \exp{(-\rho_m d_m)}} .$$

For $\alpha=s$, $g_m=n_m \cos \phi_m$, and for $\alpha=p$, $g_m=\cos \phi_m/n_m$ where n_m is the index of refraction of the mth layer and ϕ_m is the angle of incidence in the mth layer. The thickness of the mth layer is designated by d_m, and $\rho_m=2\pi i n_m \cos \phi_m/\lambda$ where λ is the vacuum wavelength of the incident radiation.

In accord with the results from the x-ray study, it was assumed that a gradient in the refractive index exists across the oxide and that the average refractive index of the oxide is a function of film thickness. The functions chosen to express these variations are shown below for the refractive index of the jth layer, $\tilde{n}_j=n_j-ik_j$.

$$n_j=n_m+\frac{b}{d^a} \left(1-\frac{j-1}{m-1}\right)^c \qquad (1)$$

$$k_j=k_m+\frac{b'}{d^{a'}} \left(1-\frac{j-1}{m-1}\right)^{c'} \qquad (2)$$

where n_j, k_j, n_m, and k_m are the real and imaginary parts of the refractive indexes of the jth and mth layers, m is the total number of layers, a, a', b, b', c, and c' are constants, and d is the oxide thickness.

The three unknown quantities in the classical Drude equation for reflection are the thickness, d, and the index of refraction of the oxide, $\tilde{n}_1=n_1-ik_1$. The usual procedure for determining $\tilde{n}_1$ involves varying n_1 and k_1 until $\tan \psi$ and Δ values computed for a series of thicknesses agree with a corresponding set of experimentally determined values of $\tan \psi$ and Δ. Equations (1) and (2) introduce an additional set of adjustable constants $(a, a', b, b', c, \text{and } c')$ into the basic Drude equation, and values for these constants must be chosen in order to calculate $\tan \psi$ and Δ for a given oxide thickness.

These equations were programmed for an IBM 7090 computer, and values of $\tan \psi$ and Δ, expressed in terms of the corresponding analyzer (A) and polarizer (P) readings, were computed for a series of film thicknesses for specified ranges of both the real and imaginary parts of the index of refraction of the oxide.

The object of these calculations was to find those values for n_m, k_m, and the other adjustable constants which produce a fit between plots of calculated and observed A and P values. To this end the differences between A_{calc} and A_{obs} were determined for each value of P_{obs} and the squares of these differences summed. The combination of

n and k for the oxide yielding a minimum for $\Sigma(A_{calc}-A_{obs})^2$ was taken as the value of the refractive index providing an optimum fit between calculated and observed data.

4. Results

The equations described above do not take into account the existence of optical anisotropy in the oxide films, and, as might be expected, considerably greater success was achieved in applying the equations to data for oxide films on the (111) face of copper than for films on the (110) face where, as already pointed out, the oxide is distorted anisotropically. Only the results for the (111) films will be discussed in this paper.

A comparison of calculated and observed data for an oxide film formed at 200 °C and 1 atm O_2 pressure on the (111) face of copper is shown in figure 5. Analyzer readings are plotted against polarizer readings. As may be seen, the two curves match reasonably well, especially for small thickness values. On the basis of curve fitting alone, however, it was very difficult to select a unique value for the index of refraction of the oxide; the nature of the problem is illustrated in figure 6, which shows a plot of k_m (the imaginary part of the index of refraction, the plotted value being that at the oxide/gas interface) versus $\Sigma(A_{calc}-A_{obs})^2$. Each curve represents tests of the fit between observed and calculated data for a fixed value of the real part of the index of refraction of the oxide while the imaginary part is varied. Clearly, for each real value of the index, there exists a value of k which minimizes $\Sigma(A_{calc}-A_{obs})^2$, and while it is possible to identify an "optimum curve," the improvement in fit, measured in terms of the average deviation per experimental data point, lies within experimental error for a modest range of values for the index of refraction

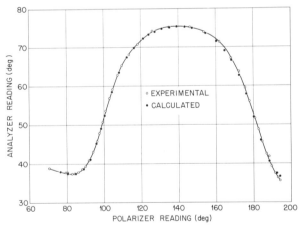

FIGURE 5. *Plot of polarizer versus analyzer reading for oxide film grown on the (111) face of copper at 200 °C and ~1 atm oxygen pressure.*

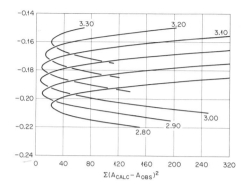

FIGURE 6. *Curves measuring the "fit" between calculated and observed ellipsometer data for various values of the real and imaginary parts of the index of refraction of the oxide.*

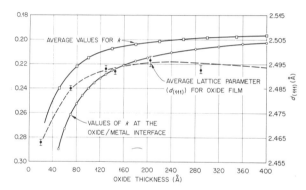

FIGURE 7. *Plot showing the variation of d_{111} and k, the imaginary part of refractive index of the oxide, as a function of oxide film thickness.*

of the oxide. This problem is especially serious for films <250 Å where uncertainties in thickness values corresponding to uncertainties in the index of refraction of the oxide may run as high as ± 50 percent.

For these reasons it was concluded that the construction of a thickness calibration curve for the ellipsometer by curve-fitting procedures was not satisfactory. Instead a purely empirical approach to the problem was adopted, and a comparison was made between a series of thicknesses obtained by x-ray measurements and film thicknesses calculated for the ellipsometer. The best agreement was obtained using the gradient model for the oxide film with $n_m = 3.00$, $a = b = c = 0$, $k_m = 0.190$, $a' = c' = 1$, and with the value of b' chosen so that the variation of the average value of k for the oxide and its value at the oxide/metal interface were those shown in figure 7. As may be seen, the change in the average index of refraction for the oxide corresponds roughly to the change in d_{111} as a function of film thickness.

A comparison of thickness values from x-ray measurements with those from ellipsometer data is shown in table 2. The two sets of ellipsometer thickness values correspond to thicknesses determined from the "gradient" model for the oxide and from the classical equations in which the oxide is assumed to be homogeneous and isotropic.

TABLE 2. *Comparison of thickness values obtained by x-ray and ellipsometer measurements*

x-ray	Ellipsometer	
	Gradient model	Isotropic model
$\overset{\circ}{A}$	$\overset{\circ}{A}$	$\overset{\circ}{A}$
76	92	126
130	125	169
148	141	197
205	205	296

The data for the isotropic oxide model were obtained with the index of refraction for the oxide of 2.50 to 0.265 i, which was the index producing the "optimum" fit for that oxide model. The average deviation per experimental data point between the calculated and observed curves over the thickness range tested was 0.25° for the isotropic model and 0.11° for the gradient model.

Compared to the isotropic model, the gradient model for the oxide not only produced a better fit between calculated and experimental data but also gave thickness values in much better agreement with the x-ray data. Thus, it seems reasonable to assume that the thickness calibration curve obtained with the gradient model is accurate to thicknesses of at least ~250 Å. It should be noted, however, that the changes made in the optical equations take the form of the addition of adjustable constants in the equations. A better fit of experimental and calculated data is, hence, to be expected, but it is questionable that real significance should be attached to the index of refraction values obtained from the equations.

5. Summary

Optical and x-ray studies of thin Cu_2O films on copper crystals demonstrated that the classical equations for reflection from a film-covered surface are not adequate when the films are crystalline and subject to epitaxial forces. A more realistic optical model for the oxide was proposed on the basis of these studies. This new model permitted an empirical thickness calibration curve to be constructed for the ellipsometer, but it was felt that little physical significance could be attached to the refractive index values for the oxide indicated by the model.

6. References

[1] K. R. Lawless, and A. T. Gwathmey, Acta Met. **4,** 153 (1956).
[2] J. V. Cathcart, J. E. Epperson, and G. F. Petersen, Acta Met. **10,** 699–703 (1962).

[3] B. S. Borie, Acta Cryst. **13,** 542 (1960).
[4] B. S. Borie and C. J. Sparks, Acta Cryst. **14,** 569 (1961).
[5] B. S. Borie, C. J. Sparks, and J. V. Cathcart, Acta Met. **10,** 691–697 (1962).
[6] J. V. Cathcart, G. F. Petersen, and C. J. Sparks, Lattice disregistry in very thin oxide films on copper, Proc. Symp. on Nucleation Processes in Gas-Metal Reactions, Paris (1963).
[7] C. J. Sparks, unpublished research.
[8] A. B. Winterbottom, J. Opt. Soc. Am. **38,** 1074–82 (1948); K. Danske vidnskabernes selskab Skrifter, 1955 NR 1, p. 1.
[9] H. Wolter, Optik dünner Schichten, Handbuch der Physik, Vol. XXIV, pp. 461–544, Springer-Verlag, Berlin-Götingen-Heidelberg (1956).
[10] A Vašíček, Opt. and Spectr. **11,** 128–130 (1961).

Discussion

H. E. Bennett (Michelson Laboratory):

I have two questions. First, could you tell us about the surface preparation of the copper? Was it electropolished, and did you look at surface damage using electron diffraction or a similar technique? Second, could you give a fuller description of the gradient model used? Was the variation linear with thickness or exponential?

J. V. Cathcart:

To answer the first question, we used electropolished copper crystals which were nominally 99.999 percent copper. The surfaces of these crystals, as far as we could tell from replica studies with the electron microscope, were essentially featureless after electropolishing. We used the standard phosphoric acid polishing solution for the specimens.

With regard to the form of the gradient of the index of refraction in the oxide, we assumed the film to consist of m homogeneous layers, the index of refraction of the jth layer then being given by

$$n_j = n_m + \frac{b}{d^a}\left(1 - \frac{j-1}{m-1}\right)^c.$$

n_j and n_m are the refractive indices of the jth and mth layers, respectively, d is the oxide thickness, and a, b, and c are constants. In most of our calculations we set $a = c = 1$.

K. H. Zaininger (Radio Corporation of America):
How sensitive is this x-ray method that you mentioned?

J. V. Cathcart:

We think it is very sensitive. The method is based on the assumption that all the oxide film present is very highly oriented; in other words, all of the oxide film that the x-ray beam intercepts is in position to diffract when the specimen is rocked through a modest angle. Within the limits of this assumption, which I think is a fairly good one based on electron diffraction evidence, films approximately 20 Å thick can easily be studied. This technique, which was developed by B. S. Borie and C. J. Sparks at the Oak Ridge National[1] Laboratory, is described in two papers that appeared in Acta Crystallographica **13**, 542 (1960) and **14**, 569 (1961). Two additional papers describing the application of the technique to thin Cu_2O films on copper crystals may be found in Acta Metallurgica **10**, 691–97 and 699–703 (1962).

F. L. McCRACKIN (National Bureau of Standards):
What is the modification of the Drude equation by Vašíček and where is it published?

J. V. CATHCART:
Vašíček's paper appeared in the Russian Journal of Optics and Spectroscopy **11**, 128–30 (1961). The basic change he makes comes from applying the Stokes reversibility principle in deriving the reflection equations. Such a consideration leads to the substitution in the denominator of the general equation for reflection from a thin film of the complex conjugate of the reflection coefficient for the first interface of the system.

Optical Study of the Formation and Stability of Anodic Films on Aluminium

M. A. Barrett

Norges Tekniske Högskole, Trondheim, Norway

The ellipsometer has been employed in a study of anodic films on aluminium primarily with the aim of understanding the effect of this type of film on the corrosion resistance of aluminium in hot water. Measurement of the thicknesses of the two layers resulting either from pore formation during anodising, or hydration by the action of hot water was accomplished by a combination of total thickness measurements and determinations of the anodic polarization necessary for the recommencement of the film growth, a quantity dependent only on the thickness of the inner compact layer.

1. Introduction

The ellipsometer built by Tronstad [1] [1] has been used in a study of anodic films formed on aluminium, and on the corrosion of aluminium in hot water [2]. Visual half shades have been used in making most of the measurements, rather than a photomultiplier, enabling observations to be made which relate to specific small areas when the reaction rate varies markedly over the surface. In all cases, measurements were made *in situ*, and it has been found profitable to combine data from the ellipsometer with electrical measurements, since the combination provides a means of studying the porous outer layer and the compact inner layer independently.

The two types of film substance involved, the anhydrous and the mononydrated aluminium oxide, are both completely transparent, but they vary markedly in the ease with which the results can be interpreted. To obtain a growth curve for the anodic film, the electrolyte 3 percent ammonium tartrate was chosen. This produces an essentially nonporous film. Films produced with this electrolyte yielded a closed curve when the delta and tan psi data from the ellipsometer were plotted on a polar graph for a series of thicknesses (fig. 1), corresponding to the growth of a homogeneous, transparent film. The extent to which the curve is retraced on the second cycle can be seen on the figure, where the circles represent readings taken in the first cycle and the triangles those in the second cycle. The dashed line represents the theoretical curve for growth of film in the electrolyte with those optical constants that have been chosen as best fitting the data. Agreement between the experimental and theoretical curves is not perfect, and the small discrepancies have not yet been explained.

---

[1] Figures in brackets indicate the literature references on p. 226.

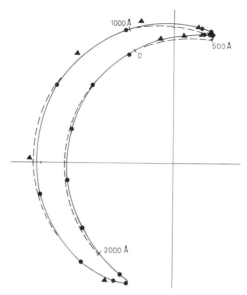

FIGURE 1.   *The reflection coefficients are plotted for a growth curve for aluminium anodized in 3 percent ammonium tartrate electrolyte.*

The closed circles represent observations in the first cycle, triangles are for the second cycle.   The dashed curve is one computed for a substrate with optical constants $1.0 - 6.7j$ for a transparent film with refractive index $n_2 = 1.66$ immersed in a transparent medium with refractive index $n_1 = 1.346$.

2. Determination of the Refractive Index of Aluminium

The complex refractive index of aluminium would be determined by a single observation on a film-free surface, but it is extremely difficult to obtain massive aluminium in this state, and it is doubtful whether evaporation under the best vacuum conditions would produce deposits strictly comparable optically to massive aluminium.   However, the following conclusions can be reached from the experimental observations thus far described.   The reading of a clean surface lies along the experimental line of figure 1 in the vicinity of the estimated zero point, and certainly to the left of all observations made on freshly polished surfaces.   This effectively determines the minimum possible value of the absorption coefficient as well as the relation between this and the real part of the refractive index.   A shift of the zero point results in only a minor shift of the growth curve, and making observations at other angles of incidence does not remove the uncertainty of the zero point.

In an attempt to remove these difficulties, another method [2] was employed.   This method, which involved varying the refractive index of the surrounding medium, is theoretically a more effective approach, and was the method adopted although it presented experimental difficulties.

This technique was based on the principle that if a filmed surface is immersed in a medium of the same refractive index as the film substance, the reflection at the interface between the film and the immersion medium is eliminated. The refractive index of the substrate can then be determined directly as though the surface were film free. This method requires a knowledge of the refractive index of the film. It was here assumed to be the same as that of anodic film. Comparison of the observed individual reflection parameters for the various immersion media with the corresponding computed ones furnishes an alternative approach for interpreting the data, one that has the advantage of treating equally well the case where no medium is found matching identically the refractive index of the film.

It is advantageous to use aluminium with the least possible film in order to minimize error due to misjudgment of the film substance. The observations were made on aluminium freshly electropolished in a solution consisting of 700 ml alcohol, 200 ml perchloric acid and 100 ml 2-butoxy-ethanol. The immersion liquids used were benzene, o-dichlorobenzene, monochloronaphthalene and alpha-bromonaphthalene. The constants of aluminium at the wavelength 5461 Å were estimated as $1.0 - 6.7j$ by this method.

3. Determination of the Refractive Index of Anodic Oxide Films on Aluminium

An estimate of the refractive index of the anodic film can be made directly from the growth curve shown in figure 1 with reasonable accuracy, since a higher film refractive index results in an increase in the length of the crescent-shaped curve. The estimate obtained this manner for the anodic film was 1.66

The immersion method described above was also used. In this case there was an advantage in using relatively thick films. Two polished aluminium specimens were anodised to produce films of the same character but with such different thicknesses that the reflection coefficients in ammonium tartrate were widely different. The reflection coeficients were then determined in a series of immersion liquids with a range of refractive indices. On inspection of the observations, it was then possible to interpolate a refractive index for that immersion medium in which the two specimens would have identical values for the reflection coefficients and which therefore would have the same refractive index as the film substance.

Here again, a comparison of the individual reflection parameters with calculated ones provides a check. An example is taken from the observations of a single filmed surface immersed in the above mentioned liquids. The observations are plotted as crosses in figure 2. The match of computed points with observations naturally involves the assignment of values for the film thickness and the refractive index of the substrate. To obtain the corresponding com-

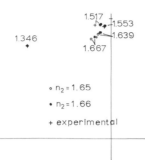

FIGURE 2. *Computed and experimental reflection coefficients for anodized specimen in various liquids, assuming* $n_2 = 1.65$ *and* 1.66.

The refractive indices of the immersion media are marked at the points.

puted points the substrate was assumed to have the refractive index $1.0 - 6.7j$ as determined in the experiment mentioned above. The film thickness was determined first assuming a film refractive index 1.65 from the observation taken in ammonium tartrate. Using this thickness, the points to be expected with immersion in the various media were computed and are shown as open circles in the plot. The procedure was repeated with a value of 1.66 for the film refractive index, and the results are shown as filled circles. Agreement was best assuming the value of 1.66 for the anodic film.

A serious uncertainty when using the immersion liquids on filmed samples, not present using the growth curve to estimate directly the refractive index of the film, arises from the assumptions that no adsorbed water is left on the surface, but that any water incorporated in the film during formation (approximately 15 percent for compact anodic films) remains in the film. The treatment adopted was similar to that used in botany and zoology; the specimens were immersed in absolute alcohol for several hours after formation. The method depends also on the various immersion liquids replacing one another in the pores if the film is porous.

Alterations in the film as a result of reaction in the course of a series of immersions would be expected to give rise to differences in the ellipsometer readings on repeating observations in the earlier immersion liquids. Alteration in water adsorbed or absorbed in porous films would give similar indications. In the immersion experiments made, the films appeared reasonably stable except that there were indications of some action with alphabromonaphthalene.

4. Refractive Index of the Corrosion Film

Regardless of which method is used, direct estimation from the growth curve or the immersion method, the problem of interpreting results obtained during the corrosion of aluminium in hot circulating water is much more complex than that for the anodised aluminium. The difficulties associated with the growth curve method are evident from a typical curve for corroding freshly electropolished aluminium,

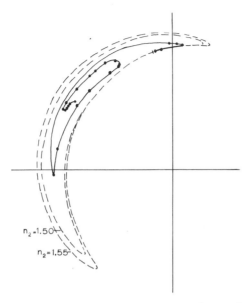

FIGURE 3. *Typical curve for changes in reflection coefficients during corrosion of aluminium in hot water compared to theoretical curves (dashed lines) for films with refractive indices 1.50 and 1.55.*

as shown in figure 3. It does not repeat itself, but follows a spiral track whereas computations of curves for growth of homogeneous transparent films with various refractive indices give a series of closed curves with the characteristic crescent shape. The lower the film refractive index, the smaller the loop, while the apparent loop center approaches the zero point or point for a clean metal substrate reading. The spiral curve in figure 3 has diminishing convolutions that might be associated with a lower film index, but the location of the center is displaced from the expected location. Electron diffraction studies indicate that the corrosion product in these conditions is a monohydrate whose refractive index is reported to be $n_D = 1.65$.

The position of the curve suggested that each reading might be the average of a series of points on the growth curve for a uniform homogeneous film. Such an averaging process might be conceived as arising from a surface consisting of a patchwork of small areas with different film thicknesses or different refractive indices. In figure 4 a curve has been computed for film growth in which the parameters delta and tan psi have been averaged for 10 thicknesses ranging from 60 to 140 percent of the nominal value, in which no interference effects are assumed to arise between adjacent areas. The computed curve shows some resemblance to the observed curve in figure 3. Similar curves could presumably be derived on the

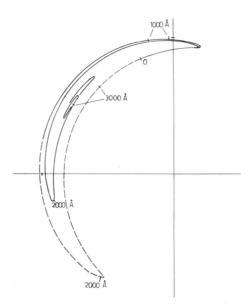

FIGURE 4.   *Computed curves where each reflection coefficient is averaged over a range*
of thicknesses from 60 to 140 percent of the nominal thicknesses.

The dashed curve is the normal growth curve for the same constants.   The optical constants employed
are $n_1 = 1.326$ (water at 70 °C), $n_2 = 1.54$, $n_3 = 1.66$ (inner barrier layer with constant thickness of 20 Å), $n_4 =$
$1.0 - 6.7\,j$.

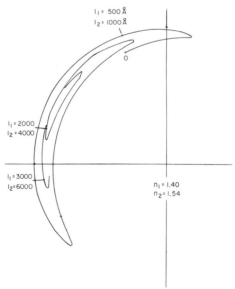

FIGURE 5.   *Computed curve assuming a double film in which the outer layer* (n=
1.40) *is half the thickness of the inner layer* (n=1.54).

assumption of the film refractive index varying over small areas with the same film thickness, i.e., variations in the density of the film. Computations have also been made for the case of a double-layered film in which the layers grow in constant proportions. The results of some computations of this type are presented in figure 5, and it is apparent that it is possible to obtain a curve similar to that observed on these assumptions.

It seems reasonable to assume that a variety of models could lead to curves for progressive changes in the optical parameters that would resemble the observed ones. In other words the optical observations alone cannot be expected to yield an unambiguous interpretation and it would therefore be reasonable to apply several independent techniques to distinguish between such alternative interpretations.

Immersion in a series of media of various refractive indices would be expected to be fraught with extra difficulties on account of the probability that these heterogeneous films would change on immersion and replacement of liquids in pores by subsequent immersion in different media might be rather incomplete. Nevertheless the estimate made by this method must be considered the most reliable at present. The observations were compared with theoretical points calculated on the basis of homogeneous films only, and the best match was obtained by taking the refractive index to be 1.54 for the corrosion product.

5. Stability of Anodic Films in Hot Water

The changes occurring in anodic films in hot water have been studied quite extensively in connection with the process of sealing of porous anodised films. It is accepted that this process involves the formation of the hydrated oxide, boehmite, which plugs or seals the pores. There is, however, some doubt as to whether the boehmite arises from conversion of existing film substance or from the reaction of further metal ions transmitted through the film.

It seems that anodising is not effective in increasing protection above the boiling point for any length of time, and the implication is that the anodic film has been destroyed under these conditions [4].

In the present studies the ellipsometer was used to follow the change in anodised surfaces exposed to doubly distilled water at 70 and 90 °C. Observations for the initial experiment with rapidly circulating water are plotted in figure 6. The first changes in the optical parameter were a retracing of the forming curve from point R to E in the figure, at an approximate rate of 5 Å/min. After reaching E, corresponding to a thickness of only about 100 Å, the film growth recommenced, and the further behaviour was similar to that observed in the direct corrosion of aluminium already discussed.

Further experiments, in which the water conditions were varied, produced the whole spectrum of results ranging from the type shown in figure 6, with vigorous circulation to those made with stagnant water in which the reflection coefficients remained stationary for

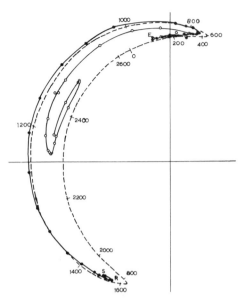

FIGURE 6. *Experimental curve representing an aluminium surface previously anodized in ammonium tartarate, then exposed to circulating hot water.*

Observations started at *S*. There was first a slight increase of film to *R*, then steady changes following closely the computed growth curve of fig. 1 (shown dashed), in the reverse direction. At *E* reversal again took place and the open circles represent this final phase of formation of corrosion product. (Reproduced from [2].)

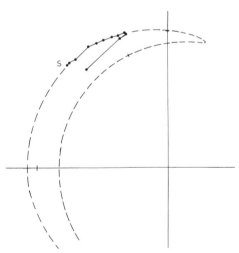

FIGURE 7. *Experimental curve representing changes of a pre-anodized aluminium specimen exposed to still water at 70° C.*

The initial point is at *S*. The dashed curve is the theoretical growth curve for anodic film.

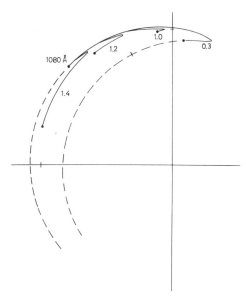

FIGURE 8. *Theoretical curve for the two-layer film model in which the inner layer (anodic film, n=1.66) is progressively replaced at the outer interface by hydrated film (n=1.54).*

The numbers represent the thickness ratio of the loss of the inner film to the gain of the outer film. The dashed curve is the theoretical growth curve for a single anodic film.

some minutes, and then spiraled in anticlockwise. A typical curve of the intermediate type is shown in figure 7. It is tempting to interpret the initial section of all curves of this type as representing dissolution, possibly accompanied by hydration, and the second portion as representing corrosion film growth. However, some computations were made for a model process assuming homogeneous films, in which a film 1080 Å thick with a refractive index 1.66 was progressively converted to a film with refractive index 1.54 accompanied by some loss by dissolution. The ratio of the decrease of the inner compact layer to the increase of the outer layer was varied in different series with the values .3, 1, 1.2, and 1.4 to represent varying degrees of dissolution. It will be noted (see fig. 8) that in all these hypothetical processes the curves change direction during the progress of the assumed reaction. Consequently an alteration in the sign of the change in delta is not necessarily indicative of a change in process; it is often merely the result of the periodic character of the optical phenomena for uniform growth or conversion of films. Conversely, the change of process to pure corrosion film growth when the entire anodic film has been consumed is not accompanied by any appreciable change in the direction of the curve, except for examples similar to figure 6. In other words, the commencement of the last stage is generally not detectable by a plot of the reflection coefficients alone.

On the other hand, the location of the turning point might be useful in estimating the ratio characterising a conversion process. Unfortunately, this requires a knowledge of the refractive index of the film formed. It is not to be expected that the final corrosion product on corroding previously anodised aluminium will necessarily be the same as for the corrosion of freshly electropolished aluminium, and the corrosion behaviour over a longer time indicated that the two products must differ in some respects. Characteristic of the curves of the type shown in figure 6 was that the last section, representing corrosion film growth, proceeded at a rate an order of magnitude slower than that for corrosion of freshly polished aluminium under similar conditions. Curves of the type of figure 7, or those indicating higher ratios of anodic film lost to corrosion film gained, if continued for a longer time, were impossible to interpret as they did not resemble any of the theoretical curves thus far computed. Taking the value of 3.2 for the specific gravity of anodic film and 2.8 for the specific gravity of corrosion film [4], the ratio should be 1.3 if the anodic film is simply hydrated without loss by dissolution or gain by further reaction with the metal. Even allowing for the uncertainty of the film refractive index it can be stated that values considerably above and below this were obtained in practice. The amount dissolved was clearly dependent on the speed of circulation. In still water the value of the ratio did not fall below about 1.2. Some dependence was also found on the amount of aluminium already present in the water, dissolution occurring more readily if the water had previously been boiled with aluminium shavings. This seemingly anomalous result is in agreement with the findings of the Institutt for Atomenergi [4], and Draley [5].

6. Determination of Barrier Layer Thickness

An independent method of measuring the amount of compact anodic type film in the presence of an overlying porous film is based on the difference in electrical properties of the two oxide types. The method as first devised by Hunter and Fowle [6] involves the study of current flow when anodically polarising the surface under study in a suitable electrolyte, e.g., ammonium tartrate, at gradually increasing voltages until the occurence of a sudden increase of current. This increase is characteristic of the resumption of film formation. The voltage at which this occurs may then be taken as a measure of the barrier layer film thickness, since the anodic film formation is dependent on ionic conduction which only occurs when the field strength is above about 10^7 V/cm. It is assumed that the entire potential drop lies across the barrier layer.

However, by using the ellipsometer to detect the onset of film growth, this technique can be applied to less perfect films, where leakage currents are substantial and interfere with the detection of the onset of formation by current measurements. An example of the application of the ellipsometer to the determination of the barrier

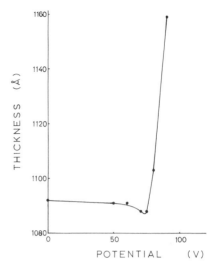

FIGURE 9. *Thickness curve for the determination of the voltage for re-anodisation for aluminium anodized previously at 80 V.*

layer thickness is given in figure 9. Each increment in voltage was maintained for 5 min before the optical reading was taken. The slight dip in the thickness curve that occurs before the rise indicating resumption of film formation is thought to be due to the dissolution of the film being stimulated by the polarisation.

It would not be possible to employ optical measurements for this purpose of growth if the barrier layer occurred solely at the expense of the outer layer since the optical effect of such conversion would be only minor. This mode of barrier layer growth would immediately be evident in that all barrier layer determinations would then simply give the total film thickness as the barrier layer thickness. Conversely, the fact that this is not so gives an indication that barrier layer growth occurs partially within the layer itself or at the metal oxide interface. The slope of the curve such as that in figure 9 when anodising has recommenced should give an indication of the extent to which further anodic oxidation takes place without the conversion of the porous layer, a steep slope indicating relatively independent growth of the barrier layer. The maximum possible slope would be 13.7 Å/V as found when the entire film is of the barrier type.

The slope found in an experiment with a porous anodic film was 10.3 Å/V. If it is assumed that the formation of the inner barrier layer film in all cases corresponds to the factor found in the formation of compact film, then for each volt applied, an increase of 13.7 Å in the barrier layer thickness follows. If, however, the optical indication is that an increase of only 10.3 Å has occurred in total film, then the difference must represent either that part of the potential drop lies in the outer layer, or that there is a reduction in the fraction of the film that is porous as shown diagrammatically in figure 10. The film substance of both layers is supposedly the same and therefore

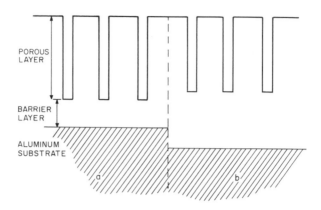

FIGURE 10.   *Suggested model of film growth.*
(a) film as formed after several hours at constant voltage, (b) structure
after further anodisation at increased voltage.

conversion of porous to barrier type film would result from further anodic oxidation occurring at the base of the pores filling them up. This is the reverse of the process of porous anodic film formation which is believed to take place by dissolution at the base of pores, consuming the outside of the barrier layer, which is replenished elsewhere within the barrier layer by further oxidation to maintain the equilibrium thickness approximate to the applied voltage. A porous layer is formed, although slowly, even in ammonium tartrate [7] which is normally considered to produce compact film. The above results relate to films formed in this electrolyte at constant voltage for many hours.

From the evidence that oxide formation may take place in part at the solution interface at the base of the pores as well as at the metal film interface or within the barrier layer, it can be argued that both anions and cations diffuse through the film during the formation process. Mott and Hoar have proposed that both Al^{+++} and O^{--} or OH^- diffuse, cation migration predominating at high field strengths and anion migration at low field strengths [8]. The mobility of both ions has been demonstrated experimentally by Bernard [9].

It would be interesting to apply a similar analysis to the case where the barrier layer is covered with boehmite as in the hydration process described above. The optical inhomogeneity of the hydrated layer is again a hindrance to interpretation, and no certain conclusion has yet been reached. A value for the voltage for re-anodisation can be found, but the slope of the curve above this point, requiring thickness evaluation, is in doubt.

7. Influence of Field Strength on Film Dissolution

Another aspect of the anodising process studied with the ellipsometer was the influence of field strength on the solution rate at the

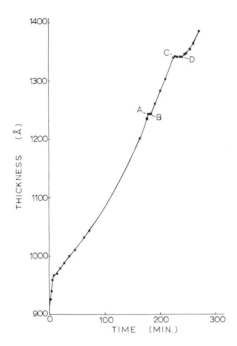

FIGURE 11. *Film growth during anodizing.*

The initial applied voltage is 70.25 V. At point A
the voltage is lowered to 69.25 V and at C to 64.25 V.

base of the pores. The first indication that this could be of importance
came from the invariable small decrease in thickness just prior to
the sharp bend upwards in curves such as that in figure 9.

For this study ellipsometer readings were made during the formation of a two-layer film in the ammonium tartrate electrolyte. During
the first ½ hr of anodising with constant voltage a linear rate of
growth of porous film was established (see fig. 11). After a period
of such growth the applied voltage was reduced by 2 V at A, when
film growth stopped immediately and was resumed after 4 min at B.
After a further period the applied voltage was reduced by 5 V at C
when growth again stopped and resumed after 15 min at D.

If it is assumed that when uniform growth of porous film is occurring,
there is also established an equilibrium barrier layer thickness corresponding to the applied voltage, then this thickness has decreased
during the pause by an amount corresponding to the voltage reduction
of two V for the first time and five V for the second time. If the total
equivalent thickness remains constant, then this reduction in barrier
layer thickness must be balanced by a corresponding increase in the
porous layer thickness, presumably by dissolution at the base of the
pores just as during linear anodic growth. From the time taken to

resume growth the average rate of thinning of the barrier layer at the base of the pores would be about 6.5 and 4.5 Å/min respectively in the two experiments. This rate exceeds that during the linear growth of porous anodic film, which is known to be 2.5 Å/min in the example shown in figure 11, because the dissolution rate must equal the film growth rate to maintain the barrier layer at the characteristic thickness for the forming voltage. Similar results were obtained using electrolyte of pH 5.5. However, in a further experiment, a film was anodised at 85 V, after which the applied voltage was reduced to 60 V, a reduction of 25 V, or, expressed in terms of the relative field in the barrier layer, this was reduced to 0.7 of the value maintained during linear growth. Growth of the film was not resumed in this case after 26 hr at the reduced voltage, i.e., the rate of thinning of the barrier layer in this case was less than 0.2 Å/min.

These experiments tend to suggest that dissolution at the base of pores is strongly dependent on the applied field in a similar way to the barrier layer formation process itself, but that at a field strength just below that required for barrier film growth, the dissolution reaction is appreciable.

8. Concluding Remarks

The foregoing are some examples of applications of ellipsometry to the study of rather complex phenomena for which it is difficult to obtain reliable optical constants and where the film structure is probably rather complicated. In such cases it is profitable to make collateral studies with ellipsometry and other techniques applicable to films *in situ* to give independent information regarding film formation.

It is also apparent that with the increased availability of computer facilities many aspects of measurements and interpretation can now be effectively studied and elucidated by computation surveys.

The present work was initiated at the request of Institutt for Atomenergi (Kjeller Research Laboratories) and of AB Atomenergi, Stockholm, in the framework of the program of optical studies of metal surfaces at Norges Tekniske Høgskole, supported by grants from the Royal Norwegian Council for Scientific and Industrial Research. The author thanks the above-mentioned organizations for financial support and Prof. A. B. Winterbottom and Messrs. K. Videm and B. Forsen for stimulating discussions and encouragement.

9. References

[1] A. B. Winterbottom, this volume p. 91.
[2] M. A. Barrett and A. B. Winterbottom, First Intern. Congr. on Metallic Corrosion, London, 1961, p. 657, Butterworths, London.

[3] Alcoa Monograph, Tech. Paper No. 10.
[4] K. Videm, private communication, 1963.
[5] J. E. Draley, J. Electrochem. Soc. **110**, 622–27 (1963).
[6] M. S. Hunter and P. Fowle, ibid. **103**, 481 (1954).
[7] M. S. Hunter and P. Fowle, ibid. **108**, 139 (1961).
[8] T. P. Hoar and N. F. Mott, Chem. Solids **9**, 97 (1959).
[9] W. J. Bernard, J. Electrochem. Soc. **109**, 1082 (1962).

Discussion

A. ROTHEN (Rockefeller Institute):
There is one point which was not quite clear to me. What kind of formulation did you use to get your thickness from your ellipsometry data?

M. A. BARRETT:
We used the complete Drude formula, with no approximations.

H. E. BENNETT (Michelson Laboratory):
Could you tell us more about the electropolishing technique that you mentioned you used to get the optical constants of the aluminum? Also, how pure was the aluminum and how thick were the oxide films you had in that case?

M. A. BARRETT:
The aluminium used was electrolytic aluminium of purity 99.993 percent. The analysis was 0.003 percent Cu, 0.0012 percent Fe, 0.003 percent Si. The ingots were subjected to a homogenizing anneal for 24 hr at 500 °C. Some of the later anodising experiments were done with zone refined aluminium, but no difference was observed.

The electropolishing solution was 70 percent alcohol, 20 percent perchloric acid, and 10 percent 2-butoxy-ethanol. The solution was circulated during electropolishing, and around 35 V was applied. According to our best estimates the thickness after electropolishing varied from 20 to 40 Å. Above about 40 Å the sample was discarded. These thicknesses are the most difficult to determine absolutely because of the difficulty of determining the zero point on the calibration curve.

R. C. PLUMB (Worcester Polytechnic Institute):
I would like to ask whether you have observed any effects with ammonium tartrate electrolyte which indicated departure in surface topography of the oxide-solution electrolyte interface from a simple plane surface.

M. A. BARRETT:
There are deviations from the theoretical curve that we cannot explain, but there is another complication not yet mentioned. This is that with ammonium tartrate solution pore formation does occur. In fact, all the results I have given for porous anodic films were obtained with ammonium tartrate solution but anodising for a long

time at constant voltage. The pore formation is slow, 1 to 2 A/min, but a small amount of pore formation would be expected to occur in all anodising, so we must always expect some deviation from the theoretical curves derived for uniform compact film growth.

R. C. PLUMB:

The reason I bring it up is in connection with your atomistic model for the decrease in thickness as you re-anodize, which you have attributed to dissolution. I wonder if it would be appropriate to do the same experiments with an electrolyte having a higher buffer capacity. Apparently the dissolution during anodization in an ammonium tartrate electrolyte is associated with the buffer capacity. Ammonium tartrate solutions have a rather weak buffer capacity. Perhaps some other electrolytes with a greater buffer capacity would not show that decrease and perhaps substantiate that mechanism.

M. A. BARRETT:

I think that is a good point to make. We would have liked to make the same studies using a borate solution, but oddly enough the curves deviated from the closed curve that would correspond to growth of a uniform transparent film. They did not follow the first convolution in the second time round and did not pass through the starting point. Ammonium tartrate appeared to be the best electrolyte of those we have tried so far, but we hope to examine other electrolytes with different anions and differing buffer capacities later.

K. H. ZAININGER (Radio Corporation of America):

How large is your illuminated sample area? How uniform do you think the films are over this area? And how is the accuracy dependent on sample area? Have you ever tried to correlate your thickness measurements determined by ellipsometry with measurements made by multiple beam interferometer?

M. A. BARRETT:

No, multiple beam interferometry has not been used in this work. The illuminated area of the specimen in the ellipsometer is 5 mm wide and about 12 mm long. Using half shades, an uneven film shows up as an uneven field in the telescope, but the analyser and polariser adjustments can be made for a small portion of this field, say 1 x 2 mm, lying on the line of demarcation of the half shade. This involves no loss of sensitivity since with the eye the rest of the field of view has no effect, in marked contrast to measurements made with the aid of the photomultiplier.

Ellipsometry in Electrochemical Studies

A. K. N. Reddy and J. O'M. Bockris

The Electrochemistry Laboratory, The University of Pennsylvania, Philadelphia, Pa. 19104

This communication presents techniques for utilizing ellipsometry for *in situ* electrochemical studies of film formation and growth on mirror electrodes immersed in aqueous solutions. In such studies, two major problems arise: (a) the presence of electrolyte may be incompatible with the establishment of a film-free state of the metal surface, required as an optical reference state; (b) film growth may occur much faster than can be matched by methods normally used for analyzing elliptically polarized light. In this laboratory, these problems have been circumvented by the use of an electronic potentiostat which has permitted the development of new types of techniques.

1. Introduction

This Laboratory has been involved in investigations which range over most of the basic aspects of electrochemistry, such as the structure of the electrical double layer, the kinetics of metal deposition, the mechanism of hydrogen and oxygen evolution, the electrochemistry of fused salts, etc. In 1961, work was commenced on the formation and growth of anodic films, and ellipsometry recommended itself as an eminently suitable technique, particularly in view of the classical studies of Tronstadt and Winterbottom [1, 2].[1]

Ellipsometry is the optical examination of surfaces, based on the laws of reflection of polarized light. The term ellipsometry is generally defined in a more restricted sense as an optical technique for the determination of the thickness and optical constants of surface films on metals. The technique is based on the fact that when linearly polarized light is incident on film-covered metals, the polarization state (i.e., the azimuth, λ, and ellipticity, ω) of the reflected light is different from that observed (λ°, ω°) in the case of reflection from a film-free surface. The magnitude of the changes in the polarization state, introduced by surface films, depends on the thickness and optical constants of the film material. Ellipsometry is noted particularly for its sensitivity in detecting and measuring extremely thin surface films (~ 1 Å) [3].

There are two main requirements for experimental ellipsometry: (1) a film-free state of the metal surface must be produced as an optical reference state; (2) the thickness of the surface film must either be constant, or must change at a much smaller rate than the rapidity with which elliptic polarization states are determined.

In utilizing ellipsometry for *in situ* electrochemical studies of film formation and growth on mirror electrodes immersed in aqueous solutions, two major problems arise: (1) interaction between the metal mirror and the electrolyte may lead to spontaneous film formation

---

[1] Figures in brackets indicate the literature references on p. 244.

and to the necessity of reestablishing the film-free, optical reference state; (2) anodic film growth generally occurs much faster than can be matched by methods normally used for analysing elliptically polarized light.

Notwithstanding these problems, some progress has been achieved in this laboratory towards the goal of adapting ellipsometry for electrochemistry. This communication is intended to describe the new techniques which have been developed, and then to discuss future possibilities.

It will be seen that a distinctive and novel feature of the techniques described here is the use of the *electronic potentiostat* as an integral part of an ellipsometric study of electrochemical processes. The basic viewpoint implicit in this approach is that, under steady-state conditions, the state of the metal-solution interface (particularly with reference to the existence, composition and thickness of surface films) is determined by the potential difference across the interface. Thus, the potentiostat, by electronically regulating the potential of a mirror electrode with respect to the solution, also determines the state of the metal surface with respect to surface films. For example, if it is desired to obtain a film-free, optical reference state of a metal M in a solution S, then a knowledge of the electrochemistry of the metal M, often conveniently summarized in potential-pH diagrams [4], enables one to choose the potential range in which the mirror electrode is thermodynamically immune to film formation.

There are many roles which a potentiostat can play in an ellipsometric experiment, and each method of utilizing the potentiostat yields a particular type of technique.

2. Qualitative Ellipsometry of Growing Films

The potentiostat in this technique serves to maintain an *initial*, film-free optical reference state of the electrode surface. Cessation of potentiostatic control of the electrode potential makes film formation possible (either spontaneously or with the passage of anodic current or by establishing a new electrode potential with a potentiostat) and ellipsometrically detectable.

For this type of investigation, however, it is necessary that the electrolytic cell be designed to permit electrochemical and ellipsometric experiments to be conducted simultaneously. Requirements of current density distribution and minimization of natural convection restrict the choice of cell and electrode geometry. In this laboratory, rectangular, fused-quartz cells were used with the metal under study covering the cell bottom. A pair of opposite walls of the cell serve as entry and exit windows for the light beam. The cell cover is designed to permit introduction into the cell of a reference electrode and a counter-electrode.

The assembled cell is mounted on the specimen carrier of an ellipsometer having a vertical plane of incidence (fig. 1). The horizontal metal functions as an electrode for the electrochemical experiment and as a mirror for an optical experiment. Thus, the state of the metal

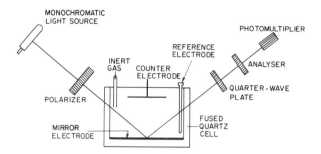

FIGURE 1. *Fused quartz cell mounted on specimen carrier of ellipsometer.*
(Reproduced from [7].)

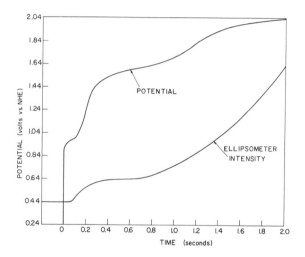

FIGURE 2. *Potential-time and ellipsometer intensity-time transients obtained from platinum in 0.1 N H$_2$SO$_4$ at a current density of 1 mA/cm^2.*

surface is continuously monitored *in situ* both electrochemically and optically.

The experimental technique consists of the following steps:

(1) the potentiostat is switched on and a suitable potential difference is maintained across the electrode-solution interface to ensure that the mirror surface is in a film-free state;

(2) when the mirror is in the film-free, optical reference state, the optical components of the ellipsometer (polarizer, analyzer, and compensator) are adjusted for "extinction" at first visually and finally by using a photomultiplier. These settings are not altered during the course of an electrolysis experiment;

(3) the extinction intensity is fed via a preamplifier to an oscilloscope;

(4) a fast switch is used to switch off the potentiostat and to impose a constant anodic current across the mirror electrode-solution interface;

(5) the formation of a surface film on the mirror anode degrades the fixed settings of the components into "off-extinction" settings and the off-extinction is manifested as an intensity increase.[2]   With increasing film thickness (for thin films) the fixed settings of the optical components depart more and more from the true extinction settings at any particular instant, and, therefore, the intensity of light incident on the photomultiplier also increases;

(6) if a dual-trace oscilloscope is used, a simultaneous record of potential versus time can be made.   In this manner the information from the ellipsometer intensity-time transient can be used to augment the information gained from the potential-time transient.

Such a study has been carried out on the anodic oxidation of platinum in 1 N H_2SO_4 solutions [5].   It suffices to point out here that the transients (fig. 2) show that an "oxide" is formed only at potentials greater than about 1.0 V (versus normal hydrogen electrode).

3. Chronoellipsometry

In the case of the anodic formation of calomel, the potential-time and ellipsometer intensity-time transients (fig. 3) (obtained by the technique described in section 2) presented an interesting problem [6]. The galvanostatic charging transients showed that the calomel

---

[2] Film formation can be made to reveal itself more distinctly when the optical components are set slightly off-extinction when the mirror is in its initial, film-free state.   To the extent that the settings of the optical components are not used to calculate thickness and optical constants, the actual intensity emerging from the analyzer serves only as an arbitrary "zero."

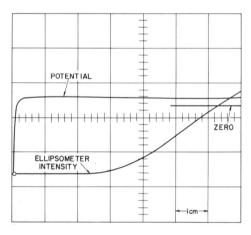

FIGURE 3. *Anodic formation of calomel films.*
Potential-time and ellipsometer intensity-time transients recorded with a 2 sec/cm Time Base on a Tektronix RM35A Oscilloscope, with a Type CA Dual-Trace Plug-in. Potential versus time transient with 200 mv/cm amplification. Initial potential held at −440 mv versus SCE with Wenking potentiostat. Zero of potential is indicated in figure. (Reproduced from [6].)

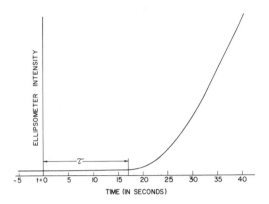

FIGURE 4. *Ellipsometer intensity versus time transient to illustrate induction time τ_i.*
[Reproduced from [7].)

potential was attained in a few hundred milliseconds (the integral capacity corresponding to this process being of the order of 120 μfarads/cm^2). In contrast, an *induction time* (τ_i) of several seconds was required for the formation of a calomel film (signalled by an intensity jump in the ellipsometer intensity transient) (fig. 4).

The induction time, τ_i, was found to be dependent on mass transport factors. Thus, the induction time increased considerably when the solution was stirred during the passage of anodic current.

The mechanism of growth of the calomel film was elucidated by switching off the galvanostatic current *during* the growth of the film. It was observed that the film continued to grow for some time even after the cessation of the current.

The anodic formation of calomel films on mercury electrodes was, therefore, interpreted in terms of a dissolution-precipitation model, a brief version of which can be written thus:

1. Specific adsorption of chloride ions:

$$2\ Hg + Cl^- \longrightarrow 2\ Hg \ \dots \ Cl^-$$

2. a. Dissolution of mercury with formation of chloromercurous ions
   b. Disproportionation of chloromercurous ions:

$$2\ Hg \ \dots \ Cl^- \xrightarrow{-2e} (Hg_2Cl)^+$$
$$\downarrow\uparrow$$
Mercuric entities

3. Precipitation of calomel:

$$(Hg_2Cl)^+ + Cl^- \longrightarrow Hg_2Cl_2 \downarrow.$$

The solution of the diffusion problem [7] showed that the induction time τ_i should increase with a decrease of current density, and that $i\tau_i^{1/2}$ should increase with current density, and above a critical current

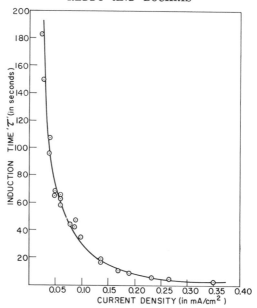

FIGURE 5. *The induction time* (τ_i) *required for calomel film formation observed at various current densities.*
(Reproduced from [6].)

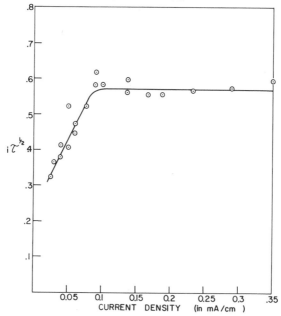

FIGURE 6. *The function* $i\tau_i^{\frac{1}{2}}$ *plotted against current density* (i).
(Reproduced from [6].)

density, should become constant with current density. The experimental results on the induction time for the formation of calomel are shown in figures 5 and 6. We see, therefore, that the dissolution-precipitation model is consistent with the pattern of experimental results, as is argued in detail elsewhere [6].

A preliminary study has also been carried out on the mechanism of film formation during the anodic passivation of nickel in acid solutions. The ellipsometer intensity-time and potential-time transients are shown in figure 7. An induction time was observed for the formation of a film on a nickel mirror electrode. The general behavior of the induction time was similar to that in the case of the anodic formation of calomel. It increased with stirring, and varied with current density as shown in figure 8. These results will be analyzed in greater detail in a forthcoming publication [8]. It will only be mentioned here that the surface film (not necessarily the passivating film itself) is apparently formed by a dissolution-precipitation mechanism.

The experimental determination and theoretical analysis of induction times was termed "chronoellipsometry" in view of its close analogy with "chronopotentiometry." In the latter technique, the "transition time" is determined from the potential "jump" in the potential-time plot obtained at constant current density, and is theoretically significant as the time required for the concentration of the reducible species to attain the value $C_{x=0}=0$. In chronoellipsometry, the "induction time" is determined from the intensity "jump" in the ellipsometer intensity-time plot obtained at constant current. The induction time is theoretically analyzed as the time required for the product of anodic dissolution to attain a concentra-

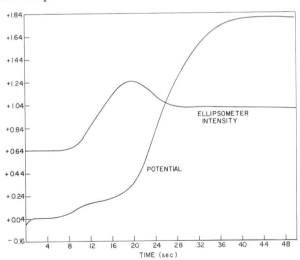

FIGURE 7. *Potential-time and ellipsometer intensity-time transients obtained from nickel in 0.5 M K_2SO_4 + 0.01 M H_2SO_4 (pH = 3.1) at a current density of 1.5 mA/cm².*

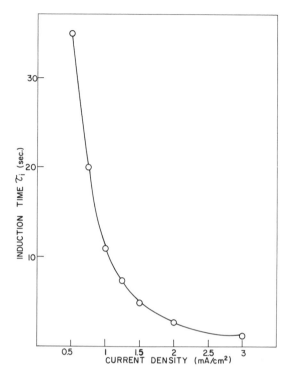

FIGURE 8. *The induction time* (τ_i) *required for a formation of a surface film on nickel as a function of the constant (anodic) current density.*

tion C^* near the electrode, C^* being determined by the solubility product of the insoluble salt which forms the anodic film by precipitation.

In the qualitative ellipsometry of growing films, the record of ellipsometry intensity versus time curves serves to provide ellipsometric monitoring of the surface and yields the following information: (a) whether a surface film is formed or not; (b) the time, after the commencement of anodic polarization, at which a film is formed on the surface; and (c) whether the film thickness increases with time or remains constant. It is to be noted, however, that though chrono-ellipsometry provides only qualitative information on the characteristics of surface films, it yields quantitative data on induction times.

4. Quantitative Ellipsometry of Growing Films

The ellipsometric analysis of growing films is bound to rest on a qualitative level until one is able to determine the time variation of the thickness and optical constants of a film. This advance, however, can be achieved only if the elliptic polarization states of the reflected

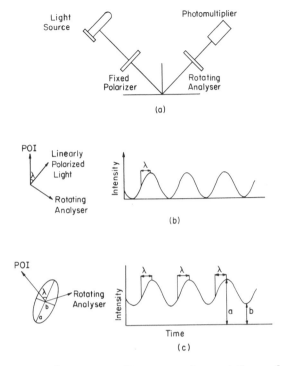

FIGURE 9. *An automatic ellipsometer using a rotating analyzer.*
(a) Schematic of ellipsometer.
(b) Sinusoidal intensity output in the case of linearly polarized light.
(c) Sinusoidal intensity output in the case of elliptically polarized light.

light can be continuously determined by methods other than the classical method of analysis. The latter method requires the manual alteration of the azimuths of the compensator and analyzer by means of independent mechanical controls and demands that the film be stable over several minutes. There is a vital need therefore for an automatic recording ellipsometer.

An attempt has been made in this laboratory to use a rotating analyzer.[3] If one provides a "phase marker" to register the time when the transmission direction of the analyzer is parallel to the plane of incidence, the azimuth and ellipticity of the reflected elliptically polarized light can be determined from the phase of the maxima, and the ratio of the maxima to minima respectively of the sinusoidally varying intensity emerging from the rotating analyzer (fig. 9). For time-independent elliptic polarization states, the method has proved successful [9]. For growing films, at least one complete rotation of the analyzer should be completed before there is any significant change in film thickness. The problems arising from the mechanical "wobble" of the rotating analyzer and from accurate (to 0.01°)

3 We are grateful to Mr. V. Radhakrishnan (Department of Radio Astronomy, California Institute of Technology, Pasadena, Calif.) for this suggestion.

determination of the phase and amplitude ratio of sine waves of increasing frequency (the faster the film growth, the higher should be the rpm of the rotating analyzer) have not yet been solved in detail but the method seems sufficiently promising to merit further attention.

At the present juncture, therefore, the best that can be achieved is to resort to approximation methods and to recover a thickness-time plot from the ellipsometer intensity-time curves. A significant step in this direction has been taken by Archer [10], who developed a method (which he called "photoelectric ellipsometry") in the course of a study of the adsorption of water on silicon substrates.

A derivation of his equations is presented here in terms of the Poincaré sphere representation [11], and an ellipsometer geometry in which the quarter-wave plate is situated in the incident beam, its fast axis being set at a 45° azimuth with respect to the plane of incidence. The present treatment is based on a well-known property of the Poincaré sphere [11] viz, given an analyzer which transmits completely light of polarization state $A(\lambda_A, \omega_A)$, the fraction (I) of the intensity of light of polarization state $Z(\lambda_Z, \omega_Z)$ emerging from the analyzer A is given by

$$I = \cos^2 \frac{\widehat{ZA}}{2},$$

where $\widehat{ZA}$ is the arc on the Poincaré sphere joining the points Z and A.

If the azimuth (a) of the analyzer is known, then the problem is to express the polarization state Z of the reflected light in terms of the polarizer azimuth, p, the relative phase retardation (Δ) and the relative amplitude diminution (ψ) introduced by the reflection. The transformations of polarization state as the light passes through various optical components is shown in figure 10. From the Naperian triangle $||Z°K_F$, we have

$$\delta = 2p - 90°,$$

where δ is the phase difference introduced by the quarter-wave plate. Expressions for $\sin 2\lambda_Z$ and $\cos 2\lambda_Z$ are obtained from the Naperian triangle $||ZX$. Then $\cos \widehat{ZA}$ is determined from a well-known formula giving the distance on a sphere between two points whose latitude and longitude are known. In this manner we obtain

$$I = \sin^2 (\psi + a) - \sin 2\psi \sin 2a \sin^2 \left(\frac{\Delta + 2p - 90°}{2} \right)$$

which is Archer's expression. If the analyzer is set in the extinction azimuth $\psi = a$, then

$$I \propto \sin^2 \left(\frac{\Delta}{2} + p - 45° \right).$$

It is obvious, therefore, that changes of intensity can result either from

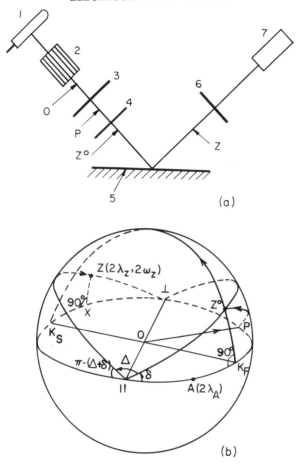

FIGURE 10. (a) *Sequence of optical components.*

1. Mercury light source; 2. collimator and monochromator; 3. polarizer; 4. quarter-wave plate; 5. mirror; 6. analyzer; 7. photomultiplier. Polarization states at various stages indicated by $0 \rightarrow P \rightarrow Z^\circ \rightarrow Z$.

(b) *Poincaré sphere representation of transformation of polarization states*
$0 \rightarrow P \rightarrow Z^\circ \rightarrow Z$.

|| and ⊥ represent linearly polarized light vibrating parallel and perpendicular to plane of incidence respectively, K_F and K_S, the fast and slow axes of quarter-wave plate.

changes in Δ due to film formation or from changes in the polarizer azimuth. The following procedure is therefore adopted:

(a) the mirror surface is maintained in a film-free state in which the relative phase retardation is Δ°;

(b) starting from an initial polarizer azimuth of p° (yielding an extinction intensity I°), the polarizer azimuth is decreased in steps of say 0.1° and at each value the deflection on the instrument which records the intensity is noted;

(c) the polarizer is returned to the $p°$ azimuth;

(d) the film formation process is allowed to proceed revealing itself as an intensity-time plot;

(e) from the initial calibration, the intensity-time curve can be reduced to a Δ-time curve.

A basic assumption in this whole approach is that film growth results only in changes of Δ, leaving ψ constant. The conditions under which this approximation is justified can be defined by taking the Drude-Tronstad thin-film equations from which [12]

and

$$\frac{d\Delta}{dL} = -\alpha$$

$$\frac{d\psi}{dL} = \beta.$$

Expressions [4] for the coefficients α and β are available in the literature [12] and it is found that $\beta/\alpha = \frac{d\psi}{d\Delta}$ depends essentially on the magnitude of the extinction coefficient (K) of the reflecting substrate and the angle of incidence, θ. If $K \to 0$ and $\theta = \theta_B$, where θ_B is the Brewster angle, then $\frac{\beta}{\alpha} \to 0$. In Archer's experiments on silicon [10], $\left|\frac{\beta}{\alpha}\right| = \frac{0.003}{0.256}$. The above approximation is less suited for metal substrates, but even here its validity increases as film thickness decreases.

Once α is calculated on the basis of a known (or assumed) value for the refractive index of the film, the Δ-time plot yields a thickness-time plot from which the kinetics of film formation can be interpreted.

[If, during the course of an ellipsometric experiment on growing films, the intensity becomes constant with time (even for a matter of minutes) indicating that the film is stable, then the stable thickness of the film can be determined by rapidly carrying out an extinction experiment to analyze the reflected elliptically polarized light. From the ellipse parameters the thickness can be calculated either by using approximate formulae for thin nonabsorbing films or by solving exact equations by computer techniques. In experiments on the anodic formation of calomel, it was observed that on switching off the electrolysis current during film growth, the film continued growing for some time and then was stable over several minutes. Under these circumstances, its thickness was calculated [6].]

5. Quantitative Ellipsometry of Steady-State Films

The functional relationship between the potential of a metal-solution interface and the state of the metal surface can be used not only to maintain a film-free metal surface but also a steady-state thickness of anodic film. This can be achieved once again with the aid of a potentiostat set to a suitable anodic potential. Under these conditions of constant

[4] α and β are functions of the angle of incidence (θ_i), the index of refraction of the surface film n_F, the complex index of refraction of reflecting substance $n^* = n\,(1-iK)$ and the wavelength (λ).

potential and therefore steady-state thickness, the parameters of the elliptically polarized light reflected from the film-covered metal surface can be determined by setting the optical components to extinction. From the ellipse azimuth and ellipticity, the relative phase retardation (Δ) and relative amplitude diminution (ψ) of the parallel and perpendicular components of the reflected light, and thus the thickness and optical constants of the surface film can be quantitatively determined. By analyzing the reflected light at various potentials, a thickness versus potential curve can be plotted.

It has been hitherto customary to use cells with optical windows normal to the light beam. In electrochemical studies, it is often convenient to use rectangular cells made of optical-grade, synthetic quartz with highly reflecting metal tape held between the bottomless cell and a bottom glass plate. The tape projects outside the cell and electrical contact can be made to the projecting part. Such an arrangement corresponds to the ideal current distribution of a rectangular conductor.

It is important, however, to ensure that the cell is alined with its sides parallel and perpendicular to the plane of incidence. A very sensitive method of carrying out this alinement has been described in a communication which deals with the theory and practice of the use of rectangular cells in ellipsometry [12].

FIGURE 11. *Sequence of optical components and optical path through the ellipsometer.*

1. Hg vapor lamp; 2. 5461 Å filter; 3. collimator; 4. polarizer; 5. quarter-wave plate; 6. analyzer; 7. photomultiplier. The polarization states at the various stages in the optical path: 0, P'', P', P, Z, Z', Z'', and L are represented on the Poincaré sphere (see fig. 12). θ_i'' is the angle of incidence read on the ellipsometer, and θ_i is the true angle of incidence at the mirror. (Reproduced from [6].)

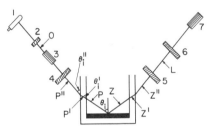

Apart from this experimental precaution of cell alinement, the use of a rectangular cell requires that careful Fresnel corrections be made at four interfaces (Air-Glass I, Glass-Electrolyte I, Electrolyte-Glass II, and Glass-Air II). The optical path through the ellipsometer is shown in figure 11 and the Poincaré sphere representation of the polarization state of the light beam at various stages in the optical path is shown in figure 12. The changes in polarization state $P'' \rightarrow P' \rightarrow P$ are due to the entry of the light beam into the electrolyte after traversing two interfaces, Air-Glass I and Glass-Electrolyte I. These azimuthal changes are given by

$$\tan \alpha_i = (\tan \alpha_i'') / \{ \cos (\theta_i - \theta_i') \cos (\theta_i - \theta_i'') \}.$$

When the plane polarized light is reflected from the metal, a relative phase retardation Δ and a relative amplitude diminution $\tan \psi = \dfrac{\tan \alpha_r}{\tan \alpha_i}$ results in elliptically polarized light 5. On exit from the cell and

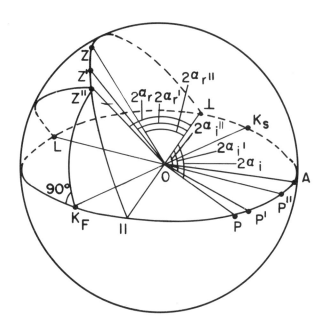

FIGURE 12.   *Poincaré sphere representation of polarization states at the various stages in the optical path shown in figure 11.*

(Reproduced from [6].)

traversing Electrolyte-Glass II and Glass-Air II interfaces, two more changes (5→6→7) in polarization state occur which are once again given by equation:

$$\tan \alpha_r = \tan \alpha_r'' \cos (\theta_i' - \theta_i'') \cos (\theta_i - \theta_i').$$

Thus, it is seen that the Fresnel corrections $P'' \to P' \to P$ and $Z \to Z' \to Z''$ can be quantitatively determined knowing the angle of incidence, θ_i, and the refractive indices of the glass and the electrolyte.

The results of a quantitative study of steady-state oxide films on platinum in $1N$ H_2SO_4 solutions are shown in figure 13. Prior to a computer calculation of the thickness and optical constants of the oxide films, preliminary calculations were made. Assuming a value of $n_F = 2$ for the refractive index of the oxide, the thickness of the oxide at various potentials has been calculated (fig. 14). The significance of these results has been discussed elsewhere [5].

6. Adsorption of Organic Molecules on Solid Electrodes

A knowledge of the adsorption behavior of organic materials is of crucial importance to electrochemistry from both a theoretical and an applied point of view [14]. It is our intention here to follow a suggestion made by Devanathan [15], and to point out the method of using ellipsometry in such studies.

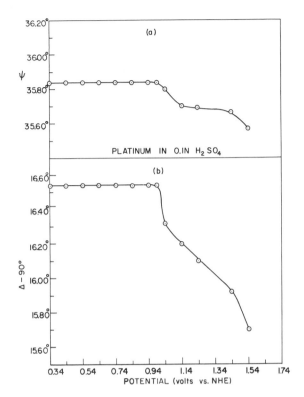

FIGURE 13. (a) *Change of relative amplitude diminution* (ψ) *with potential;* (b) *Change of relative phase retardation* (Δ) *with potential*

Consider the adsorption of an organic molecule L Å long and let us assume that the molecule adsorbs "head-on." A potentiostat is used to hold the solid electrode at various potentials and at each value of potential the extinction settings of the optical components of the ellipsometer are determined. The instrument readings would correspond to a hypothetical film of thickness L and refractive index n which would depend on the percentage coverage of the solid electrode with the adsorbent. The observed film refractive index (n_F) can be related to the coverage by referring to calibration curve giving the refractive index of *bulk* mixtures of the organic substance and the electrolyte as a function of the percentage of the organic ranging from zero (pure electrolyte) to 100 (pure organic). In this manner the variation of the adsorption with potential can be determined.

The authors acknowledge financial support from the Aeronautical Systems Command, Air Force Systems Command, U.S. Air Force under Contract No. AF 33(616)–8150, and from the National Aeronautics and Space Administration under Contract No. NsG–325.

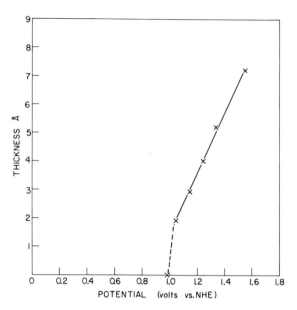

FIGURE 14.   *Approximate thickness of platinum "oxide" at various potentials.*

They thank E. Passaglia, R. Stromberg, and J. Kruger of the National Bureau of Standards for helpful discussion, and Dr. R. J. Archer of Bell Telephone Laboratories for a preprint of his paper on "Photoelectric Ellipsometry." One of us (A. K. N. R.) thanks the Council of Scientific and Industrial Research, India, for the grant of Leave of Absence.

5. References

[1] L. Tronstadt, Det Kgl. Norske Videnskabers Selskabs Skrifter, No. 1 (1931).
[2] A. B. Winterbottom, Det. Kg. Norske Videnskabers Skrifters, No. 1 (1955).
[3] D. S., Heavens, Optical Properties of thin Solid Films, Butterworths Scientific Publications, London (1955).
[4] M. Pourbaix, Atlas d'Equilibres Electrochimiques a 25°C, Gauthier-Villars & Cie, Paris (1963).
[5] A. K. N. Reddy, J. O'M. Bockris, and M. Genshaw, in preparation.
[6] J. O'M. Bockris, M. A. V. Devanathan, and A. K. N. Reddy, Proc. Roy. Soc. **279**, No. A1378 (1964).
[7] A. K. N. Reddy, M. A. V. Devanathan, and J. O'M. Bockris, J. Electroanalytical Soc. **6**, 61 (1963).
[8] A. K. N. Reddy, and J. O'M. Bockris, in preparation.
[9] W. Budde, Appl. Optics. **1**, 201 (1962).
[10] R. J. Archer, HP Associates, Palo Alto, Calif., private communication.
[11] G. N. Ramachandran, S. Ramaseshan, Handbuch der Physik, Vol. XXV/1 (1961).
[12] R. J. Archer, J. Electrochem. Soc. **104**, 619 (1957).
[13] A. K. N. Reddy, in preparation.
[14] J. O'M. Bockris, and D. A. J. Swinkels, in preparation.
[15] M. A. V. Devanathan, private communication.

Application of Ellipsometry to the Study of Phenomena on Surfaces Prepared in Ultra-High Vacuum

J. F. Dettorre, T. G. Knorr, and D. A. Vaughan

Battelle Memorial Institute, Columbus 1, Ohio

A bakeable vacuum system has been built which allows ellipsometric observations of evaporated films as prepared and held at pressures of 10^{-9} torr or lower. Valving permits the introduction of controlled atmospheres. The dispersion of evaporated and bulk copper specimen show significant differences between samples oxidized in dry oxygen and samples corroded in air. Changes in optical properties immediately after deposition indicate the films are losing surface material at room temperature. This can possibly be explained as desorption of gases collected during film formation. In the case of aluminum the changes reverse direction, and after about 4 hr indicate the growth of a surface film approximately 10 Å thick.

1. Introduction

There have been no reports, as yet, of the *in situ* study of the surface of metal films evaporated in ultra-high vacuum. This paper contains such observations and indicates some of the potential of a system specifically designed to make measurements of this type [1].[1] The observations reported are somewhat preliminary inasmuch as they were used to both evaluate the vacuum system and to establish possible directions for fundamental investigations.

1.1. Apparatus and Techniques

The vacuum system developed for these studies has been discussed in detail elsewhere [1]. A brief description of the system and its capabilities will be listed here for completeness. Space limitations were imposed upon the system design, since it was intended for use on an unmodified commercial ellipsometer. Construction was of 304 stainless steel with connections made through standard copper shear seals. Ion pumping was used exclusively to maintain the highest degree of cleanliness. The system can be isolated for bakeout to assure operating pressures in the range of 10^{-9} torr or below.

Samples were mounted in a furnace made from a copper block, treated to prevent oxidation at high temperatures in air. Heating of the samples was achieved by means of coiled, platinum-wire heaters contained in ceramic tubes passing through the block. Substrates for evaporated film samples were clamped in the furnace with chamfered stainless steel jaws which also define reproducible edges. The furnace was mounted such that the sample substrate could be

---

[1] Figures in brackets indicate the literature references on p. 252.

alined with respect to the windows before sealing the vacuum system. Leads for simultaneous electrical measurements made contact to the films through spring clips and baked-on platinum probes. The sample and furnace were contained in a chamber which also contained a coil of copper tubing used with coolants for supplemental cryogenic pumping.

The windows used for the ellipsometric observations were 1-in. circles of ¼-in.-thick quartz or Pyrex. These windows were sealed to the main chamber with indium gaskets held in stainless steel containing rings. The use of indium limits bakeout temperature to 150 °C which nevertheless has been found to be sufficient to insure operating pressures in the range 10^{-9} torr or below. The windows were fixed in position and the sample was alined such that the angle of incidence was 66 deg.

An auxiliary chamber containing an evaporation source was located on a direct line in front of the sample. The distance between source and substrate was about 6 in. Pumping, gaging, and valving connections for the introduction of controlled atmospheres were contained on a manifold at the opposite side of the main chamber.

Copper was chosen for most of the investigations since comparisons could then be made with other studies already reported for this material. Such comparisons provide a most effective method for evaluating the usefulness of the technique and apparatus discussed above. Data were taken at points of equal intensity around the minimum for both the analyzer and polarizer. Averages of these readings were used as the input to a computer program which calculated values for ψ and Δ. These values were ultimately used to determine optical constants of either the base material or the combination of base material plus added film. Kinetic data for the changes ψ and Δ with increase in oxygen partial pressure were obtained by following these parameters as a function of time. The data were typical of those expected and observed elsewhere on samples cleaned by various techniques. Analysis of the kinetics permitted evaluation of activation energies for oxide development which, however, are not included in the present discussion. The oxide overgrowth studied on the copper films reported here had an index of refraction of $2.80-i0.165$ and grew at room temperature, to a thickness of about 40 Å as determined from the ellipsometric data. Some of the most interesting data were obtained from the dispersion relations and will be discussed below.

1.2. Experimental Results

Figure 1 shows the dispersion of the real portion of the complex dielectric constant for a copper film 1500 Å thick evaporated and measured on a substrate held at room temperature. Copper films of this thickness do not possess bulk electrical properties but are almost optically opaque. Effects of the glass substrate on the observed values of ψ and Δ were assumed negligible in the range of film thickness

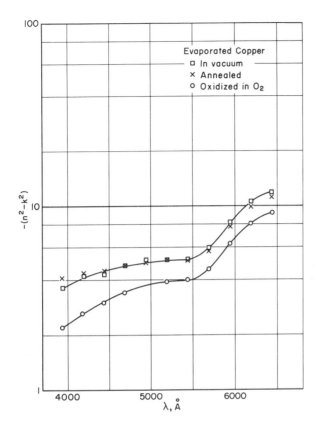

FIGURE 1. *The real portion of the complex dielectric constant for a copper film 1400 Å thick.*

Three conditions are shown; as evaporated in vacuum, after anneal at 150 °C for 2 hr, and after oxidation in dry oxygen. All measurements were taken at room temperature.

studied here. Three dispersion curves are shown; the curve labeled "in vacuum" was measured as soon as the sample stabilized. In the case of copper, these data were usually taken about an hour after formation. The second dispersion curve, "annealed," was measured at room temperature after the copper film had been held at 150 °C for 2 hr. Treatment of this type was sufficient to significantly anneal lattice defects in the evaporated film. Measurements on other samples of similar thickness indicated that the change of electrical resistivity was less than one percent during the last half hour of anneal. On this basis, the anneal was arbitrarily taken as complete. The third dispersion curve, "oxidized," was measured after the film had stabilized at atmospheric pressure, usually at least 24 hr after formation. The three curves in figure 1 indicate no significant changes in

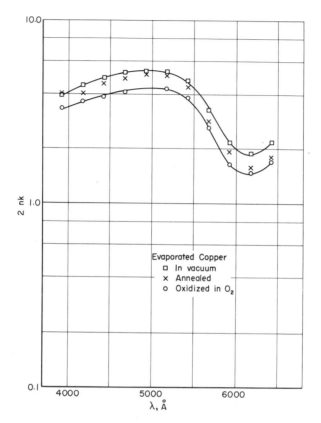

FIGURE 2.   *The imaginary portion of the complex dielectric constant for the copper film shown in figure 1.*

dispersion after annealing, whereas the oxidation treatment appears to have resulted only in a vertical downward displacement of the curve.

The values shown in these curves are in fair agreement with Roberts' [2] values when the difference in thickness of the samples is considered. The dispersion curves after oxidation are made for two reasons: (1) to determine the effect of oxide layers on the dispersion curve, and (2) to determine any window effects. Corrections for the effects of strain birefringence are made in the following manner: with the specimen inside the system the dispersion curve is measured after the sample is allowed to stabilize at atmospheric conditions. The specimen was removed from the vacuum system and the dispersion curve measured again. The difference in readings represents the effects of strain birefringence and is the correction that must be applied to measurements taken when the specimen was inside the vacuum chamber. Corrections measured in this way were of the order of two degrees.

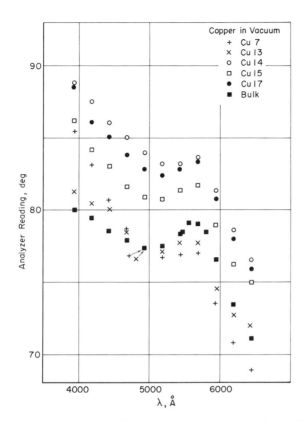

FIGURE 3.   *Analyzer readings for the six copper samples studied.*
The data are corrected for the strain birefringence of the windows in the vacuum system. All measurements were taken at room temperature.

Figure 2 shows the dispersion of the imaginary portion of the complex dielectric constant for the same film.   The general shape of the curves is similar to that shown by Roberts [2]; however, the minima are not as deep.   Likewise, the changes in magnitude of the values shown for $-(n^2-k^2)$, see figure 1, are not as great as those reported by Roberts.   Some preliminary data, other than that shown, suggest that the dispersion observed in both parts of the complex dielectric constant are related to the thickness of the metal film.

Relative changes among specimens can be compared more easily by direct inspection of the data after correction for the strain birefringence of the windows.   Corrected analyzer readings for five evaporated copper specimens of different thickness, and a bulk specimen, are shown in figure 3.   These data are measurements of the dispersion in vacuum.   The curves indicate a relationship between the dispersion and film thickness for four of the films and the bulk specimen.   The exception is Cu 17.   There is no experimental evidence to suggest exclusion of the Cu 17 data.   The thicknesses of

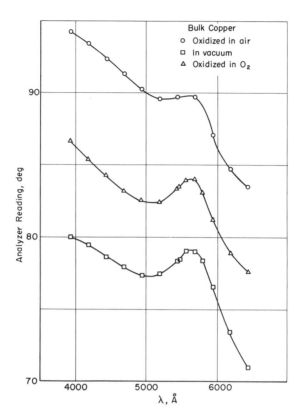

FIGURE 4.   *Corrected analyzer readings for the bulk copper specimen.*
Three conditions are shown: as prepared in atmospheric conditions (labeled "oxidized in air"), after hydrogen reduction in vacuo, and after oxidation in dry oxygen. All measurements were taken at room temperature.

the samples measured were Cu 14, 650 Å; Cu 15, 1500 Å; Cu 13, 1700 A; Cu 17, 1800 Å; Cu 7, 3300 Å.   Polarizer data for all samples are essentially the same and typical measurements will be shown in figure 5.

Data obtained for a polished bulk specimen are shown in figure 4. This specimen was mounted in a small glass vacuum system, hydrogen reduced and sealed in high purity dry nitrogen.   The system was then baked to 400 °C for 18 hr which resulted in a pressure of 10^{-9} torr. The corrected analyzer data of the bulk specimen are shown in the upper curve in figure 4, which is labeled "oxidation in air."   The curve measured in vacuo is again shown for comparison.   The effect of oxidation at 1 atm of pure dry oxygen at ambient temperature can be seen from the middle curve.   The shapes of these three curves are also characteristic of those observed for evaporated films treated similarly.   There is a significant difference between the dispersion charac-

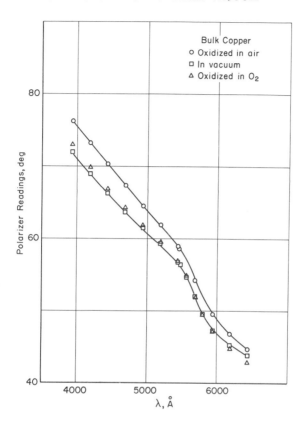

FIGURE 5. *Corrected polarizer readings for the bulk copper specimen shown in figure 4.*

teristics of specimens oxdized in oxygen and those corroded in air. In the case of the bulk specimen, the air oxidized curve, which represents the "as prepared condition," probably contains the effects of cold work introduced during the polishing procedure which possibly was modified or removed during the high temperature cleaning. Corrected polarizer data for the bulk specimen are shown in figure 5. Two of the curves are drawn and indicate the typical spread in data observed for all samples studied. In addition, the two curves drawn in figure 5 define a band of values which contains all of the curves measured for the evaporated copper films.

Observations of oxidation rates at reduced pressures have also been made. In the case of the bulk copper specimen just described, no changes in analyzer and polarizer readings were observed at oxygen pressures equal to or less than 100 μ. At this point the oxygen pressure was increased to atmospheric and the oxidation rate followed. The observed absence of change at pressures below 100 μ is in agreement with an extrapolation to room temperature of Yoda and Siegel's

[3] electron diffraction studies of the nucleation of copper oxide. Similar observations were made in the case of evaporated copper studied here, except that immediately after evaporation there was an initial period of change indicating the loss of surface film material. Although not completely understood, this change is probably due to the desorption of gases pumped by the evaporant stream during deposition.   After about 20 min the surface stabilized and again no changes were observed at oxygen pressures up to 100 μ.

Observations of the behavior of aluminum evaporated and maintained at 10^{-9} torr and room temperature exhibit a behavior similar to that discussed above.   However, after the initial period of observations, indicating the loss of surface film material which could be desorption or possibly annealing in the case of aluminum, the changes in the measurements reversed direction indicating the formation of a surface film.   The growth, at 10^{-9} torr, is completed in 3 to 4 hr. It is of interest to calculate the time required for a monolayer to form at this pressure.   If one assumes the residual gas in the system is 20 percent oxygen and the sticking factor is unity, it would require approximately 4 hr for the surface to be covered by a monolayer of oxygen.   The ellipsometric data indicate the thickness of oxide formed at 10^{-9} torr is approximately 10 Å.   This value agrees with the limiting thickness proposed by Lanyon and Trapnell [4] based on a place exchange mechanism of oxidation.   This mechanism has also been employed by Eley and Wilkinson [5] to explain the oxidation of aluminum at 10^{-6} torr.

A limited amount of electron microscopy has been done on surface replicas to investigate the possibility of observing nucleation phenomena in the oxide overgrowth.   There is evidence to suggest nucleation in the oxides grown in dry oxygen, however the density of sites varies by orders of magnitude from sample to sample.   No correlation with preparation conditions or film surface have been investigated as yet.   The overgrowth produced by corrosion in air is observed to be much rougher and does not contain obvious nucleation sites.   A group of experiments has been started in another ultra-high vacuum system where the availability of multiple evaporations will allow us to compare simultaneously deposited specimens immediately after evaporation and after oxidation.

One of the most interesting questions still to be investigated is the interpretation of the data immediately after evaporation.   In addition, the effects of evaporation parameters, annealing, desorption, and oxidation must be isolated and characterized.   Also, the meaning of "index of refraction" and "thickness" must be established when the film consists of isolated nuclei or small patches.   Future investigations are being directed toward a fundamental understanding of the processes involved.

2. References

[1] J. F. Dettorre, T. G. Knorr, N. F. Hartman, and G. G. Cocks, Rev. Sci. Instr. **35**, 503 (1964).

[2] S. Roberts, Phys. Rev. **118,** 1509 (1960).
[3] E. Yoda, B. M. Siegel, J. Appl. Phys. **34,** 1512 (1963).
[4] M. A. H. Lanyon and B. M. W. Trapnell, Proc. Roy. Soc. A. **234,** 405 (1956).
[5] D. D. Eley and P. R. Wilkinson, Structure and Properties of Thin Film, ed. C. A. Neugebauer et al., John Wiley & Sons Inc., New York (1959), page 508.

Discussion

H. T. Yolken (National Bureau of Standards): I wonder if (in the aluminum studies) you made any effort to get back to the beginning point before your 20 minutes were up by using bombardment, heating, or some other method; or do you think this is an annealing process relative to the film growth?

J. F. Dettorre: No, we have not. These were deposited and observed at room temperature with no special treatments.

H. T. Yolken: Could the difference between the oxidized in air specimens and the oxidized in dry oxygen specimens be due to surface preparation? The oxidized in air specimens were never heated or reduced with hydrogen prior to oxidation while the oxidized in dry oxygen specimens were given a hydrogen anneal and bake at 400 °C.

J. F. Dettorre: You are referring to the bulk specimen. Yes, the differences could be due to surface preparation in this case. For the bulk specimen air oxidation data were taken after the specimen was prepared, that is, after the specimen was placed in the vacuum system, but had not been evacuated. Measurements were made at that time, then the specimen was hydrogen reduced, sealed off in nitrogen and baked at 400 °C. Surface preparation, however, can not explain differences, similar to those observed in the bulk specimen, between thin film samples prepared under equivalent conditions but oxidized either in air or dry oxygen.

C. Del Carlo (Chrysler Corporation): This change in Δ which you described with respect to time, we observed also with aluminum films, and at a pressure of 5×10^{-8} torr; we found the effect is largely reversible with the subsequent heating of the film after evaporation. The process can be repeated a number of times.

H. T. Yolken: I wondered if you were able to determine any differences in your equilibrium film at the end for different pressures?

J. F. Dettorre: From 10^{-9} torr to less than 100 microns we reproduced our instrument settings to the nearest 0.02 degree at each pressure, so we essentially observed no changes until greater than 100 microns. At 100 microns we stopped our pressure variation, and increased the pressure to atmospheric.

H. T. Yolken: How do you account for no film growth up to the high pressure of 100 microns?

J. F. DETTORRE: I can't exactly. We observed this in the case of copper. A possible explanation is that if there is an adsorbed film already on the copper, it must be replaced by another gas before changes could be observed. The work of Yoda and Sigel extrapolates to this case, if the extrapolation is valid and indicates that you must have an oxygen pressure greater than 2,000 microns to observe changes in copper.

H. T. YOLKEN: We have done work with iron where the sticking probability appeared to be 5×10^{-3} after the first monolayer is formed. We did oxidations from 1×10^{-7} torr oxygen to 1×10^{-3} torr oxygen; the rate changes, but the equilibrium film thickness is almost independent of pressure.

J. F. DETTORRE: At any given pressure the maximum time we used was around 10 to 12 hours and the minimum time was about 8 hours. Any changes that might have occurred for times much longer than these would not have been detected. All changes observed occurred in the first few minutes at any given pressure.

A. K. N. REDDY (University of Pa.): The statement you made about the nodules raises a very interesting problem of the optics of such discontinuous films. I wonder whether there could be some discussion on this subject? Perhaps Dr. Passaglia would like to comment on this.

E. PASSAGLIA (National Bureau of Standards): The problem we have been concerned with is scattering from inhomogeneous films, in which the refractive index varies in directions parallel to the surface as well as normal to the surface. The films were polymer films and are discussed in "Application of Ellipsometry to the Study of Adsorption from Solution" by R. R. Stromberg, E. Passaglia and D. J. Tutas, this book, p. 281. In a very crude approach, I assumed the films would scatter much like a polymer solution of the same concentration. Then, assuming that the scattering would do the worst possible thing, namely subtract from the p component, and not the s component, etc., one can get a rough estimate of the error in ψ due to this scattering. This was less than $0.01°$ in this case.

In the case of nodules, I have always thought, rather naively, that one takes the horizontal projection of the area, if the surface is rough, for everything else reflects off in other directions and does not enter the analyzer. However, if such a rough surface is covered with a film, the simplest thing one can do is assume the refractive index to be a linear combination of the index of the substrate and of the film, weighted by volume fraction or some other means. Dr. Archer discusses this in his paper, "The Measurement of the Physical Adsorption of Vapors and the Chemisorption of Oxygen on Silicon by the Method of Ellipsometry", this book p. 255.

Measurement of the Physical Adsorption of Vapors and the Chemisorption of Oxygen on Silicon by the Method of Ellipsometry

R. J. Archer [1]

Bell Telephone Laboratories, Incorporated, Murray Hill, N.J.

Physical adsorption isotherms for water, carbon tetrachloride, and acetone have ellipsometric thickness scales which agree with the dimensions of the adsorbed molecules for substrate surfaces prepared by etching at the maximum rate in an HNO_3–HF solution. All other methods of preparing the substrate surface result in isotherms which have ellipsometric thicknesses at monolayer coverage which are smaller than the diameters of the adsorbed molecules by factors as small as one-half to one-third. The effect is attributed to the degree of irregularity of the substrate surface. A calculation for a specific model of an irregular surface predicts effects of the same magnitude as observed experimentally. The adsorption of water is found to be sensitive to the chemical structure of the silicon surface.

The chemisorption of oxygen on atomically clean, cleaved silicon surfaces gives ellipsometric thicknesses for the monolayer of 2.5 to 2.8 Å. Sticking coefficient as a function of coverage for four pressures of oxygen from 7×10^{-8} to 1.6×10^{-6} mm of Hg shows that the sticking coefficient is independent of pressure, and that the average value, 6×10^{-3}, is independent of coverage up to coverages of 0.6 to 0.7. The magnitude of the sticking coefficient agrees, within a factor of two, with most previous measurements.

1. Introduction

The use of the exact equations of reflection theory to obtain the optical constants and thicknesses of films on silicon by the method of ellipsometry has been recently reported [1].[2] The emphasis was on relatively thick films in the range from 10^{-6} to 10^{-4} cm. This paper is concerned with the use of the method for measuring very thin films. The phenomena studied are the physical adsorption of water vapor and some organic compound vapors on practical silicon surfaces and the chemisorption of oxygen on atomically clean silicon surfaces. The thickness range of concern is from submonolayer coverage up to several layers, with an upper limit of the order of 10 Å.

This paper is divided into three main sections plus a summary. The remainder of the present section deals with the principles and theory of interpreting ellipsometric measurements on very thin films. The presentation and discussion of experimental results will occupy the following two sections. The first will be concerned with physical adsorption, the second with chemisorption.

The effect of such very thin films on the state of polarization of reflected light requires some discussion. The experimentally measured

---

[1] Present address: HP Associates, Palo Alto, Calif.
[2] Figures in brackets indicate the literature references on p. 277.

255

quantities are Δ and ψ, the angles which define the ratio of the Fresnel coefficients for the p and s component waves, i.e.,

$$\frac{R_p}{R_s}=\tan\psi e^{i\Delta}. \tag{1}$$

The formation of a surface film and changes in its thickness are detected as changes in Δ and ψ. The dependence of Δ and ψ on the properties of very thin films can be derived from two points of view. The film may be considered to be a three-dimensional phase characterized by a thickness and an index of refraction, or, for the specific case of monolayer films, a two-dimensional model may be used in which the film is treated as a surface distribution of Hertzian oscillators. The results of both derivations will be discussed.

1.1. Three-Dimensional Theory

The general, exact relationship between Δ and ψ and the properties of the surface film when the film is characterized by a thickness and an index of refraction is given, for example, as eq (3) in ref. [1]. By the use of electronic computer techniques it is easy to determine the dependence of Δ and ψ on the film properties from this equation. However, first-order approximate equations can be derived which are accurate for very thin films and which allow easier illustration of the properties of the relationships.

For the ratio of the Fresnel coefficients, first-order theory [2, 3] gives

$$\tan\psi e^{i\Delta}=\tan\overline{\psi}\,e^{i\overline{\Delta}}\left\{-1\frac{i4\pi\cos\varphi\sin^2\varphi}{\lambda\left(1-\frac{1}{\overline{n}^2}\right)\left(\cos\varphi-\frac{\sin^2\varphi}{\overline{n}^2}\right)}\left[\left(\frac{1}{n_1^2}-\frac{1}{\overline{n}^2}\right)(n_1^2-1)d\right]\right\}. \tag{2}$$

(See the Glossary of Symbols for definitions.) From eq (2) are derived

$$\Delta=\overline{\Delta}-\alpha d \tag{3}$$

and

$$\psi=\overline{\psi}+\beta d \tag{4}$$

where

$$\alpha=\frac{\left[4\pi\cos\varphi\sin^2\varphi(n_1^2-1)\left\{\left(\frac{1}{n_1^2}-a\right)[\cos^2\varphi-a +\sin^2\varphi(a^2-a'^2)]+a'^2(1-2a\sin^2\varphi)\right\}\right]}{\lambda\{[\cos^2\varphi-a+\sin^2\varphi(a^2-a'^2)]^2+a'^2(1-2a\sin^2\varphi)^2\}} \tag{5}$$

and

$$\beta = \frac{\left[\begin{array}{c} 2\pi \sin 2\bar{\psi} \cos \varphi \sin^2 \varphi (n_1^2 - 1)a' \left\{ \left(\frac{1}{n_1^2} - a \right) \right. \\ \left. (1 - 2a \sin^2 \varphi) - [\cos^2 \varphi - a + \sin^2 \varphi (a^2 - a'^2)] \right\} \end{array} \right]}{\lambda \{ [\cos^2 \varphi - a + \sin^2 \varphi (a^2 - a'^2)]^2 + a'^2 (1 - 2a \sin^2 \varphi)^2 \}}. \qquad (6)$$

Equations (5) and (6) contain more terms than the expressions usually quoted [4, 5], and have been given before [6]. They are repeated because of typographical errors in the indicated reference.

In all of the work described here, the following conditions have been constant: $\varphi = 70.00°$, $\lambda = 5461$ Å, and $\bar{n}(Si) = 4.050 - 0.028i$[1]. Evaluation of α and β for these parameters using $n_1 = 1.5$ gives

$$\alpha \sim 0.3 \text{ deg/Å} \qquad (7)$$

$$\beta \sim 0.001 \text{ deg/Å} \qquad (8)$$

so that for films in the thickness range under consideration, ψ is effectively constant, and changes in film thickness are detected only as changes in Δ. In order to calculate the change in thickness corresponding to a measured change in Δ it is necessary to assume a value for the index of refraction of the film in order to evaluate α.

The limitation of having to guess a value for n_1 is not too severe. This can be shown with reference to figure 1 which plots α as a function

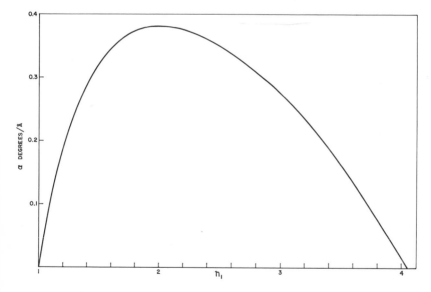

FIGURE 1. *Calculated dependence of the thickness coefficient, α, on the index of refraction, n_1, of a surface film.*

of n_1.   Assuming a likely lower limit for n_1 of 1.2 for any film leads to the condition $0.188 \leq \alpha \leq 0.380$ for all films in the range $1.2 \leq n_1 \leq 3.4$.   An intermediate value, $\bar{\alpha}$, can be selected for evaluating *all* films.   It follows that if

$$\bar{\alpha} = \frac{2(0.188)(0.380)}{0.188 + 0.380} = 0.252, \tag{9}$$

the *maximum* error is ± 34 percent of the thickness calculated from

$$d = \frac{\bar{\Delta} - \Delta}{\bar{\alpha}}. \tag{10}$$

The question of the effect of multiple films on Δ arises in the physical adsorption work.   The surfaces used for physical adsorption have permanent films 10 to 20 Å thick upon which the adsorbed layer forms.   Also, the interpretation of some of the data uses a model of the surface which pictures adsorption as resulting in multiple films. For multiple, very thin films, each film affects Δ independently and the change in Δ due to any one film is the same as that which would occur if the film were present as a single layer.   That is,

$$\Delta = \bar{\Delta} - \sum \alpha_i d_i, \tag{11}$$

subject to the condition $\Sigma d_i \ll \lambda$, where the α_i's are calculated for each film from eq (5).   Equation (11) may be derived by expanding the exact expressions for the Fresnel coefficients of a multiple film system and retaining only terms in thickness to the first power.

The use of the three-dimensional theory to deduce the properties of very thin films must be questioned.   A reasonable criterion for its validity, and for the validity of the concept of index of refraction, is that the thickness of the film be large compared to the dimensions and separations of the constituent atoms or molecules.   For monolayers, for example, it is *a priori* unreasonable to expect the quantity n_1 in eq (2) to be of the same magnitude as the index of refraction of the film material in a bulk phase.

For films which consist of only partial monolayer coverage, the interpretation of measurements with the three-dimensional theory, even assuming its validity for such films, is complicated by the fact that for whatever value for the coverage, θ, the thickness, d, of the film is constant, at least for the case of spherical atoms or molecules, or for any other case if the orientation of the atoms or molecules relative to the surface is independent of coverage.   Only the density and index of refraction of the film vary with θ, and to deduce θ from changes in Δ requires a knowledge of the functional dependence of n_1 on θ.   One might, for example, assume that n_1 is the sum of the indices of refraction of occupied and unoccupied adsorption sites, each weighted by relative coverage.   Then,

$$n_1 = (1 - \theta) + \theta n_0,$$

where n_0 is the index of refraction of a complete monolayer. Again, one might assume a surface corollary of the Clausius-Mosotti relationship so that

$$\theta \propto \frac{n_1^2 - 1}{n_1^2 + 2}.$$

Neither model is convincing, and both lead to complicated relationships between Δ and θ. Fortunately a very simple relationship is predicted by the derivation of the Fresnel coefficients based on a two-dimensional, monolayer model of the film.

1.2. Two-Dimensional Theory

Strachan [7] and more recently Sivukhin [8] have derived the Fresnel coefficients on the basis of a monolayer model with identical results except for differences in terminology and symbolism. Strachan's results will be given.

Strachan postulates that a monolayer is equivalent to a two-dimensional distribution of scattering centers and assumes that an element of surface dS when influenced by a light wave whose electric vector has components with amplitudes A_1, A_2, and A_3 becomes a Hertzian oscillator of strengths

$$dS\{\sigma_1 A_1 + \sigma_2 A_2 + \sigma_3 A_3\} \tag{12}$$

parallel to the axes x_1, x_2, and x_3. x_1 and x_2 are mutually perpendicular directions in the plane of the surface. x_3 is normal to the surface. The possibility of molecular orientation in the film is allowed for by the use of the three scattering indices σ_1, σ_2, and σ_3. Generally, $\sigma_1 = \sigma_2$.

From this point of view, Strachan derives the following first-order expression for the ratio of the Fresnel coefficients

$$\tan \psi e^{i\Delta} = \tan \overline{\psi} e^{i\overline{\Delta}} \left\{ 1 - \frac{i4\pi \cos \varphi \sin^2 \varphi}{\lambda \left(1 - \dfrac{1}{\overline{n}^2}\right)\left(\cos^2 \varphi - \dfrac{\sin^2 \varphi}{\overline{n}^2}\right)} \right.$$
$$\left. \left[2\sigma_1 \left(\frac{1}{\overline{n}^4} - \frac{\csc^2 \varphi}{\overline{n}^2}\right) + 2\sigma_2 \left(\frac{\cot^2 \varphi}{\overline{n}^2} - \frac{1}{\overline{n}^4}\right) + 2\sigma_3 \right] \right\}. \tag{13}$$

This equation is identical to the corresponding three-dimensional relationship, eq (2), except for the quantities in brackets which contain the terms that characterize the film, scattering indices in the present case, and thickness and index of refraction in the former case.

Corresponding to eqs (3) and (4), eq (13) gives

$$\Delta = \overline{\Delta} - \sum \alpha_i' \sigma_i, \tag{14}$$

$$\psi = \overline{\psi} + \sum \beta_i' \sigma_i. \tag{15}$$

Since the scattering indices define the oscillator strengths per unit area, it is reasonable to assume that they are proportional to coverage. Writing $\sigma_i = \theta\sigma_i'$, it follows that

$$\Delta = \overline{\Delta} - \theta\sum\alpha_i'\sigma_i', \tag{16}$$

$$\psi = \overline{\psi} + \theta\sum\beta_i'\sigma_i'. \tag{17}$$

Equation (16) is the simplest possible relationship between coverage and changes in Δ, namely, proportionality.

1.3. Measurement of Δ and ψ

The instrument and the measuring technique have been described before [1, 6, 9]. To recapitulate briefly, the ellipsometer is a standard polarizing spectrometer with divided circles which can be read to 0.01°. The light source is a mercury arc with an interference filter for the 5461 Å line. The quarter-wave plate transmits the incident beam and is fixed in orientation with the fast axis inclined at 45° to the plane of incidence. Δ and ψ are given by

$$\tan\Delta = \sin\delta\tan(90° - 2P) \tag{18}$$

$$\tan\psi = \tan(-A)\cot L \tag{19}$$

where

$$\cos 2L = -\cos\delta\cos 2P. \tag{20}$$

δ is the retardation of the compensator, A and P are the orientations of the analyzer and polarizer which extinguish the beam. The detector is a photomultiplier tube at the exit of the telescope. A and P are measured by determining settings of equal intensity on each side of the extinction minimum, using the procedure described in ref. [1]. Extinction settings can be made rapidly, e.g., 20 sec, and with a reproducibility equal to the precision with which the divided circles can be read. The relative retardation of the wave plate is approximately 90°, therefore $\Delta \approx 90° - 2P$, and since P can be measured to ±0.01°, Δ can be determined to at least ±0.02°. If Δ is changing rapidly with time, the precision will be less good, depending on the rate of change. It follows, that since $\alpha \sim 0.3°/\text{Å}$, changes in thickness of ±0.07 Å can be measured.

2. Physical Adsorption

2.1. Technique

Physical adsorption was measured on surfaces which were prepared and cleaned chemically in air. Such surfaces are relatively complex, compared, for example, to atomically clean surfaces, so that it is necessary to give some of the details of their preparation and chemical properties.

The substrate material was single-crystal, 10 ohm-cm, p-type silicon with, in most cases, surfaces parallel to the (110) crystal plane. Plates $2\times1\times0.1$ cm were mechanically polished to optical flatness. After polishing, the surfaces were cleaned in hot organic solvents, hot nitric acid, and hot quartz-distilled water. In addition to the polished surfaces, measurements were also made on etched surfaces, on heavily oxidized surfaces, and on cleaved surfaces. In all cases the substrate was covered with a permanent film 10 to 20 Å thick. Depending upon the chemical treatment, the permanent film may be either silicon dioxide or silicon hydride, and the surface may be either hydrophobic or hydrophilic.

Etched surfaces were prepared by agitating a polished silicon plate in a solution composed of concentrated nitric acid (70 percent) and concentrated hydrofluoric acid (48 percent). Because the adsorption results depend on the composition of the etchant, some details must be specified. Three different solutions were used; designated by the volume proportions of nitric acid and hydrofluoric acid, they are: 10:1 (10 parts HNO_3, 1 part HF), 3:1, and 3:7. The approximate etching rates for the three etches, in mils per minute, are, respectively, 1, 3.4, and 65 [10]. The last rate is the maximum for HF–HNO_3 solutions.

The etched surfaces without subsequent treatment are hydrophobic and have permanent films 15 to 20 Å thick which are probably mixtures of silicon hydrides and oxides [11].[3] The surfaces are rendered hydrophilic and have permanent films 10 to 15 Å thick of silicon dioxide, presumably vitreous silica, if they are treated as follows: (1) hot nitric acid; (2) rinse in hydrofluoric acid; (3) hot nitric acid; (4) hot quartz-distilled water. This treatment will be referred to below as the hydrating treatment. From the fact that these surfaces are hydrophilic, from the water adsorption results, and by analogy to the surface structure of hydrophilic silica gel [12], it is concluded that the oxide films are terminated by a two-dimensional array of hydroxyl groups bonded to silicon atoms in the permanent film. This is the so-called silanol structure.

The cleanest chemically prepared surfaces, on the criterion of the thickness of the permanent film, result from rinsing the hydrated surfaces in hydrofluoric acid. For this case, ellipsometric measurements indicate permanent film thicknesses of 5 to 10 Å. Such surfaces are hydrophobic.

The cleaved surfaces (111) used for physical adsorption are obtained by cleaving a specially machined silicon bar in air. Details are given below in describing the chemisorption work.

The following are some details of the vacuum apparatus and technique. The silicon substrate was mounted at the axis of the

---

[3] Unpublished measurements by the author, G. W. Gobeli, and G. E. Becker of the infrared absorption spectra of stain films on silicon substantiate the speculation in ref. [11] that these films are silicon hydride.

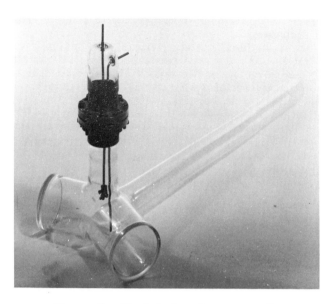

FIGURE 2.   *Physical adsorption vacuum cell.*

spectrometer in an all-Pyrex vacuum cell, figure 2, with fused-in
optically finished windows 1.5 in. in diameter and 0.25 in. thick.
The windows were oriented for an angle of incidence of 70°, and the
light beam was normal to the windows within 2 to 3°.   Normally
the beam was reflected from an area about 0.5 cm in diameter at the
center of the sample and was transmitted by the center portion of
the windows.   The windows were strain-free before evacuation, but
under the pressure differential caused by evacuation, they introduced
a few tenths of a degree change in Δ.   In no case was it necessary to
measure the absolute magnitude of Δ, so that this small strain
birefringence was unimportant.

The vacuum system consisted of an oil mechanical pump in series
with a three-stage mercury diffusion pump separated by two liquid
nitrogen traps from the vacuum cell.   There were no greased joints or
valves.   The gas delivery system and manometers were isolated with
all metal valves.   The vacuum cell could be evacuated to 10^{-7} mm of
Hg.   Water vapor pressures were measured with a Dubrovin mercury
gage accurate to ± 0.02 mm of Hg.   Organic compound vapor pressures were measured with a Wallace and Tiernon aneroid manometer
accurate to ± 0.2 mm of Hg.   The liquids were multiply distilled and
outgassed under vacuum.

The silicon plate was mounted in the vacuum cell in only approximate alinement relative to the spectrometer.   Precise alinement was
effected by adjusting the position of the spectrometer which, for this
purpose, was mounted on a milling machine head on an adjustable
tripod base.

After mounting and alining the sample, the cell was evacuated to 10^{-6} to 10^{-7} mm of Hg, and Δ and ψ were followed until they were constant. Most of the small change observed following evacuation was due to strain birefringence in the windows. To measure the adsorption isotherm, the vapor was admitted to the vacuum cell to the desired pressure and Δ was measured as a function of time until both the pressure and Δ were constant. Usually this condition was obtained within 10 min. This time lag is caused by the relatively slow equilibration of the vapor with the walls of the vacuum system. In some cases subsequent points for the isotherm were obtained by changing the pressure in small increments up to near saturation values. In other cases, each point on the isotherm was obtained by completely evacuating the system before and after each change in pressure.

2.2. Results

Figure 3 presents data which show the influence of the chemical nature of the substrate surface on water adsorption at room temperature. $\delta\Delta$ is plotted as a function of relative humidity. p_s is the equilibrium vapor pressure of liquid water. Since Δ decreases with increasing thickness, $\delta\Delta$ is the negative of the change in Δ relative to the value before adsorption. The thickness scale is calculated using

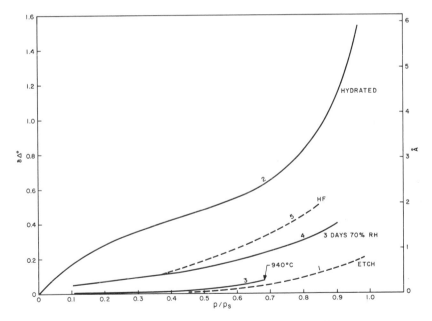

FIGURE 3.   *Water adsorption on silicon 25 °C.*

(1) normally etched (3:1) surface; (2) etched surface after hydrating treatment; (3) hydrated surface after heating to 940 °C for 30 minutes; (4) 3 days in water vapor at 70 percent relative humidity (25 °C) after heat treatment; (5) hydrated surface after immersion in HF.

$\alpha = 0.260/\text{Å}$ from figure 1 assuming $n_1 = 1.33$, the value for liquid water at room temperature. Curve 1 is for a normally etched (3:1) surface with no subsequent treatment. The extremely meager adsorption is consistent with the hydrophobic nature of etched surfaces. Following the hydrating treatment, curve 2 is obtained. This type II isotherm, according to the BET classification [13], indicates strong interaction between the adsorbed film and the substrate surface. If the hydrated surface is heated in vacuo, curve 3 results. For this case the silicon was heated, by passing a current, to 940 °C for 30 min at 10^{-6} mm of Hg. Like curve 1, this type III isotherm shows little interaction between adsorbed film and substrate. By analogy to the effect of heat treatment on the structure of a silanol surface on silica [12], it is concluded that the heat treatment causes a condensation of the hydroxyl groups to evolve water and to form a hydrophobic terminating layer of Si-O-Si groups, the so-called siloxane structure, on the permanent silica film. Long exposure to water vapor causes a partial rehydration of the surface, as shown by curve 4, which is obtained after the heated surface is exposed to water vapor at 70 percent saturation (25 °C) for 3 days. If the heated surface is immersed in liquid water it is completely rehydrated and curve 2 is obtained again. Following a rinse in hydrofluoric acid, the initially hydrated surface shows a partial hydrophobic character, curve 5. The hydrophobicity is attributed to the replacement of hydroxyl groups in the terminating layer by fluoride ions.

These data exemplify chemical effects on water adsorption. The following results show what may be characterized as a physical effect on ellipsometric thickness measurements and bring into question the interpretation of measurements on very thin films.

Figure 4 gives isotherms for water adsorption on silicon surfaces with identical chemical properties but with different physical structures. The five isotherms are for substrates prepared by different methods except that the final treatment was in all cases, the hydrating treatment described above that produces hydrophilic silanol surfaces. The substrates were prepared as follows: (1) mechanically polished; (2) normal etch (3:1); (3) very rapid etch (3:7); (4) following a 3:1 etch, this surface was oxidized in steam (1 atm) at 1000 °C to produce a film about 5000 Å thick, the adsorbed film thickness was calculated from the exact Fresnel coefficient relationship for a two film system using an electronic computer (the Δ scale does not apply for this curve); (5) cleaved in air.

It is interesting to compare these isotherms with one obtained on silica by conventional manometric measurements. The broken curve 6 is such an isotherm reported by Livingston [14] for water on crushed quartz. His data (micromoles per square meter, η) are converted to the thickness scale using the assumption that the density, ρ, of the adsorbed film is the same as that of liquid water, i.e.,

$$d = \eta \frac{M}{\rho} \times 10^{-2} \text{ Å}. \tag{21}$$

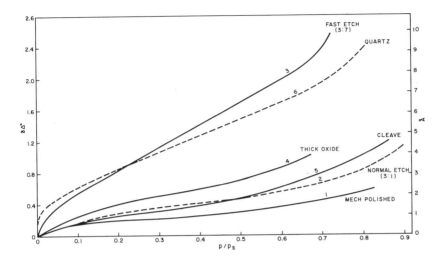

FIGURE 4. *Water adsorption on hydrated silicon surfaces, 25 °C.*

(1) mechanically polished; (2) normal etch (3:1); (3) fast etch (3:7); (4) 5000 Å silica film ($\delta\Delta$ scale does not apply to this isotherm); (5) cleaved surface; (6) Livingston's data for water on crushed quartz.

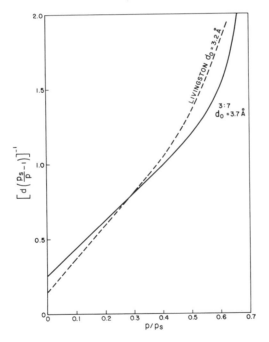

FIGURE 5. *Water adsorption isotherms plotted according to the BET equation using the data for the rapidly etched (3:7), hydrated surface and the data of Livingston for water on crushed quartz.*

M is the molecular weight of water. It is seen that the thicknesses for all of the isotherms are considerably smaller than Livingston's result, except for the case of the very rapidly etched substrate, which agrees closely.

All of the data of figure 4 have been analyzed by the BET method [13] to determine the film thicknesses at monolayer coverage. According to the BET theory,

$$\frac{1}{d\left(\frac{p_s}{p}-1\right)}=\frac{1}{d_0c}+\left(\frac{c-1}{d_0c}\right)\frac{p}{p_s}. \tag{22}$$

d_0 is the thickness of the film at monolayer coverage. The symbol c is a measure of the heat of absorption of the first layer. Figure 5 plots Livingston's data and the 3:7 etched isotherm according to eq (22). The deviation from the predicted linearity at high pressures is typical of the fit of all adsorption data to BET theory. From the linear parts of the curves at low relative saturations and eq (22), are calculated the values 3.2 Å for the monolayer thickness of Livingston's isotherm and 3.7 Å for the rapidly etched substrate.

The value for d_0 obtained for Livingston's data gives credence to the BET analysis for the water adsorption isotherms because it agrees nearly exactly with the diameter of a water molecule calculated from the density of liquid water,

$$d_0=\left(\frac{M}{\rho N_A}\right)^{1/3}=3.1 \text{ Å}. \tag{23}$$

N_A is Avogardro's number. The reproducibility of the 3:7 isotherm and the uncertainty in assessing the best straight line on the BET plot lead to a variation of about 20 percent in the values for d_0.

Values for d_0 for curves 1, 2, 4, and 5 of figure 4 are, respectively, 0.8 Å, 1.1 Å, 1.6 Å, and 1.0 Å, all of which are anomalously small in view of the diameter of a water molecule.

The same kind of dependence of the isotherms on the method of preparation of the surface is found for the adsorption of the vapors of carbon tetrachloride and acetone. Curves 1, 2, and 3 of figure 6 for carbon tetrachloride show the dependence of the isotherm on the composition of the etch. The compositions are, respectively, 10:1, 3:1, and 3:7. The dependence is not as strong as for the water case, but qualitatively the effect is the same—the more rapid the etching rate, the larger the calculated thickness (again, thicknesses are calculated using the index of refraction of the liquid, 1.46). The cleaved surface, curve 4, and the mechanically polished surface, curve 2 (the same isotherm as for the 3:1 etched surface) have isotherms that are intermediate in thickness. BET analysis of the data gives d_0 values for curves 1, 2, 3, and 4, respectively, of 2.0 Å, 3.1 Å, 3.6 Å, and 2.7 Å.

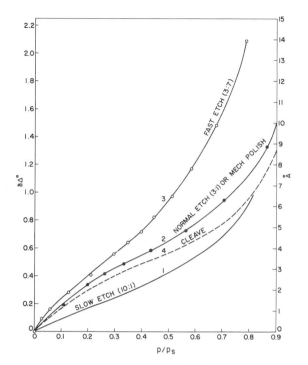

FIGURE 6. *Carbon tetrachloride adsorption on silicon, 25 °C.*

(1) slow etch (10:1); (2) normal etch (3:1) or mechanically polished; (3) fast etch (3:7); (4) cleaved surface.

The largest value, 3.6 Å, for the very rapidly etched case, is 66 percent of the molecular diameter, 5.5 Å, calculated from eq (23). Consistent with the inertness of carbon tetrachloride toward silica at room temperature, the isotherms are not affected by the chemical nature of the substrate surface. The same results are obtained for either hydrophobic or hydrophilic surfaces.

Two isotherms for acetone on silicon are given in figure 7. The cleaved surface has a d_0 value of 2.1 Å ($n_1 = 1.36$). The surface etched in the 3:7 etchant has a value for d_0 of 3.9 Å which is 78 percent of the value 5.0 Å calculated from eq (23). Palmer's data [15] for acetone on vitreous silica powder obtained by the conventional manometric method are also plotted (the broken curve). d_0 for this isotherm is 6.1 Å.

It is concluded that for all of the vapors—water, carbon tetrachloride, and acetone—the monolayer thicknesses from BET theory are comparable to the diameters of the adsorbed molecules for adsorption on the very rapidly etched surfaces (3:7) but that for other methods of preparing the substrate, the monolayer thicknesses are smaller than the molecular dimension by factors as large as 2 or 3.

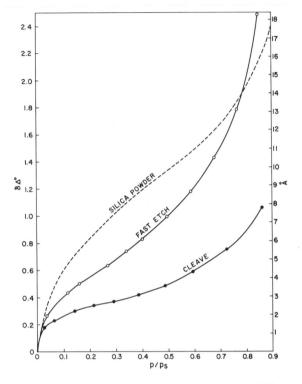

FIGURE 7.   *Acetone adsorption on silicon, 25 °C.*

Results for a cleaved surface and a rapidly etched surface are compared with the results of Palmer on powdered silica.

2.3. Discussion

This section will be concerned with a proposed explanation of the effect of the method of preparation of the substrate on the ellipsometric thicknesses of adsorbed films.   The basis for the explanation of the differences in the isotherms is the following hypothesis.   For the data of figures 4, 6, and 7 the amount of adsorbed vapor, for a given pressure and vapor, is the same for all of the isotherms, and the differences in the ellipsometric thicknesses are owing to differences in the smoothness or regularity of the substrate surface on a microscopic scale.   A model will be proposed to explain the influence of surface regularity on the effect of the thickness of the adsorbed film on Δ.

First, a qualitative picture of the effect of surface irregularities on ellipsometric thicknesses.   Consider a chemically clean surface which is irregular on a scale small compared with the wavelength of light.   The region of the irregularities, e.g., hills and valleys, constitutes a surface film with an index of refraction smaller than that of the substrate. If the valleys of the irregular region are filled by an adsorbed film, the average index of the surface region increases, and the surface film becomes optically more like the substrate. Depending upon the exact structure of the irregular region, Δ could decrease less following adsorption on such a surface than for a film of the same thickness on a perfectly smooth surface, or even, for some cases, Δ could increase following adsorption. That is, the surface could ellipsometrically appear to be cleaner after adsorption than before.

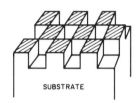

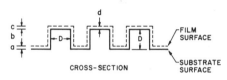

FIGURE 8.   *Model for irregularities of substrate surface.*

A quantitative treatment will be given from this point of view for the specific model of the irregular surface shown in figure 8. This model is arbitrary and is selected for ease of computation. The irregularities are taken to be a periodic distribution of cubes with the dimension D for the cube edge. It is assumed that there is no permanent film on the surface. If an adsorbed film of thickness d forms, the surface region consists of three optically homogeneous regions (D is taken as small compared to the wavelength of light). That is, the surface region is composed of the three films a, b, and c, as sketched. The index of refraction of each of the films is some averaged value of the indices of the media constituting the film. The simple assumption will be made that the index of each film is the sum of the indices of its constituent regions each weighted by its volume fraction. From this point of view, one obtains the following relationships for the indices of refraction and the thicknesses of the three films.

$$n_a = (n + n_1)/2 \tag{24}$$

$$d_a = d \tag{25}$$

$$n_b = [nD^2 + (4Dd - 4d^2)n_1 + (D + 2d)^2]/2D^2 \tag{26}$$

$$d_b = D - d, \qquad (D > 2d) \tag{27}$$

$$n_c = [(D^2 + 4Dd - 4d^2)n_1 + (D - 2d)^2]/2D^2 \tag{28}$$

$$d_c = d \tag{29}$$

where n_1 is the index of refraction of the adsorbed film material and n is the index of refraction of the substrate (the substrate is assumed to be nonabsorbing, a reasonable assumption in view of the small absorption coefficient of silicon). In the absence of an adsorbed film, the surface region is a film of thickness D and index of refraction $(n+1)/2$.

Using the above expressions for the indices of refraction, α can be calculated for each of the three films as a function of the index of refraction and thickness of an adsorbed film and also for the single film of the chemically clean condition. Designating the latter quantity α_0, the change in Δ that results from the formation of an adsorbed film is given from eq (11) by

$$\Delta_0 - \Delta = \alpha_a d_a + \alpha_b d_b + \alpha_c d_c - \alpha_0 D, \tag{30}$$

where Δ_0 is the value for the chemically clean surface.

It is desired to compare the ellipsometric thickness, d', of the film with the true thickness, d, where the former quantity is:

$$d' = \frac{\Delta_0 - \Delta}{\alpha} \tag{31}$$

and α is calculated from the index of refraction of the absorbed film material. Effects comparable to the experimental findings are obtained if $D = 50$ Å. Using this value and $n_1 = 1.46$, $n = 4.05$, it is found that for $d = 5$ Å, $d' = 2.0$ Å and for $d = 10$ Å, $d' = 5.4$ Å. Thus, the model predicts differences between true thicknesses and ellipsometric thicknesses of the same magnitude as the differences between the isotherms of figures 4, 6, and 7. The implication is that the very rapidly etched (3:7) surfaces are smooth on a scale of tens of atomic dimensions and that the other methods for preparing the substrate yield surfaces that are rough on this scale. There is at present no independent evidence concerning the relative smoothnesses of the different surfaces, so that the proposed theory as an explanation of the data is speculative. However, it is clear that surface irregularities can lead to calculated thicknesses that are smaller than the true values.

3. Chemisorption

3.1. Technique

The formation of the first layer of chemisorbed oxygen was measured on atomically clean, cleaved silicon surfaces in ultra-high vacua by following the change of Δ with time when the clean surface was exposed to oxygen gas. The kinetics of the formation of the second and subsequent layers were also measured. Those results, as yet incomplete, will be reported elsewhere.

The cleavage technique was developed by Gobeli and Allen [16], to which reference the reader is directed for details. The surfaces obtained by this technique consist of two regions. Part of the surface fractures irregularly; the other part, generally the smaller of the two, is a flat, nearly ideal (111) cleavage plane. Electron micrographs show that the better examples of the flat region consist of plateaus several thousand Ångstroms in width with steps between plateaus ranging from 50 to 300 Å. The plateaus are featureless to ± 30 Å, the resolution of the microscope. The ellipsometric measurements were made by reflecting light from the flat region by masking the incident beam with an iris diaphragm in front of the polarizer. This condition often entailed using surface areas as small as 10^{-2} cm^2.

Figure 9 is a photograph of our optical cell and associated vacuum apparatus. The stainless steel cell contains a vise which holds a silicon plate several inches long, 1 cm wide, and 0.2 cm thick with an L-shaped cross section as described in reference [16]. The rod extending from the top of the cell manipulates a diamond scribing point and the cleaving hammer by means of a sylphon bellows. Pressure is measured with the Baird-Alpert ionization gage. The pump is an 8-liter-per-minute Vac-Ion pump. Oxygen is admitted to the system by means of a silver leak. This is contained in the long tube above the pump and consists of a silver cylinder wrapped

FIGURE 9. *Chemisorption vacuum cell and associated apparatus.*

with a heating element.   The rate at which oxygen enters the system depends on the temperature of the leak.   The oxygen transmitted by the leak is spectroscopically pure.

Our procedure will be illustrated by describing a typical experiment. The vacuum tube is loaded with the silicon bar and is sealed to a conventional high-vacuum station which is pumped and baked at 300 °C for 12 hr.   The tube is then sealed off from the baking station and after several hours the Vac-Ion pump exhausts the vessel to a pressure of about 5×10^{-10} mm of Hg.   The vacuum tube is mounted so that the axis of the cell coincides with the axis of the spectrometer and the silicon bar is cleaved.   Immediately the spectrometer is alined relative to the cleaved face and measurements of Δ are begun. The time after cleavage before the first measurement is made is generally not more than 10 to 15 min. Δ in the ultra-high vacuum is measured continuously for 10 to 15 min, during which time it is always constant to the precision of the measurements.   Then, with the pump still on, the silver leak is heated by controlling the current in its heating element.   Any desired pressure can be obtained within a few minutes and maintained indefinitely with occasional adjustments of the heating current. Δ is measured continuously during this process and as frequently after the establishment of the desired pressure as the rate of adsorption warrants.   At the termination of an experiment the leak current is turned off and within from 1 to 12 hr, depending upon the pressure during the experiment, the vessel again pumps down into the 10^{-10} range.   This process has been repeated as many as five times before a new silicon cleavage bar was inserted and the vessel was again baked out.

3.2 Results

A typical result is shown in figure 10.   The points plot Δ, relative to the average value before introducing oxygen, as a function of time. The broken curve is the pressure of oxygen versus time.   For times greater than 8 min, the pressure was constant at 3.1×10^{-7} mm of Hg.   These and all other measurements were made at room temperature (about 24 °C).   Typical of chemisorption kinetics, the rate is relatively rapid at first and becomes very slow near the completion of a monolayer.

Chemisorption kinetics are conveniently described in terms of the dependence of the sticking coefficient, s, on the coverage, θ.   The sticking coefficient is the fraction of the molecules colliding with the surface which is adsorbed.   The number of molecules impinging on the surface per unit time and area is νp; p is the pressure and ν is a kinetic factor given by $nc/4$, where n is the number of molecules per unit volume per unit pressure and c is the average velocity of the molecules. For oxygen at 300 °K, $\nu = 3.48 \times 10^{20}$ cm^{-2} sec^{-1} mm^{-1}.   Defining N_0 as the total number of oxygen molecules required to form a complete monolayer, it follows that

$$\frac{d\theta}{dt} = \frac{s\nu p}{N_0}.$$

(32)

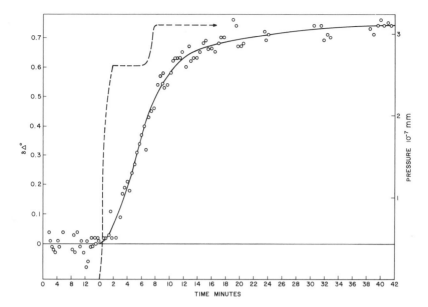

FIGURE 10. *Chemisorption of oxygen on cleaved silicon at room temperature.*
$\delta\Delta$ and oxygen pressure as a function of time.

Using the two-dimensional formulation resulting in eq (16), and defining $\delta\Delta_0$ as the change in Δ corresponding to complete monolayer coverage, one obtains

$$\theta = \frac{\delta\Delta}{\delta\Delta_0}. \tag{33}$$

Combining eqs (32) and (33), the sticking coefficient is given by

$$s = \left(\frac{N_0}{\delta\Delta_0 \nu}\right) \frac{1}{p} \frac{d\delta\Delta}{dt}. \tag{34}$$

A point-by-point graphical differentiation of the kinetic curves, such as figure 10, yields the plots of $\frac{1}{p} \frac{d\delta\Delta}{dt}$ versus $\delta\Delta$ given in figure 11 for the four indicated oxygen pressures. The plotted quantities are proportional, respectively, to sticking coefficient and coverage. These data appear to fall into two sets of similar curves, and although the characteristics of the curves are different, the average behavior indicates an approximately constant sticking coefficient up to $\delta\Delta$ equal to about $0.45°$ followed by a rapid decrease. In order to arrive at values for s and θ, values for $\delta\Delta_0$ must be deduced from these curves. For the lowest pressure curve, 7.2×10^{-8} mm, Δ stopped changing after about 100 min and remained constant at $0.63°$ for another 300 min. The

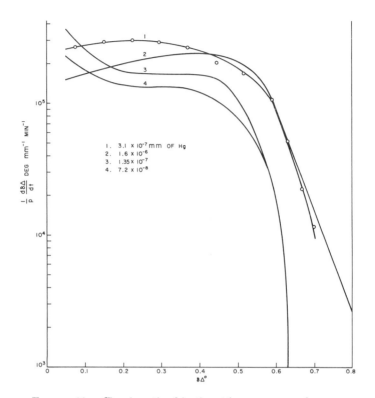

FIGURE 11. *Chemisorption kinetics at four pressures of oxygen.*

$\frac{1}{p}\frac{d\delta\Delta}{dt}$ is proportional to the sticking coefficient and $\delta\Delta$ is proportional to coverage.

curve for a pressure of 1.35×10^{-7} mm was terminated at $\delta\Delta=0.60°$ while Δ was still changing slowly with time. From the similarity of these two curves it seems reasonable to take the value $\delta\Delta_0=0.63°$ for both. In the region of the rapid decrease of s with $\delta\Delta$ the curves for the two higher pressures are displaced about $+0.08°$ on the $\delta\Delta$ scale relative to the lower pressure curves. We take therefore the value $\delta\Delta_0=0.71°$ for the two higher pressures. We have no explanation for this 12 percent difference in the values for $\delta\Delta_0$ for the two sets of curves. Perhaps differences in the nature of the surface from cleavage to cleavage account for the effect.

From the measurements of Law [17], Law and Eisinger [18], and Green and Maxwell [19] for the total amount of oxygen taken up in forming the first layer of chemisorbed oxygen, we conclude that approximately one oxygen atom per surface silicon atom is the monolayer coverage. The number of surface silicon atoms on the (111) surface is 7.8×10^{14} cm^{-2}; therefore N_0 of eq (34) has the value 3.9×10^{14} cm^{-2} oxygen molecules.

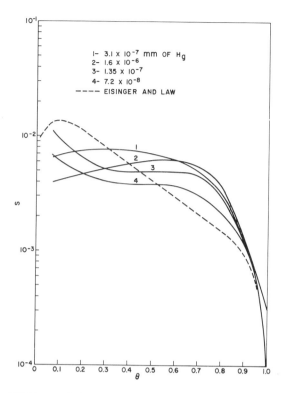

FIGURE 12. *Sticking coefficient as a function of coverage at four pressures of oxygen.*

It is assumed that at monolayer coverage there is one oxygen atom per surface silicon atom, and $\delta\Delta_0$ is taken to be $0.63°$ for the two lower pressure curves and $0.71°$ for the two higher pressure curves. The broken curve is the average of the results of Eisinger and Law obtained by flash filament manometry.

With these values for $\delta\Delta_0$ and N_0 we arrive at the plots of s versus θ of figure 12. The average characteristics of these curves indicate that the sticking coefficient is nearly constant at about 6×10^{-3} up to values for coverage between 0.6 and 0.7, after which values of s decrease at a rate that increases with θ. From the fact that the data represent a range of pressures of a factor of 20, it is concluded that there is no dependence of s on pressure.

3.3. Discussion

Included in figure 12 as the broken curve is the result of Eisinger and Law [18] obtained by flash-filament manometry. Their values for s vary by about a factor of 2 from run to run. We plot the average of their curves. Our values for s agree with theirs within a factor of 2 for all values of coverage, but their finding that s decreases exponentially with coverage throughout most of the range is in disagreement with the characteristics of our curves. This differerence is probably attributable to differences in surface structures. Their flashed filaments are considerably roughened by heat treatment and have roughness factors of the order of 3.

Hagstrum [20] from measurements of the Auger effect, and Allen [21] from field emission microscopy, deduce values for s at low coverages of 1×10^{-2} and 1.7×10^{-2}, respectively, in order of magnitude agreement with our results. Schlier and Farnsworth [22], using slow electron diffraction, obtained values for s that range from a factor of 5 to 20 larger than all other results, depending upon crystal orientation and the method of interpreting the measurements.

The value for the thickness of the monolayer, 2.5 to 2.8 Å, obtained from $\delta \Delta_0$ and $\bar{\alpha}$ of eq (9), is reasonable for a layer of oxygen atoms and suggests that there is no anomaly in thickness of the kind found in physical adsorption and attributed to surface irregularity.

It is possible that our results were affected by the use of the ion gage to measure pressures. CO is known to be formed [23] when a tungsten filament is heated in oxygen, and the possibility exists that CO could be produced by the tungsten filament of the ion gage. To eliminate, or at least minimize, CO formation, the gage was operated in oxygen at 10^{-4} mm for many days for the purpose of removing carbon contamination from the tungsten filament. Because of the CO problem and because other species might be produced by the ion gage which could contaminate the oxygen ambient at low pressures, we are repeating the measurements without using the ion gage. Initial results indicate that the magnitude of s and the variation of s with θ are essentially the same with or without the ion gage. There is an indication, however, that the rate of growth of subsequent layers of oxide is strongly affected by the use of the ion gage. When completed, these results will be published elsewhere.

4. Summary

Measurements of physical adsorption of vapors on silicon are interpreted using the standard theory of ellipsometry. The ellipsometric thicknesses at monolayer coverage obtained from a BET analysis of the isotherms agree with the dimensions of the adsorbed molecules for water, carbon tetrachloride, and acetone if the substrate surface is prepared by etching in the HNO_3-HF solution which gives the maximum etching rate. For all other surfaces, however prepared, monolayer thicknesses are smaller than molecular diameters by factors as small as $\frac{1}{2}$ to $\frac{1}{3}$. This effect is attributed to the influence of irregularities in the structure of the substrate surface on the scale of tens of atomic dimensions. Such irregularities can cause the change in Δ resulting from the formation of a surface film to be smaller than that which a film of the same thickness would cause on a perfectly smooth, flat surface. On the basis of the theory proposed, a calculation is made for a specific model of the irregular surface region. Calculated effects agree with experimental ones if the dimension of the irregularities is taken to be 50 Å.

Water adsorption depends on the chemical structure of the silicon surface. Surfaces which are macroscopically hydrophobic have very thin absorbed films even at high relative humidities and the isotherms are type III, according to the BET classification. Macroscopically hydrophilic surfaces have type II isotherms and correspondingly thicker adsorbed films.

The kinetics of the formation of the first layer of chemisorbed oxygen were measured on cleaved silicon surfaces produced in ultrahigh vacua. On the basis of the standard, three-dimensional, theory of ellipsometry the thickness of the monolayer is 2.5 to 2.8 Å, in reasonable agreement with the assumption that the layer consists of one oxygen atom per surface silicon atom. Interpretation of the kinetics using the two-dimensional theory, which allows the assumption that changes in Δ are proportional to coverage, gives curves of sticking coefficient versus coverage which have, on the average, constant values for the sticking coefficient of about 6×10^{-3} up to coverages of about 0.6 to 0.7, after which the sticking coefficient decreases rapidly. Sticking coefficient does not depend on pressure in the range from 7×10^{-8} to 1.6×10^{-6} mm of Hg. The magnitude of the sticking coefficient agrees, within a factor of two, with previous measurements.

The author acknowledges the active cooperation of G. W. Gobeli in the study of the chemisorption of oxygen on cleaved silicon. A joint paper covering in more detail this aspect of the present paper will be published elsewhere.

5. Glossary of Symbols, Equations (2) through (6)

a—$(1-\kappa^2)/n^2(1+\kappa^2)^2$.
a'—$2\kappa/n^2(1+\kappa^2)^2$.
d—thickness of film.
n_1—index of refraction of film.
$\bar{n}$—index of refraction of substrate$=n-ik=n(1-i\kappa)$.
$\bar{\Delta}$—Δ for a film-free surface.
$\bar{\psi}$—ψ for a film-free surface.
λ—vacuum wavelength of light.
ϕ—angle of incidence.

6. References

[1] R. J. Archer, J. Opt. Soc. Am. **52,** 970 (1962).
[2] C. E. Leberknight and B. Lustman, J. Opt. Soc. Am. **29,** 59 (1939).
[3] M. Born, Optik, p. 36, Verlag, Julius Springer, Berlin (1933).
[4] P. Drude, Wied. Ann. **36,** 532, 865 (1889); ibid., **39,** 481 (1890).
[5] L. Tronstad, Trans. Faraday Soc. **31,** 1151 (1935).
[6] R. J. Archer, J. Electrochem. Soc. **104,** 619 (1957).
[7] C. S. Strachan, Proc. Cambridge Phil. Soc. **29,** 116 (1933).
[8] D. V. Sivukhin, Soviet Phys. JETP **3,** 269 (1956).
[9] R. J. Archer, Phys. Rev. **110,** 354 (1958).
[10] H. Robbins and B. Schwartz, J. Electrochem. Soc. **106,** 505 (1959).
[11] R. J. Archer, J. Phys. Chem. Solids **14,** 104 (1960).

[12] R. K. Iler, The Colloid Chemistry of Silica and Silicates, Cornell Univ. Press, Ithica N.Y. (1955).
[13] S. Brunauer, The Adsorption of Gases and Vapors, Princeton Univ. Press, Princeton, N.J. (1945).
[14] H. K. Livingston, Adsorption and Free Surface Energy of Solids, Ph. D. dissertation, Univ. of Chicago (1941).
[15] W. G. Palmer, Proc. Roy. Soc. **160**, 254 (1937).
[16] G. W. Gobeli and F. G. Allen, J. Phys. Chem. Solids **14**, 23 (1960).
[17] J. T. Law, J. Phys. Chem. Solids **4**, 91 (1958).
[18] J. Eisinger and J. T. Law, J. Chem. Phys. **30**, 410 (1959).
[19] M. Green and K. H. Maxwell, J. Phys. Chem. Solids **13**, 145 (1960).
[20] H. D. Hagstrum, J. Appl. Phys. **32**, 1020(1961).
[21] F. G. Allen, J. Phys. Chem. Solids **8**, 119 (1959).
[22] R. E. Schlier and H. F. Farnsworth, J. Chem. Phys. **30**, 917 (1959).
[23] R. E. Schlier, J. Appl. Phys. **29**, 1162 (1958).

Discussion

A. C. HALL (Socony Mobil Oil Company):

I should like to know at what relative pressure of water vapor the water monolayer was complete, and also whether your measurements go to high enough relative pressures to confirm Deryagin's observation that isotherms of polar substances intercept the ordinate $P/P_0 = 1$, while isotherms of nonpolar substances become asymptotic to it?

R. J. ARCHER:

In most cases the monolayer is complete at relative saturations of about 20 percent. There are no definite indications in the data of the behavior of the isotherms at 100 percent saturation.

A. C. HALL:

Is the phase difference, Δ, a function of surface coverage below a monolayer? It seems to me that the physical models used in deriving the relationship of Δ and film thickness may be invalid below a monolayer. In Strachan's theory it is possible that whereas a complete monolayer would give rise to coherent scattering, an incomplete one would scatter incoherently.

R. J. ARCHER:

For submonomolecular coverages, changes in coverage should produce proportional changes in Δ according to my interpretation of Strachan's theory. Only for separations not small compared to the wavelength of light would incoherent scattering be expected.

A. N. SAXENA (Fairchild Semiconductor):

Would you care to comment how you arrived at the value of $k = 0.007$?

R. J. ARCHER:

It is in the literature [1]. On the basis of accumulated experience in measuring silicon surfaces we are able to deduce fairly well the thickness of the permanent film on the surface. One can prepare surfaces so that this film is only about 10 Å thick. This thickness is taken into account in calculating optical constants. There is an independent measurement of this 0.007 by Dash and Newman by transmission through silicon plates. Their curve must be extrapolated a little but the agreement is clear.

A. N. SAXENA:
I thought you used 0.028 in the paper you wrote? Or perhaps it is $k=n$ $k=4.050 \times 0.007 \cong 0.028$.

R. J. ARCHER:
The complex index of refraction of silicon at 5461 Å is $4.05 - 0.028i = 4.05(1 - 0.007i)$.

M. KOPP (University of Pittsburgh):
It is remarkable that, unlike transparent media and though the absorption coefficient is so small, a cleaned silicon surface does ellipticize light at an incidence so far from Brewster's. The effect must however be very weak for the ideal interface. Haven't you observed the better marked ellipticization near or at principal incidence (maximum) on reflection by a bare new surface protected from any contamination (e.g., cleaved in vacuo), and subsequently followed the building up of the transitional film?

R. J. ARCHER:
The angle of incidence, 70°, is not far removed from the principal angle, 76°. Most of the ellipticity is caused by surface films. Identical results would be obtained on transparent substrates. It is a fact that α is a maximum near the principal angle. Our measurements were limited to 70°.

Application of Ellipsometry to the Study of Adsorption From Solution [1]

Robert R. Stromberg, Elio Passaglia, and Daniel J. Tutas

National Bureau of Standards, Washington, D.C., 20234

Ellipsometry has proved to be a valuable tool in the study of the adsorption of polymers on solid surfaces from solution. Polystyrene with molecular weights of 76,000 and 537,000 was adsorbed from cyclohexane on chrome surfaces, and the thickness and refractive index of the adsorbed film were measured *in situ*. The swollen film thicknesses measured were 200 Å for the lower molecular weight polymer at 24 °C for most of the concentration range studied and 500 Å for the higher molecular weight polymer at 34 °C for a solution concentration of 0.23 mg/ml. The concentration of polymer in the film and the amount adsorbed are also determined from ellipsometry measurements. The application of ellipsometry to this type of problem, including the use of multiple reflection techniques, as well as the results obtained are discussed.

1. Introduction

Ellipsometry has proved to be a valuable tool in the study of adsorption from solution on solid surfaces. Using this technique, measurements can be made *in situ* and both the thickness and refractive index of the adsorbed film, as well as the amount of material adsorbed, can be simultaneously determined.

The determination of these parameters for a film under liquid is of particular importance in the case of polymer adsorption. One of the principal objectives in polymer adsorption studies is information concerning the conformation of the adsorbed molecule on the surface. Much is known about the shape of polymer molecules in a solution, coil dimensions, interaction between polymer and solvent, etc.; however, only little is known about the molecular dimensions of a molecule adsorbed on a surface. Experimental results have been interpreted as evidence for both very thin and very thick adsorbed films. (See ref. 1 for discussion.) Different theoretical treatments have also predicted both thin and thick layers. (See ref. 1.) It is, therefore, very desirable to study the thickness of these films, exposed to the solution and still in a swollen state. The simultaneous measurement of the refractive index also permits determination of the concentration of polymer in this film.

This paper reports the type of calculations employed, the techniques used, and some of the results obtained from a study of the adsorption of polystyrene from dilute solutions on metal surfaces.

[1] This work was supported, in part, by the Army Research Office (Durham).

2. Calculations

The programming of the original exact Drude equations [2],[2] for high-speed computers has permitted their use without any limiting assumptions [3, 4]. For the purpose of analysis, the electric vector of the light is considered to be resolved into two components, one in the plane of incidence and one in the plane of the surface. The ellipsometer measures the ratio of the reflection coefficients of these two components. For single reflection this can be represented by

$$\rho = \frac{r^p}{r^s} = \tan \psi e^{i\Delta} \tag{1}$$

in which ρ is the ratio of the reflection coefficients, r^p is the reflection coefficient for the component in the plane of incidence, r^s for the component in the plane of the surface, $\tan \psi$ is the relative amplitude reduction, and Δ is the relative phase change.

For a bare surface, r^p and r^s are given by the Fresnel equations,

$$r^p = \frac{n_3 \cos \phi_1 - n_1 \cos \phi_3}{n_3 \cos \phi_1 + n_1 \cos \phi_3}$$

$$r^s = \frac{n_1 \cos \phi_1 - n_3 \cos \phi_3}{n_1 \cos \phi_1 + n_3 \cos \phi_3} \tag{2}$$

where n_1 is the refractive index of the surrounding medium, n_3 (which may be complex) is the refractive index of the surface, and ϕ is the angle of incidence. For a film-covered surface with a film of refractive index n_2 and thickness d_2 on a substrate of refractive index n_3, the whole in a medium of refractive index n_1, the total reflection coefficients are given by

$$r^p = \frac{r_{12}^p + r_{23}^p \exp D}{1 + r_{12}^p r_{23}^p \exp D}$$

$$r^s = \frac{r_{12}^s + r_{23}^s \exp D}{1 + r_{12}^s r_{23}^s \exp D} \tag{3}$$

where r_{12} and r_{23} are the reflection coefficients at the film-medium and film-substrate interfaces respectively, and D is given by

$$D = -4\pi i n_2 \cos \phi_2 d_2 / \lambda \tag{4}$$

in which ϕ_2 is the angle of incidence on the substrate, and λ is the wavelength of the light in vacuo.

The optical constants for a bare metal surface can be determined by measurements of Δ and ψ on that surface. If a film has a real refractive index, a single measurement of Δ and ψ for the film-covered

[2] Figures in brackets indicate the literature references on p. 295.

surface will permit determination of the refractive index and thickness of that film if the optical constants of the substrate are known [3].

The ellipsometer measurements become more and more insensitive to the thickness and refractive index of a film as the refractive index of the film approaches that of the substrate or surrounding medium. For the cases to be discussed here, the refractive index of the metallic substrate is very different from that of the films and immersion medium. However, the adsorbed layer on the metal surface consists of a highly swollen polymer, resulting in a film with a refractive index very close to that of the solvent. It is, therefore, essential to increase the sensitivity of the measurements. This can be accomplished by means of multiple reflection.

The relationships between the measured values, p and a, obtained from the polarizer and analyzer, respectively, to Δ and ψ have been described [3, 5]. Extinction of the reflected light from a surface can be accomplished by a number of arrangements of the polarizer, analyzer, and compensator scale settings. The arrangement of the possible values of p and a into four zones, and the calculations required to determine the zone of a specific combination of p, a, and compensator values have also been described for single reflection [3]. The basic criterion applied is that the values of Δ and ψ are within the limits

$$0 \leq \Delta \leq 2\pi \tag{5a}$$

$$0 < \psi \leq \pi/2. \tag{5b}$$

However, for multiple reflections of the light, the value of the total relative phase change, Δ_n, may be greater than 2π and this must be taken into account; thus eq (5a) will no longer apply. For an unknown surface it may therefore be desirable first to determine Δ and ψ for a single reflection. The zone corresponding to a given reading of p and a may then be determined quite easily and the values of Δ and ψ determined accordingly. The limits for ψ are not affected by multiple reflections.

The ratio of the reflection coefficients for n reflections is

$$\rho_n = \rho_1^n \tag{6}$$

and, therefore, from eq (1),

$$\rho_n = (\tan \psi)^n e^{in\Delta} = \tan \psi_n e^{i\Delta_n} \tag{7}$$

where ψ and Δ are the values to be expected for a single reflection, and ψ_n and Δ_n are the overall values determined for n reflections.

We can now examine the benefits and limitations that result from multiple reflections. The measurement error may change slightly as a result of multiple reflections. In our case we have determined the standard error in the measurement of Δ to be 0.042 for a single reflection and 0.052 for three reflections from a chromium surface.

The standard error in the measurement of ψ was 0.018 for single reflection and 0.009 for triple reflection.

The value of Δ required for eq (1) is related to Δ_n by

$$\Delta = \frac{\Delta_n}{n}. \tag{8}$$

If the error in the measurement of Δ is $\delta\Delta$, then the error in the value of Δ required for eq (1) for a measured Δ_n is

$$\delta\Delta = \frac{\delta\Delta_n}{n}. \tag{9}$$

Therefore, increasing the number of reflections decreases the error in Δ without limit, assuming that no additional errors, e.g., the two surfaces not being completely parallel, are introduced. For measurement of Δ it is desirable to increase the number of reflections until the measurement error, $\delta\Delta_n$, is increased as a result of additional reflections. For reflection from a metal surface using a conventional light source, this would eventually occur as a result of decreased light intensity. For total internal reflection when no loss in intensity results from a reflection, the number of such reflections can be made very large [6].

The relation between the measured value of ψ_n and the value of ψ required for eq (1) is

$$\tan \psi = (\tan \psi_n)^{1/n}. \tag{10}$$

If the error in ψ is $\delta\psi$, then the error in the value that is required for use in eq (1) for a measured ψ_n is

$$\delta\psi = \frac{1}{n} \frac{[(\tan \psi)^{2n}+1] (\tan \psi)^{1-n}}{\tan^2 \psi+1} \delta\psi_n. \tag{11}$$

The difference between the values of $\delta\psi$ and $\delta\psi_n$ which results from multiple reflections is not, as in the case of Δ, related only to the number of reflections. It also varies with the value of $\tan \psi$, which is dependent on the surface. Further, $\delta\psi$ is not necessarily smaller than $\delta\psi_n$. If eq (11) is represented as

$$\delta\psi = k\delta\psi_n \tag{12}$$

where k is dependent upon the value of ψ and n, it is clear that $\delta\psi$ will be smaller or greater than $\delta\psi_n$ as k is less or greater than unity.

For a gold or a silver surface the value of ψ is about 40°. The value of k decreases from approximately 0.6 for two reflections to approximately 0.2 for seven reflections. It then increases to a value of approximately 0.3 for 10 reflections and is approximately unity at about 20 reflections. It is possible, therefore, for gold and silver surfaces to increase the precision in ψ with multiple reflections, and have as many as 20 reflections without losing any precision. As the value of n increases beyond 20, the value of k increases to values greater than 1, decreasing the precision.

If the value of tan ψ is 1/2, which is the case when ψ is approximately 26.5°, then eq (11) becomes

$$\delta\psi = \frac{1}{5n} \frac{1+2^{2n}}{2^{n-1}} \delta\psi_n. \tag{13}$$

Here an increase in the number of reflections is not nearly as favorable for reducing the value of $\delta\psi$ as it was for values of ψ near 40°. The value of k is approximately unity for three reflections and becomes larger as n increases. Equation (13) approximates the relationship between $\delta\psi$ and $\delta\psi_n$ for steel and chrome surfaces which have a value of ψ near 30°. For such surfaces there is a slight advantage in three reflections, as k is approximately 0.8.

Multiple reflections, therefore, are of considerable aid in improving the precision. The precision of Δ is improved by a factor directly proportional to the number of reflections. The precision of ψ can be either improved or at least not changed, depending on the surface and the number of reflections. All of the measurements on chrome

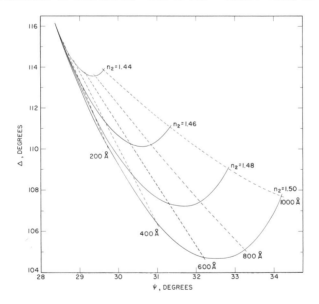

FIGURE 1. *A plot of Δ versus ψ of several possible refractive indexes for an adsorbed polystyrene film on a chrome surface immersed in cyclohexane.*

The solid lines are constant refractive index and the dashed lines are constant film thickness. The refractive indexes and the film thicknesses in angstrom units are given on the figure.

$n_1 = 1.4268$; $n_s = 3.3006 - 4.2456i$; $\lambda = 5461$ Å; $\phi = 70°$.

surfaces reported here were carried out with three reflections. The precision of Δ, therefore, was improved by a factor of 3, although that of ψ was increased by only a small amount.

The need to decrease the values of $\delta\Delta$ and $\delta\psi$ for the investigation of adsorbed polymer films, measured *in situ*, can be demonstrated by figure 1. Here Δ is plotted against ψ using the optical constants of a typical chrome surface for the substrate and the refractive index of cyclohexane for the immersion medium. The film is an unknown mixture of polystyrene and cyclohexane, requiring consideration of all refractive indexes, ranging from that of the solvent, 1.4268, to that of polystyrene, 1.59. Curves for four possible refractive indexes included in this range are given.

On this plot, curves of constant refractive index and curves of constant thickness form a network, or mesh. The thickness and refractive index represented by the mesh point with a value of Δ and ψ equal to the experimental values are the desired thickness and refractive index. However, because of the experimental errors, any mesh point which falls in the area of the rectangle defined by $\delta\Delta$ and $\delta\psi$ also represents allowed values of thickness and refractive index.

It can be seen from figure 1 that the number of mesh points per unit area is much greater for thin films and films whose refractive index is close to that of the medium. Hence, the thinner the film and the closer its refractive index is to the index of solution, the greater the range of values of film refractive index and thickness permissible within the experimental error. In this work we are unfortunately working just in the region of thin films with refractive index near that of the solution. The use of triple reflection and the consequent lessening of $\delta\Delta$ will clearly increase the experimental precision.

Although the graphical method demonstrated here will permit the determination of the best fit values of index and thickness as well as the range of values falling within experimental error, it is more convenient and rapid to determine these quantities by computation [1, 3]. A number of refractive indexes, n_2, are assumed for the adsorbed film and the corresponding thicknesses, d_2, calculated for the experimental Δ and ψ. Because of the method of calculation [3], calculated values of d_2 will, in general, consist of a real and an imaginary part. The true thickness of the films must of course be real. The size of the imaginary component is taken as an indication of the error in the assumed value of n_2.

This error can be related more directly to the experimentally determinable values $\delta\Delta$ and $\delta\psi$. The imaginary portion of d_2 is discarded and Δ and ψ calculated by means of eq (1) combined with eq (3), using the real portion only. These calculated values of Δ and ψ are compared with the experimental values. There will generally be a difference, $\delta'\Delta$ and $\delta'\psi$, between these calculated values and the observed values. The best fit value of the refractive index and thickness is then that value of n_2 and d_2 for which the differences between the calculated and measured values of Δ and ψ are zero. However, a range of values for n_2 and d_2, determined by the experimental error, are also permissible. These are determined for the system studied here by finding the range of n_2 and d_2 for which $\delta'\Delta = \pm 0.052/3$ and $\delta'\psi = \pm 0.009$.

3. Experimental Details

3.1. Experimental Procedure

A diagram of the cells used to study adsorption under liquid is shown in figure 2. The cells were fabricated from optical glass. The optically flat windows were attached either by fusion or by means of epoxy resin. The epoxy seals generally were found to be more successful, as there was less distortion of the window resulting from the attachment. The principal difficulty encountered was to obtain windows with no birefringence. The windows were arranged so that light entered and left at normal incidence to the window.

For studies at 24 °C, the measurements were carried out in a constant-temperature room. Two cells were usually placed side by side on the ellipsometer stage, thus permitting two sets of measurements to be made at the same time. For measurements above room temperature, the cells were placed in a hollow-walled chamber through which water at constant temperature was circulated. This chamber, which was sufficiently large to accommodate two cells, was placed on the ellipsometer stage.

The arrangement of the metal surfaces for three reflections is also shown in figure 2. The upper slide was placed on two gage blocks which provided a level, constant height from the lower reflecting surface. By moving the ellipsometer stage it was possible to make measurements at two locations on each set of slides.

The work reported here was carried out on the chrome surfaces of 1×2 cm slides sheared from commercial chrome ferrotype plate. They were cleaned by immersion in warm sulfuric acid–chromic acid cleaning solution, followed by thorough washing in hot distilled water. The slides had a hydrophilic surface after this procedure, but upon standing in the laboratory air for a short period of time, grad-

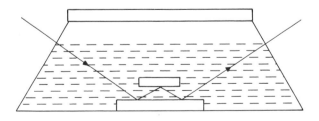

FIGURE 2. *Cell and metal surfaces arranged in cell for triple reflection.*

ually became hydrophobic. It was possible to keep the surfaces hydrophilic for longer periods of time by storing in a dessicator under clean nitrogen. It was also possible to restore the hydrophilic character of the surface by passing the slide through an oxygen-gas flame. The slides were flamed and placed, while still warm, under solvent in the cells.

The optical constants of the metal were obtained under the solvent. These optical constants are, of course, an average of the constants at the three reflection points. The solvent was then removed from the cell with a hypodermic syringe and polymer solution placed in the cell. Measurements at the same location were made of the film-covered surface as a function of time.

3.2. Materials

Polystyrene was chosen for study because of its availability in relatively narrow molecular weight fractions and because of the wealth of knowledge about this polymer. Two samples of different molecular weights, kindly provided by Dr. H. W. McCormick of the Dow Chemical Company, were used in this study. Both had been prepared by anionic polymerization. One sample, of relatively low molecular weight (Dow Sample No. S–102), had a number average molecular weight, as determined by the supplier, of 78,500 with a $\overline{M}w/\overline{M}n$ ratio of 1.05. For some of the experiments, this sample was used as received (unfractionated). For most of the experiments, a fraction with a viscosity average molecular weight of 76,000 was used. This fraction was prepared by conventional precipitation methods. The other sample was of much higher molecular weight (Dow Sample No. S–1195, $\overline{M}w/\overline{M}n$=1.09). From this a fraction with a viscosity average molecular weight of 537,000 was prepared and used for the experiments reported here.

4. Results

The measured thickness of the layer of the 76,000 molecular weight polystyrene sample, adsorbed on a chrome surface from a cyclohexane solution with a concentration of 0.18 mg/ml, is given in figure 3 as a

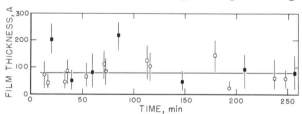

FIGURE 3.   *Thickness of adsorbed film of polystyrene, M.W.=76,000, versus time, for solution concentration of 0.18 mg/ml at 24 °C.*

Each set of points was obtained on a different set of slides.
○, Fractionated polymer
□, ■ Unfractionated polymer.

function of time. The film was measured in contact with the solution and consisted of a mixture of polymer and solvent. The points represent the best-fit values for each individual measurement. The vertical lines represent the range of thicknesses that fit within experimental error, determined as described earlier. In some cases, the lower thickness value was determined by physical considerations, i.e., the upper value of the refractive index of the film was limited to the index of the bulk polymer.

Three runs are shown in figure 3, one using fractionated polymer and the other two using unfractionated. There are no differences among the three runs. The average film thickness, shown by the curve drawn through the average of the best-fit values, is approximately 80 Å. There was no measurable change in thickness during the time interval studied. The range of film thicknesses that fit within experimental error for each point is relatively large. This is a result of two factors. The films are highly swollen, with a refractive index of about 1.465, which is fairly close to that of the solvent, 1.4268, and they are also relatively thin. As previously discussed, and as can be seen from figure 1, a relatively large range of refractive indexes and thicknesses of the adsorbed film are allowable within the experimental error of the measurements.

The curves shown in figure 4 represent the measured thickness values obtained for the 76,000 molecular weight polymer at a concentration of 5.0 mg/ml. Curves A and B were obtained using the fractionated sample and curves C, D, and E using the unfractionated material.

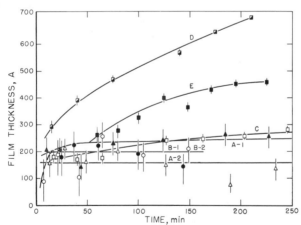

FIGURE 4.   *Thickness of adsorbed film of polystyrene, M.W.=76,000, versus time, for solution concentration of 5.0 mg/ml at 24 °C.*

Curves A and B were obtained using fractionated polymer, curves C, D, and E, using unfractionated. Curves A–1 and A–2 refer to measurements made on different portions of the same set of slides, curves B–1 and B–2 to measurements on different portions of another set of slides.
▲, Curve A–1   □, Curve C
△, Curve A–2   ◪, Curve D
●, Curve B–1   ■, Curve E
○, Curve B–2

Curves A–1 and A–2 represent two different locations on one set of slides; curves B–1 and B–2, two different locations on a second set of slides. The differences among these four sets of data are most probably caused by differences in amount adsorbed at the different locations on the surfaces. The differences in measured thicknesses can be larger between two locations on the same set of slides than between different sets of slides. The average thickness obtained from the four curves for the fractionated polymer is approximately 200 Å.

Although the range of thicknesses within experimental error for each point on curves A and B are somewhat smaller than those in figure 3, they are still relatively large. The films represented in figure 4 are thicker; however their refractive index of 1.45 is closer to that of the solvent than was the index of the films obtained from the 0.18 mg/ml solution. As can be seen from figure 1, the benefit derived from the increased film thickness is almost lost by the decrease in film refractive index. The experimental values of Δ and ψ are again located in a region where a large range of film thicknesses fall within the values of $\delta\Delta$ and $\delta\psi$.

The range of possible thicknesses for the points on curves C, D, and E is much smaller than those for curves A and B. The film thicknesses represented by curve C are approximately the same as those given by curves A and B, although curves A and B are flat and curve C continues to rise for the entire time period. The refractive index of the film shown by curve C was approximately 1.468, which was near that for the films represented in figure 3. The effect of the increased refractive index in reducing the uncertainty in the calculation of the thickness can be seen, therefore, by comparing the spread of the data on curve C with the spread in figure 3.

The refractive index of the films represented by curves D and E was approximately 1.442. Although this was closer to the index of the solvent than was the index of the films represented by curves A and B, the range of possible thicknesses for each experimental point was reduced. It can be seen from figure 1 that as the film thickness increases, the curves of constant refractive index diverge, resulting in a smaller range of permissible thickness values within the experimental error.

The differences between the curves for the fractionated sample and those for the unfractionated probably are caused by precipitation of higher molecular weight components in the unfractionated sample even though such components made up only a very small portion of this sample. The fact that precipitation occurred was immediately apparent from curves D and E. Although the thickness of the film represented by curve C continued to rise, while those of curves A and B remained flat for most of the time interval studied, it is not completely evident from the thickness curves alone that precipitation occurred, but does become evident when the refractive index of the film, and hence the concentration of polymer in it, is considered.

The concentration of polymer in the film can be readily determined if the refractive index increment, dn/dc, is known. The relationship between the concentration of polymer and refractive index was determined experimentally to be 0.168 ml/g and was found to be linear for the concentration range studied. Assuming additivity of specific volumes, a linear relation for this concentration range was also obtained using the molar refraction relationships of Lorentz and Lorenz. Therefore, the concentration of polymer in the film can be determined directly from the refractive index. The product of this concentration and the film thickness gives the amount of polymer adsorbed or deposited per unit area. The computer program designed to determine the refractive index and thickness of the adsorbed films from the experimental ellipsometer quantities can also compute the amount deposited, using the Lorentz-Lorenz relation [4].

The curves in figure 5 represent the same films whose thicknesses are given by curves A, B, and C in figure 4. In figure 5 the adsorbance (amount adsorbed per unit area) in mg/cm² is plotted versus time of immersion. The symbols for the individual points and the lettering of the curves are identical to those used in figure 4. The average adsorbance of the fractionated sample was approximately 2×10^{-4} mg/cm². Although the thickness values of curve C (fig. 4) were near those of curves A and B, the larger refractive index, and consequently the more dense nature of the film resulted in an "adsorbance" curve markedly different from those of the fractionated sample. The range of uncertainty for each point on all the curves in figure 5 is relatively small and within the dimensions of the symbols used.

The thickness of the adsorbed layer of the fractionated 76,000 molecular weight polystyrene sample is shown in figure 6 for the entire concentration range studied, 0.18 to 9.7 mg/ml. Each point represents the average of several runs at that concentration. Differences

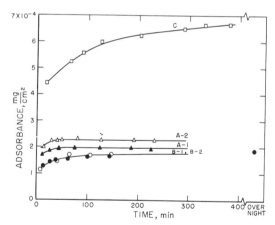

FIGURE 5.   *Adsorbance of polystyrene, M.W.=76,000, for solution concentration of 5.0 mg/ml at 24 °C.*

▲, Curve A–1   ○, Curve B–2
△, Curve A–2   □, Curve C
●, Curve B–1

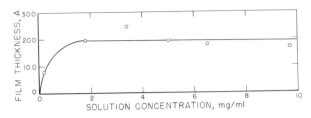

FIGURE 6. *Average swollen-film-thickness of polystyrene, M.W.=76,000, as a function of solution concentration at 24 °C.*

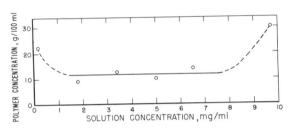

FIGURE 7. *Concentration of polystyrene, M.W.=76,000, in adsorbed layer as a function of solution concentration at 24 °C.*

among the individual runs, such as is illustrated in figure 4 by curves A–1, A–2, B–1, and B–2, were attributed to differences in the surface from one location or set of slides to another. The average of the individual best-fit point averages results in a thickness for the adsorbed polymer-solvent layer of approximately 200 Å for most of the concentration range studied, with a thickness of approximately 80 Å for the lowest concentration.

The concentration of polymer in the film is directly determined from a knowledge of dn/dc, as described earlier. This concentration is given in figure 7 for the solution concentration range studied. For most of the solution concentration range, the concentration of the polymer-solvent mixture is approximately 12 g of polymer per 100 ml of the mixture. This concentration of polymer in the film was higher at both low and high solution concentrations.

The measured thickness of the adsorbed layer of the 537,000 molecular weight sample of polystyrene on the chrome surfaces is shown in figure 8. These measurements were carried out at 34 °C for a solution concentration 0.23 mg/ml. A maximum thickness for the adsorbed film was reached much more slowly for the higher molecular weight material than for the fractionated sample of the lower. The decrease in the range of possible thicknesses for each experimental point in figure 8 at increasing times results from the increase in film thickness. The refractive index of these films was approximately 1.44 and that of the solvent 1.4200 at this temperature. The film refractive index did not change significantly with time. This difference in refractive

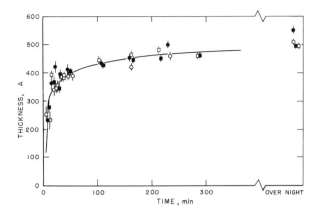

FIGURE 8. *Thickness of adsorbed film of polystyrene, M.W.=537,000, versus time, for solution concentration of 0.23 mg/ml, at 34 °C.*

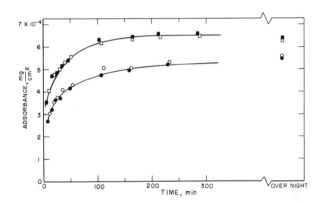

FIGURE 9. *Adsorbance of polystyrene, M.W.=537,000, for solution concentration of 0.23 mg/ml, at 34 °C.*

Curves A and B each represent measurements made on separate sets of slides. The open and closed points on each curve represent separate measurements made on that set of slides.

index between the film and solvent is approximately the same as was obtained for the lower molecular weight sample.

The adsorbance curves for these films are shown in figure 9. Although the thicknesses were approximately the same for all four films measured, the adsorbance curves were somewhat different for each set of slides, resulting from differences in the refractive index of the films.

The thickness and adsorbance for this molecular weight sample were both somewhat higher at higher solution concentrations.

5. Discussion

The ability to measure the adsorbed layer in contact with the solution is especially valuable for polymers because of the highly swollen nature of the film. Theories of polymer adsorption have led to predictions of both relatively thick [7] and relatively thin [8] films. The thicknesses reported here are based on a simple model of a single homogeneous film on a surface in contact with a liquid medium. However, the polymer segment density in the adsorbed film is probably not uniform, but rather decreases at increasing distances from the surface. The actual distribution is not known.

McCrackin and Colson [9] have theoretically studied films with refractive indexes varying between that of the solvent and that of either the pure polymer or some intermediate value between solvent and polymer, using in particular, the values for the cyclohexane-polystyrene system. Three different types of distributions which are reasonable for a polymer film adsorbed on a surface—linear, exponential, and Gaussian—were studied. They found that the thickness value calculated using the simple homogeneous single film model was approximately 1.7 times larger than the root-mean-square average of film (thickness) calculated for all of these distributions.

The values of the thicknesses shown in figures 3, 4, 6, and 8, therefore, must be divided by a factor of 1.7 to obtain the root-mean-square average thickness. This results in a film thickness of approximately 115Å for the 76,000 molecular weight sample in the plateau region of the solution concentration curve, and approximately 290Å for the 537,000 molecular weight sample reported here. These reduced values can be compared to the dimensions of the polymer in solution at the theta temperature (35 °C). The radii of gyration of the high and low molecular weights are 80 Å and 210 Å, while the root-mean-square end-to-end distances are 196 Å and 514 Å. The observed thickness is in each case somewhat larger than the radius of gyration but smaller than the end-to-end distance. Therefore, the configuration of the polymer on the surface is probably close to a random coil.

The simultaneous determination of the concentration of polymer in the adsorbed layer provides another indication of the conformation of the polymer molecule at the surface. The higher concentration of polymer in the film adsorbed from the 0.18 mg/ml solution, shown in figure 7, may indicate that the polymer molecule exists on the surface in a more uncoiled state than at higher solution concentrations, resulting in denser films. This is consistent with the lower thickness values obtained at this solution concentration. The high value of the concentration of polymer in the film for the 9.8 mg/ml solution concentration may indicate that there is entanglement of non adsorbed polymer molecules in the adsorbed layer, increasing its density, but not its thickness.

There are very few techniques by which adsorbed material can be measured on a surface directly. The determination of adsorbance by measuring changes in the concentration of a solution is a very satisfactory method for many materials. However, in the case of polymers the rate of desorption is usually many orders of magnitude slower than that of adsorption, and it is advantageous to adsorb from a system with no significant change in solution concentration resulting from adsorption. Ellipsometry provides such a system.

6. References

[1] R. R. Stromberg, E. Passaglia, and D. J. Tutas, J. Res. NBS **67A** (Phys. and Chem), 431 (1963).
[2] P. Drude, Ann. Physik. **272**, 532 (1889); ibid. **272**, 865 (1889); ibid. **275**, 481 (1890).
[3] F. L. McCrackin, E. Passaglia, R. R. Stromberg, and H. L. Steinberg, J. Res. NBS **67A** (Phys. and Chem.) 363 (1963).
[4] F. L. McCrackin and J. Colson, NBS Tech. Note 242 (1964).
[5] A. B. Winterbottom, Optical Studies of Metal Surfaces, The Royal Norwegian Scientific Society, Report No. 1, 1955, published by F. Bruns, Trondheim, Norway.
[6] E. Passaglia and R. R. Stromberg, Optical properties of thin films on transparent surfaces by ellipsometry; internal reflection for film covered surfaces near the critical angle, J. Res. NBS **68A** (Phys. and Chem.), No. 6 (Nov.–Dec. 1964) (to be published).
[7] R. Simha, H. L. Frisch, and F. R. Eirich, J. Phys. Chem. **57**, 584 (1953); H. L. Frisch and R. Simha, ibid. **58**, 507 (1954); H. L. Frisch, ibid. **59**, 633 (1955); H. L. Frisch and R. Simha, J. Chem. Phys. **24**, 652 (1956).
[8] A. Silberberg, J. Phys. Chem. **66**, 1872 (1962); A. Silberberg, ibid. **66**, 1884 (1962).
[9] F. L. McCrackin and J. P. Colson, this book, p. 61. (See table 11).

Discussion

R. Ullman (Ford Motor Co.):
If you were to take pure solvent, cyclohexane, let it sit on the surface, and then make measurements as a function of time, would you get any changes in the readings at all?

R. R. Stromberg:
Changes in Δ and ψ that occur as a result of exposure of the surface to solvent for many hours are negligible in relation to the changes occurring as a result of adsorption. The surface is usually exposed to solvent for at least 2 hours before solution is added.

R. Ullman:
How does the radius of gyration of the polymer in solution compare with the measured thicknesses either corrected or uncorrected?

R. R. Stromberg:
The radii of gyration are approximately 80 Å for the 76,000 molecular weight polymer and 210 Å for the 537,000 molecular weight sample. The root-mean-square average measured thickness values of the adsorbed polymer are 115 Å and 290 Å respectively.

R. Ullman:
What is interesting about this is that the result is in fair agreement (making appropriate corrections for molecular weight and solvent

power) with that obtained by measuring the alleged polymer thickness in terms of the flow through fine capillaries, where Öhrn found that the average thickness associated with the blocking of the fluid flow near the edge of the capillaries is of the order of 2 to 3 times the radius of gyration in solution. Now, of course, it may be that both of these methods of measurement yield awkward and different average values, but it is interesting that they are not too different from each other.

R. R. STROMBERG:

Öhrn reported thicknesses that are larger than those we measured. This was also true of the results of the other workers who have applied this capillary technique. Rowland (Polytechnic Institute of Brooklyn) reported a thickness of about 200 Å for polystyrene with a molecular weight of 110,000 adsorbed from cyclohexane. Our value of 115 Å is less than that found by Rowland.

R. ULLMAN:

Rowland's method was carried out using a sintered glass powder, not a capillary, and only a nominal average capillary dimension was calculated. This number must be corrected by some unknown factor.

C. L. SUTULA (Marathon Oil Company):

I understand you are performing radioactive isotope measurements along with your ellipsometer work. Can you comment on the agreement in the adsorption isotherms determined by both methods?

R. STROMBERG:

Using the radiotracer technique one cannot, of course, measure thicknesses; however, one can quite accurately measure the amount of polymer adsorbed. We have used the same molecular weight polymer and the same chrome surfaces with both techniques and the agreement is very good as far as we can tell.

C. L. SUTULA:

Do you find, as did Bartell and Betts, that the ellipsometer readings are linearly related to surface coverage if coverage is inferred from radiotracer measurements?

R. R. STROMBERG:

In the case of polymer adsorption we think it highly probable that at all the concentrations reported here the surface is completely covered. Differences resulting from different concentrations may be caused by differences in polymer conformation on the surface. Our studies, therefore, cannot be directly compared to those of Bartell.

Determination of Thickness and Refractive Index of Thin Films as an Approach to the Study of Biological Macromolecules

J. B. Bateman

U.S. Army Biological Laboratories, Fort Detrick, Frederick, Md.

Some years ago a stepped interference reflector, consisting of barium stearate multilayers on chromium, was devised for determining the thickness and refractive index of films deposited upon it. Tests of the method were encouraging. Thin films thus measured yielded values of refractive index in good agreement with values obtained on much thicker films by the Abelès method. Values of film thickness were often compatible with known molecular dimensions. Preliminary data contrasting the properties of "intact" and "unfolded" protein molecules will be shown in illustration. Areas for future study and possible modifications of the method will be indicated, with the warning that limitations arising from dispersion, anisotropy and film heterogeneity also require further examination.

1. Introduction

It is perhaps trite to say that phenomena in two dimensions represent a sort of halfway house between one dimension and three, but this is nevertheless the chief reason for the interest and fascination of thin films in biology. We now realize that information is most effectively stored in one dimension, on a thread or wire; but between the abstract instructions and their three-dimensional realization we must have boundary layers, films, membranes, and septa to implement the creation of structure. Since these boundary elements are far from being mere partitions, but possess activities, specificities, structures, information-bearing capabilities of their own, their study is of the greatest importance. They are, moreover, amenable in many of their aspects to *in vitro* study. Such study has both intrinsic significance and significance in the investigation of the fragile threads that store genetic information, since these can be more readily preserved and manipulated by being incorporated in films.

As an ultimate accomplishment one may imagine the message of a biological linear polymer being translated in a sort of molecular wire recorder, or a minute area of interfacial film being scanned for the distribution of specific reaction foci. In the absence of any immediate prospect of such an achievement, aside from the use of the living cell itself as translator, we are left with the necessity of drawing what inferences we can from examination of macroscopic regions of the objects of interest. The value of studies using visible light in this connection rests upon the fact that, while the cross section of the optical probe is necessarily very large, viewed on an atomic scale, the short dimensions of biological polymers are of the order of one percent of a wavelength, so that polarimetric or related methods can

297

provide significant information concerning these dimensions. This is not all, for by the same token, these methods can detect, and measure, processes involving deposition of biological macromolecules at active interfaces, or involving their release, degradation, or change of configuration.

Such considerations as these, for which we are indebted above all to the writings of Rideal [27, 28] [1] and Langmuir [19], have inspired our interest, over a number of years, in the optical study of thin films. The remainder of this paper will be devoted to the description of a method invented by Richard Mattuck, which permits the "optical thickness", or mass per unit area, of a film to be resolved into metrical thickness and refractive index. The existence of such a method carries us a step forward in the study of biological interaction at interfaces, for there is a very clear advantage in being able to distinguish, for example, between attachment of large compact molecules to a relatively small number of reaction sites, and the formation of a thinner, but denser, film covering the entire surface.

2. Principles of Determination of Thickness and Refractive Index of Thin Transparent Films

2.1. Outline

The description of the method and of the preliminary results obtained with it is spread through several papers published from 1956 to 1961 [23, 24, 6, 7, 8]. Our hope in the present paper is to consolidate this material and to present it in easily assimilable form for the interested biological scientist. The initial description will be more or less qualitative, followed by statement, without proof, of the simple approximate equations. Experimental procedures and results will then be given, while the derivation of the equations, and various other matters such as limitations on validity, sources of error, and future developments, will be dealt with later.

2.2. Qualitative Sketch of Optical Principles

In attempting a simple approach, consider a semi-infinite flat sheet of some material illuminated at some specified angle of incidence by a parallel beam of plane-polarized light. In general the light suffers complicated changes of amplitude (and therefore of intensity) and of phase upon reflection, which can however easily be understood by considering two simple special cases. In the first, the plane of polarization is adjusted so that the electric vector oscillates in the plane of incidence (*p*-, or *parallel*-vibration); in the second, the electric vector oscillates perpendicular to the plane of incidence (*s*-, or *senkrecht*-vibration). The changes of amplitude and phase upon reflection are in general different in the two cases; they are

---

[1] Figures in brackets indicate the literature references on p. 332.

described by the well-known Fresnel equations, which show a different functional dependence of the reflected amplitude and phase upon the relative refractive index of the reflector. Thus, in principle, absolute measurements of the two reflection coefficients (amplitude and phase) will describe the properties of the reflector in terms of the two components of the refractive index (refraction and absorption); if the reflector is a transparent dielectric, a single measurement will suffice.

If now the plane surface is coated with a thin film, we shall have to deal in general with reflections from the two surfaces of the film, and the amplitude and phase of the reflected ray will be the result of compounding that arising from the upper surface of the film with those emerging after successive pairs of reflections within the film. Since the appropriate Fresnel coefficients will again be involved, depending as they do upon different functions of the film refractive index, it would seem that if the substrate has been adequately characterized, further measurements of the new absolute reflection coefficients and phase changes for the s- and p-vibrations will serve to characterize the film in terms of thickness and refractive index—remembering that the optical thickness of the film also contributes to the phase change and to the resultant amplitude.

Unfortunately, this type of procedure, so transparent in principle, suffers from severe practical drawbacks. It is quite usual in optics to try to avoid absolute measurements, and at the same time to seek conditions that will provide either qualitative distinctions, as between light and dark, or at least easily recognizable extrema. In the field of thin film measurements, a useful stratagem first exploited by Drude has had a dominating influence. In illuminating the reflector we have just been discussing, the plane of polarization of the incident light can be shifted (for example) through $45°$, so that instead of using the s- and p-vibrations singly, we are in effect applying them simultaneously with equal amplitudes and exactly in phase with each other. After reflection they no longer agree either in phase or in amplitude, but if the reflected beam is passed through suitable optical devices suitably adjusted, the agreement can be restored, and the settings of the instruments that accomplish this are simply related to the ratio of the reflected amplitudes for the s- and p-rays and to the difference between the two changes of phase. When the reflector is covered with a thin film, the amplitude and phase changes are modified in a manner that is dependent upon the optical parameters of the film. The sensitivity of these polarimetric quantities to changes in the film parameters can be increased in various ways. For example, it is not necessary for the reflector to be a simple semi-infinite solid slab of the kind postulated above; more typically it is laminated, a metal base coated with a dielectric layer of optimum thickness for the purpose at hand. It is this use of a compound substrate that is partly responsible for the power and versatility of Rothen's famous "ellipsometer."

One might hope that the ellipsometric technique itself would provide a means of resolving film thickness and refractive index. Analytical approximate expressions for the effects of thin films on the reflection of polarized light, such as those of Drude [14] and Lucy [21], provide some encouragement, but the experimentally observable quantities usually turn out to be dependent essentially upon optical thickness with very slight second order sensitivity to variations in refractive index *per se*.[2] Attempts to get around this limitation, or to supplement the polarimetric measurement in some suitable manner [16] have been discouragingly unsuccessful [22].

2.3. The Stepped Interference Reflector Method

In the method now to be described, the traditional polarimetric measurements have been abandoned, and replaced by observations of reflected intensity minima that occur when the *s*- and *p*-rays are incident upon suitable compound reflectors and then upon the same reflectors coated with the "unknown" thin film.   In this respect the technique has more in common with a simple method of measuring small changes in film thickness devised years ago by Blodgett [9, 10], than with that of Drude.   The basic observation is illustrated in figure 1, adapted from Blodgett's paper.   If a plate of polished metal is coated with a layer of a dielectric such as barium stearate, which can be deposited quite conveniently in successive bimolecular sheets, each adding a constant increment of thickness, the reflection coefficient for the *s*-ray of monochromatic light at a definite angle of incidence will pass through a minimum when the thickness of dielectric is such that the optical path difference between the rays reflected at the two interfaces of the reflector is approximately 180°.   The word "approxi-

---

[2] From the recent work of McCrackin et al. [25] It appears that this statement is not always correct, and several papers in this symposium contain evidence to the same effect.   Our conclusion, right or wrong, provided the impetus for developing the method described here.

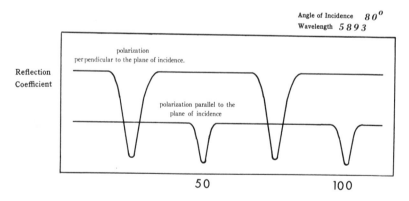

Angle of Incidence 80°

Wavelength 5893

Double Layers of Barium Stearate

FIGURE 1.   *Illustrating the conditions for formation of* s- *and* p- *fringes when different numbers of barium stearate double layers are deposited upon chromium.*

Modified from Blodgett [9]

mately" is used because the condition for minimum reflectance is determined not only by the thickness of the dielectric but by any contribution that may result from differences between the phase changes at the two interfaces. These differences are rather small with the *s*-ray. In the case of the *p*-ray, on the other hand, at large angles of incidence, they approach 180°, so that in order to produce minimum reflectance it is necessary for the optical path difference within the dielectric layer to approach 360°: thus with increasing dielectric thickness the reflection minima will alternate in the manner shown in figure 1. The underlying phase relationships that produce this state of affairs are illustrated in figure 2.

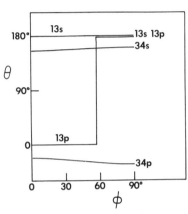

FIGURE 2. *Phase changes at air-dielectric (13) and barium stearate-chromium (34) interfaces.*

Abscissa: angle of incidence in air. Ordinate, phase change. Letters *s* and *p* prefer to plane of polarization of incident light, parallel (*p*) or perpendicular (*s*) to the plane of incidence.

The existence of a minimum in the reflected intensity depends not only upon the establishment of suitable phase relationships. It is also necessary that there should not be too great a disparity between the reflected amplitudes from the two interfaces. Obviously, if one amplitude were to be very much greater than the other, the minimum would be reduced to a mere ripple very hard to locate and to measure. Conversely, the simple equations for reflection from a dielectric coated metal reflector show that, in principle, the minimum can be converted to an extinction if, together with the correct phase relationships, the reflected amplitudes are exactly equal. Calculations using these equations and the known optical constants of metals and barium stearate show that the necessary conditions should readily be attainable in practice. There is always an angle of incidence at which the two reflection coefficient curves intersect (see examples in fig. 3). Here, then, we see the origin of the stepped interference reflector. We have, for example, a chromium-plated glass slide, one half of which has about 20, the other half about 40, double layers of barium stearate (fig. 4). At the correct wavelength and angle of incidence, the thinner step will give the *s*-ray extinction; at a slightly different angle of incidence the thicker step will give the *p*-ray extinction. Alternatively, thicker dielectric films can be used to give the corresponding first-order extinctions. If instead of using monochromatic light the slide

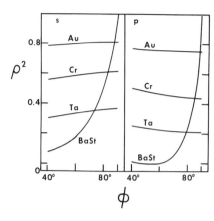

FIGURE 3.   *Illustrating first condition for formation of* s- *and* p- *extinction fringes by compound reflector of barium stearate on metal.*

Curves labeled BaSt give reflected intensity at interface between air and a semi-infinite layer of barium stearate. Curves labeled Au, Cr, Ta give the corresponding reflected intensities at a barium stearate-metal interface. Abscissa, angle of incidence in air; ordinate, square of reflected amplitude. Wavelength about 5890 Å throughout.

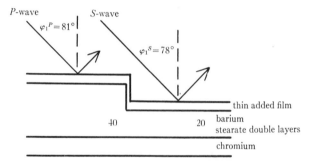

FIGURE 4.   *Chromium plated glass slide with stepped multi-layer of barium stearate-stearic acid.*
(Reproduced from [6].)

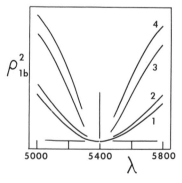

FIGURE 5.   *Calculated extinction fringes produced when stepped reflector of barium stearate on chromium is examined at the correct angle of incidence.*

Fringes are calculated to coincide at 5400 Å. Dispersion of metal is ignored. Abscissa: wavelength. Ordinate: reflected intensity. Curve 1: zero-order s-fringe. Curve 2: zero-order p-fringe. Curves 4 and 3 are the corresponding first-order fringes respectively.

is illuminated with white light and the reflected light dispersed in a spectrometer, a black band will be seen at the extinction wavelength. Figure 5 shows curves calculated for zero and first order s- and p-extinction fringes produced by barium stearate on a metal plate having optical constants resembling those of chromium, but assumed to be independent of wavelength.

What happens if a thin transparent film of arbitrary refractive index and thickness is now deposited upon both steps of the interference reflector? Clearly the reflection coefficient at the original upper surface of the dielectric substrate will be decreased; the rays reflected from this interface, now representing the boundary between the "unknown" film and the substrate (fig. 6), will continue to interfere with those reflected from the metal, with their optical path difference unchanged, and will thus produce a minimum reflected intensity at the wavelength of the original extinction. However, upon this will be imposed a second minimum produced by combining the ray reflected from the upper surface of the added film with that coming from the metal; this second minimum will occur at a new, longer, wavelength corresponding to the total optical thickness of dielectric substrate and test film (regions 2 and 3 of fig. 6). These two minima will not actually be resolved; they are introduced for purposes of exposition only. The result of combining the two hypothetical fringes will be a single rather broad minimum at an intermediate wavelength. The same process of combination will occur both on the s- and p-steps, but since the profiles of the two minima in each case will depend upon the values of the respective Fresnel reflection coefficients, and since these in turn will involve different functions of the refractive index of the unknown film, the wavelengths of the s- and p-minima will depend in distinctive ways upon film refractive index. The theory of the fringe shifts justifies this prediction and shows, furthermore, that the difference referable to film refractive index is a readily measurable quantity. After drastic approximation, the following simple equations are obtained:

$$n_2 \sim 1.5(\delta'_{3s}\Delta_s/\delta'_{3p}\Delta_p)^{1/2} = 1.5(\epsilon_s/\epsilon_p)^{1/2} \tag{1}$$

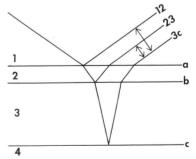

FIGURE 6. *Simplified scheme, ignoring multiple reflections, illustrating displacement of extinction fringe when thin test film is formed upon the dielectric film 3.*

Observed fringe is compounded from fringe formed (a) by addition of rays 23 and 3c, at the wavelength λ_b of the original extinction fringe, and (b) by addition of 12 and 3c, at some longer wavelength. Resultant minimum is at an intermediate wavelength λ_a.

$$d_2 \sim 0.088 \delta_3' \Delta_s / (n_2^2 - 1) \qquad (2)$$

$$\epsilon_s = \delta_{3s}' \Delta_s, \ \epsilon_p = \delta_{3p}' \Delta_p. \qquad (3)$$

These equations refer to the case of a film (fig. 6) deposited upon barium stearate of refractive index 1.5 and observed at an angle of incidence 81°. Film refractive index and thickness are denoted by n_2, d_2, respectively; fringe shifts are Δ; the δ_3' values are effective optical path differences for the barium stearate substrate, and are calibration constants measured as described later.

3. Apparatus and Procedures

3.1. Fabrication of Stepped Reflectors

Glass microscope slides coated with a thick film of chromium by vapor condensation *in vacuo* can be prepared in the laboratory as needed, or can be obtained from commercial sources.[3] Sample slides from each batch should be examined for suitability since the optical properties of the chromium films are quite variable and occasionally will fail to give extinction fringes when coated with the usual thicknesses of stearate and examined at the usual angle of incidence. A check by this means is more satisfactory than a measurement of the optical constants of the metal film since the tolerable range of variation has not been established.

Procedures for transfer of stearate multilayers vary considerably from laboratory to laboratory and have undergone many modifications in our own laboratory. Although studied by many workers, some of the factors involved are so subtle that all-inclusive specifications cannot be given. The composition of the water upon which the stearic acid is spread, for example, is certainly of major importance, but the usual electrical criterion of purity is irrelevant, and more importance must be attached to such factors as presence of impurities picked up from ion exchange materials during the course of preparation.

Our most recent procedures have been described in some detail [8]. The aqueous subphase is prepared from laboratory distilled water of specific resistance around 80,000 ohm/cm, and containing spectrographically detectable traces of B, Si, Al, Fe, Mg, Ca, and Cu; the salts added to this are barium chloride, 10^{-4} M; potassium bicarbonate, 2×10^{-4} M; cupric chloride, 10^{-7} M. The final pH is 6.8 and the temperature must not exceed 20 °C. This solution is placed in a waxed Plexiglas film tray (fig. 7). The surface is repeatedly "swept" clean with a Plexiglas barrier, and on the clean surface is placed a polyethylene float in position 2 (fig. 7). A solution of stearic acid (Eastman, M. p. 69.5 to 70 °C), 3×10^{-2} M in reagent grade benzene, is then dropped from a micropipet upon the surface at the center of the ring 3; the ring retains the solution while permitting outward spreading of the monolayer formed as the benzene evaporates. Spread-

[3] Evaporated Metal Films Corp., 436 W. State St., Ithaca, N.Y.

ing is continued, as rapidly as possible, until the float has been propelled to position 2'. A residual lens of solution is aspirated off the surface, and after a few minutes the film is compressed to 29 dynes/cm by applying a drop of purified oleic acid to the surface on the left (in fig. 7) of the floating barrier. Several clean chromium slides, made hydrophobic by rubbing with cotton wool, are then mounted on an automatic dipping device above the trough (position 4 in fig. 7) and dipped vertically at about 5 cm/min. The result of repeated dipping is a very stable, uniform multilayer of barium-copper-hydrogen stearate.

For many purposes zero-order reflectors are satisfactory, with about 20 stearate double layers on one portion and about 40 on the other. Sharper extinction fringes are obtained with first-order reflectors (61 and 80 double layers) (cf. fig. 5), with reduction of fringe shift for a given unknown film, but with an overall gain in precision and convenience.

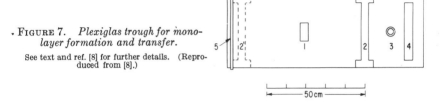

. FIGURE 7. *Plexiglas trough for mono-layer formation and transfer.*
See text and ref. [8] for further details. (Reproduced from [8].)

3.2. Optical Apparatus and Procedure

The various optical elements are shown in figure 8 and identified in the accompanying legend. The arrangement is such that at an angle of incidence of about 80° the area of the stepped reflector viewed by the photomultiplier is 2 mm high $\times$0.6 mm. The spectral bandwidth received by the photomultiplier is estimated to be about 10 Å, representing a compromise between desirable fringe resolution and available intensity.

Assuming the necessary alinement and other adjustments to have been checked, the first step is to locate the s- and p-fringe minima on the reflector. Formerly this was done at the angles of incidence for true extinction fringes, 79°10' and 82°30' respectively for s- and p-rays. A convenient practical compromise is to work at a constant angle of incidence of 81°, with negligible loss of accuracy. A manual null-searching method has proved adequate for locating the fringe minima, although scale readings taken on either side of the minimum may also be useful and are convenient indicators of any unusual change in symmetry. In general, observations are made at ten places on each step of the reflector, placed in two vertical rows on either side of the axis. The uniformity of the multilayer plates is such that discrepancies between readings exceeding 2 Å are quite

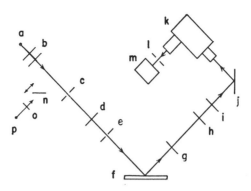

FIGURE 8.   *Apparatus used for measurement of film thickness and refractive index by the* s-p *stepped reflector method.*

a is zirconium arc; *b*, collimating lens; *c*, first collimating slit; *d*, polarizer; *e*, second collimating slit; *f*, stepped reflector with test film; *g*, analyzer; *h*, and *i* are focusing lenses; *j* is mirror; *k*, constant deviation spectrometer mounted on turntable; *l*, Hilger slit; *m*, photomultiplier; *n*, movable mirror; *o*, collimating lens for mercury vapor lamp used for calibration. (Reproduced from [24].)

unusual, and within a series of established uniformity the number of observation areas may be reduced. The test films added subsequently are generally less uniform.

After locating the minima at λ_{os} and λ_{op}, calibration is done by adding a known small number of double layers of BaCuH-stearate to the entire reflector and repeating the fringe measurements, which now yield the wavelength values λ_{bs} and λ_{bp}. From the four wavelength values the calibration constants δ_3' of eqs (1) to (3), can be calculated by eq (69).

The reflector is now ready for the test film, deposition of which produces a further displacement of the fringe minima to λ_{as} and λ_{ap}. These displacements $(\lambda_{as}-\lambda_{bs})$ and $(\lambda_{ap}-\lambda_{bp})$, are the values Δ used in eqs (1) to (3). If more than a rough estimate of the test film parameters is required, more involved calculations can be carried out as indicated later.

4. Methods of Checking Validity of Film Thickness and Refractive Index Data

4.1. Test Criteria

Independent methods are not available for determining the optical constants, or alternatively the mass per unit area and density, of the test films deposited upon the reflector. Indirect tests must be applied, recognizing that each is open to some objection. The following criteria have been used, with results that will be presented briefly in the next section:

a. Successive transfers of monolayers of test substance: constant apparent refractive index combined with constant apparent thickness increment.

b. Agreement of film refractive index and thickness per layer with values found using multilayers built up to several higher orders (see section 4.2).

c. Variation in apparent thickness of monolayers prepared from members of homologous series correlated with molecular dimensions; apparent refractive indices compared with values for organic crystals.

d. Apparent refractive index of thin films formed by condensation of vapor compared with values for thicker films, similarly prepared, measured by the Abelès method (see section 4.3).

e. Apparent refractive index of test film formed either by vapor condensation or by monolayer transfer shown to be independent of film thickness, and correlated with refractive index of substance in bulk.

f. Demonstration that the apparent refractive index of certain porous films of very low apparent index can be increased by "filling in."

4.2. Independent Determination of Thickness and Refractive Index of Thick Multilayers

When successive monolayers can be transferred to a chromium slide in sufficient numbers to give s-ray extinction fringes of several orders, the average refractive index and thickness per monolayer can be determined by measuring the fringe wavelengths λ for various angles of incidence above and below the extinction angle (17). The fringe condition is

$$\frac{4\pi \bar{d} N}{\lambda} (n^2 - \sin^2 \phi)^{1/2} + \theta = (1 + 2m)\pi \tag{4}$$

where the first term corresponds to the optical path difference in the added film. The additional phase term θ incorporates (a) phase changes on reflection at the two interfaces, and (b) the retardation within any "rubbed-down" monolayer present on the metal surface. The fringe order, m, is $0, 1, 2 \ldots$. If θ is not wavelength dependent, the plot of N/λ against m at any angle of incidence will be a straight line:

$$m = 2\bar{d}(n^2 - \sin^2 \phi)^{1/2}(N/\lambda) - (1 - \theta/\pi)/2.$$
$$= b(N/\lambda) + a. \tag{5}$$

Equation (5) can then be solved for $\bar{d}$ and n by plotting b^2 against $\sin^2 \phi$:

$$b^2 = -4\bar{d}^2 \sin^2 \phi + 4n^2 \bar{d}^2. \tag{6}$$

Some dependence of θ upon wavelength would be expected. A basal layer, d_o, n_o, would contribute a term θ_f in λ^{-1}, and ϕ, while there would also be a dispersion term θ_r at the metal-dielectric interface dependent mainly on λ:

$$\theta = \theta_f + \theta_r = 4\pi d_o(n_o^2 - \sin^2 \phi)^{1/2}/\lambda + \theta_r. \tag{7}$$

In practice, measurements cannot be made at exactly constant wavelength; there is some variation of fringe wavelength within each set of orders at any angle of incidence, and a much larger systematic variation with changing angle of incidence, resulting in apparent dependence of the intercept a upon angle of incidence. If this is attributed to θ_f, varying according to eq (7), it is found experimentally that d_o has a large negative value, while the observed small overall values of θ (around $20°$) have to be maintained by an unreasonably large compensating value of θ_r. Thus no reliable estimate of $\theta(\phi)$ can be obtained, and it is preferable to consider it as exclusively wavelength-dependent. With this assumption, the values of a obtained at each angle of incidence can be plotted against average fringe wavelength and revised values of a can be obtained by interpolation for the fringe wavelength measured at each value of N. Each measurement then yields a new value of the slope b by the equation:

$$b = (m-a)/(N/\lambda) \tag{8}$$

and the averaged values of b plotted against $\sin^2 \phi$ lead to the corrected estimates of n and $\bar{d}$.

If consideration is being given to the nonisotropic character of the multilayers, measurements can be made at each angle of incidence with the s-ray at right angles to the direction of film deposition (the usual position of the slide) or parallel to it. In this case it is assumed that the metrical thickness of the films, $N\bar{d}$, is independent of the direction from which they are viewed [8]. Using one prime and two primes, respectively, to denote values referable to the two mutually perpendicular directions of incidence, one obtains

$$(b')^2 + (b'')^2 = 4\bar{d}^2[(n')^2] - 8\bar{d}^2 \sin^2 \phi \tag{9}$$

$$(b')^2 - (b'')^2 = 4\bar{d}^2[(n')^2 - (n'')^2]. \tag{10}$$

4.3. Determination of Refractive Index by the Abelès Method

In the Abelès method [1, 2], a portion of the surface of a plane reflector of any type is coated with the test film. The boundary between the covered and uncovered portions is illuminated with collimated monochromatic light plane polarized in the plane of incidence (p-vibration) and the angle of incidence is varied until the images of the areas on either side of the boundary appear equally bright.

The reflection coefficient of the film-covered system is obtained simply by adding the multiple reflections (see, for example, ref. [11], pp. 61, 323; ref. [18], p. 55), while that of the clean reflector can be expressed in terms of the film parameters by bringing the film thickness to zero:

$$r_{1b} = \frac{r_{13} + r_{3c} \exp(-i\delta_3)}{1 + r_{13}r_{3c} \exp(-i\delta_3)} \xrightarrow{\delta_3 = 0} \frac{r_{13} + r_{3c}}{1 + r_{13}r_{3c}} = r_{1c}, \tag{11}$$

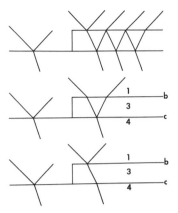

FIGURE 9.   *The two Brewster angle methods of Abelès [1, 2] for determining index of refraction of thin films.*

Top: multiple reflections between surfaces b and c of a dielectric film on an arbitrary base.   Middle: Multiple reflections abolished when light (p-vibration) is incident at Brewster angle for interface b.   Bottom: Film on dielectric substrate.   Multiple reflections abolished when incidence corresponds to Brewster angle for interface c.

where the various reflection coefficients, which may be complex, are denoted by r.   Matched fields can be obtained either by eliminating reflection at the upper film surface ($r_{13}=0$) or at the lower surface ($r_{3c}=0$), as shown in figure 9.   The second condition cannot readily be satisfied on metallic substrates.   The first condition is generally applicable; it shows that if, by eliminating r_{13}, the multiple reflections are reduced to a single reflection r_{3c} plus complete transmission at 13 and 31, the reflected amplitude r_{3c} at an internal angle of incidence of $\sin^{-1}(\sin \phi_1/n_3)$ will be equal to that at the clean substrate surface at an angle of incidence ϕ.   This is not generally the case; in a system governed by Fresnel reflection coefficients it is satisfied only when $\tan \phi_1=n_3$.   Thus the matching angle of incidence, the Brewster angle, at once gives the refractive index of the film, no matter what the optical properties of the substrate.

Abelès [1] remarks that there may be an optimum film thickness for the detection of the matching angle, and it has been noted [24] that when a metallic base is used, the condition for maximum contrast in the vicinity of the matching angle is periodic in film thickness, with δ_3, the optical path difference in the film, equal to π, 3π, 5π; this is, remembering the additional phase difference close to π between r_{13} and r_{34}, the condition for maximum r_{1b}.   The contrast is much less in the vicinity of the p-ray extinction.   The upshot of this is that the minimum film thickness for satisfactory measurements is about 1000 Å.   The method, in this form, is not suitable for direct check of results obtained by the stepped reflector method, but furnishes an interesting comparison of thin and thick films deposited under similar conditions.[4]

The apparatus used consisted of a sodium vapor source, collimating lens, two collimating irises, Nicol prism, Spencer student spectrometer table with added slide holder, and a viewing telescope focused on a dust particle at the center of the slide.   The matching condition was

---

[4] More recent work on the method is referred to in the review by Abelès [3].

established visually by simultaneous manual rotation of the slide holder and telescope arm, 10 to 20 such readings being taken.

5. Some Experimental Results

5.1. Measurements on Thick Fatty Acid Multilayers

a. Illustration of Procedure

The method outlined in section 4.2 has been used for measurements of double-layer spacing and refractive index of barium stearate, barium copper stearate, and barium copper nonadecanoate mixed in unknown proportions with the free acids. An illustration of the primary fringe wavelength measurements has been given in an earlier paper [17], while the data used for the initial calculations from equations (5) and (6) are shown graphically for a typical case in figure 10.

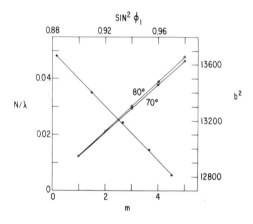

FIGURE 10. *Experimental data illustrating higher order s-fringe method of determining film thickness per monolayer and refractive index.*

Ba Cu H multilayers on chromium plated glass. Open circles: N/λ as function of fringe order, m (text eq (5)) for angles of incidence 70° and 80°. Closed circles: b^2 (sin^2 ϕ), text eq (6), for angles of incidence 70.0°, 72.5°, 75.0°, 77.5° and 80.0°. (Reproduced from [8].)

Examples of the graphs used to obtain corrected values of $a(\lambda)$, for application of eq (8), are given in figure 11. The resulting individual values of $b(m,\phi)$ are then averaged for each ϕ and eq (6) again applied for calculation, by least squares, of final values of n and $\overline{d}$. The values of $b(m)$ prove to be compatible with a straight line passing through the origin, but they nevertheless show some nonrandom variation that seems to depend upon the nature of the film substance. Illustrations of this slight systematic variation, which suggests a variation of film properties with thickness, are given in table 1.

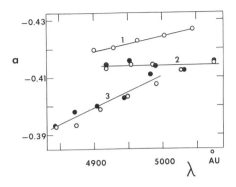

FIGURE 11. *Apparent* s-*vibration phase change at surface of "clean" chromium reflector, obtained by extrapolation of straight line relating fringe order, m, to* N/λ *(eq (5))*.

Abscissa: average fringe wavelength for 1st- to 5th-order fringes. Ordinate: a, equal to $-0.5(1-\theta/\pi)$, where θ is phase change at "clean" surface. If $\theta=0$, $a=-0.5$. Curve 1: for Ba Cu H stearate slide III; 2: Ba Cu H stearate checkerboard slide V; 3: Ba Cu H nonadecanoate slide II. See table 2.

TABLE 1. *Average variations of* b(m)

Film \ m	b/b_1					No. of slides examined
	1	2	3	4	5	
BaCuH stearate	1	0.99583	0.99464	0.99667	0.99834	3
BaCuH stearate, checkerboard	1	.99915	.99980	.99963	------------	1
BaCuH nonadecanoate	1	.99974	1.00061	.99974	.99850	2

Values averaged over five angles of incidence.

b. Results

The measurements are summarized in table 2. The variation from slide to slide is rather greater than might be hoped, apparently because of variations in the nature of the multilayer rather than poor reproducibility of the optical measurements themselves. The average spacings for stearate and nonadecanoate are compatible with a vertical orientation of the extended chains, although the extended chain lengths themselves are open to uncertainty as to the effect of the barium and copper atoms and the percentage of free acid in the films. The values of the refractive index of stearate are compatible with the assumption that the index that is effective for the s-vibration is the ordinary index n_0 if the hydrocarbon chains are normal to the slide. In the case of the nonadecanoate films, it is apparent that the chains are either more loosely packed than is the case for stearate, or that there is a certain proportion of vacancies throughout the film. An indication of this can be obtained from the values of $(n^2-1)/(n^2+2)$ since

$$\frac{n^2-1}{n^2+2}=\frac{1}{\rho}\cdot\frac{R}{M} \qquad (12)$$

TABLE 2. *Spacing and refractive index of thick fatty acid multilayers by measurement at several orders of interference*

Slide	Reference	Substance	Fringe type	d	n'	n''	n'-n''
---------------	*[15]	BaH stearate_____	s	45.7	1.508	---------	---------
---------------	*[4]	BaH stearate_____	s	47.575	1.498	---------	---------
I_____	[8]	BaCuH stearate_____	s	51.326	1.492	---------	---------
I_____	---------	BaCuH stearate_____	p	---------	1.493	---------	---------
II_____	[8]	BaCuH stearate_____	s	49.485	1.510	1.508	0.00200
III_____	[8]	BaCuH stearate_____	s	49.256	1.515	---------	---------
V_____	[8]	BaCuH stearate checkerboard__	s	48.535	1.52250	1.52269	−0.00019
I'_____	[8]	BaCuH nonadecanoate_____	s	51.409	1.5108	1.5125	−0.00170
II'_____	[8]	BaCuH nonadecanoate_____	s	54.225	1.4661	1.4649	0.00120
II'_____	[8]	BaCuH nonadecanoate, 2 months later.	---------	53.908	1.4679	1.4667	0.00120
Averages_	---------	BaH stearate_____	s	46.638	1.503	---------	---------
		BaCuH stearate+_____	s	49.762	1.508	---------	---------
		BaCuH stearate checkerboard__	s	48.535	1.522	---------	---------
		BaCuH nonadecanoate§_____	s	52.738	1.488	---------	---------

N=number of double molecular layers (range)
$\overline{d}$=thickness per double layer, Å
n'=refractive index for light incident at right angles to monolayer transfer direction
n''=value for incidence parallel to transfer direction
*=Values as given in reference. Remaining values have been revised as described in text section 4.2.
Differences from values given in reference [7] are small except for slide II' remeasured after two mouths; values given there were $\overline{d}$=52.53, $n'=n''$=1.491.
+=Weighted average, with double values assigned to II and III, since edge effects between orders were suspected in slide I.
§Weighted average, with double values to I'' and single values to each measurement of II'.

where R is molecular refractivity, M is molecular weight, and ρ is density of the solid-air mixture [5] having refractive index n. The highest value found was 3.07 for the BaCuH stearate checkerboard slide (q.v.); for stearate transferred in the usual manner, 2.90 to 3.02; for nonadecanoate, 2.76 to 3.00.

A test for vertical orientation was done by examining some of the film-coated slides after turning them through 90° in the slide holder. In the usual measurements the vertical axis of the slide coincides with the direction of dipping during film transfer, and is perpendicular to the plane of incidence; in this case, if the molecular chains are not exactly perpendicular to the dipping axis, the refractive index for the s-vibration will be a little larger than the ordinary index, n_0. Rotating the slide through 90° will then bring the refractive index back to n_0. The expected difference, $n'-n''$, would be about 0.0010 for a tilt of 5°, 0.0015 for 10°, 0.0040 for 15°. Thus the observed differences, 0.0019 for stearate and 0.0012 for nonadecanoate (table 2), suggest a tilt of about 6 to 10°.

A further test was made by building a stepped multilayer in the usual way and then adding to this a second series of steps at right angles, producing a checkerboard effect for which the refractive indices n' and n'' should be equal and, in presence of molecular tilting, slightly larger than n_0. This slide proved to be superior to all others in that the intercept a was independent of wavelength, the

[5] Although R/M is not exactly constant for the different fatty acids, the difference is probably less than 1 percent—e.g., 0.3054 and 0.3079 for palmitic and stearic acids, respectively, at 80 °C [12].

values of b showed no dependence on fringe order (table 1), and the difference between n' and n'' was reduced by a factor of 10 (table 2). At the same time, the film density was higher than usual, suggesting that transfer in two directions may be advantageous in the production of uniformly packed multilayers.

5.2. Measurements with s-p Stepped Reflector

a. Transferred Monolayers of Aliphatic Acids

Since stearate is used in determining the calibration constants δ'_{3s} and δ'_{3p}, eq (1), calculation of apparent refractive index and thickness of subsequently added stearate amounts to a further calibration and should yield the same values as those initially assumed. The fairly satisfactory check obtained is shown in figure 12. The results for stearic acid transferred from a distilled water substrate show equally satisfactory constancy of double-layer spacing and refractive index, with values that are significantly different from the calibration values for barium stearate.

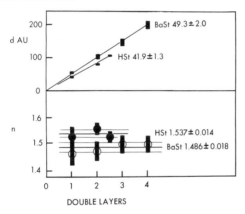

FIGURE 12.   *Thickness (above) and refractive index (below) as a function of number of double layers of stearate transferred to* s-p *stepped reflector.*

Vertical bars indicate standard deviations of each value. Overall thicknesses per double layer, $\bar{d}$, and refractive index, n_2, are given at right, together with standard deviation for each series.   Ba St indicates barium hydrogen stearate. H St is free stearic acid.

Measurements with a few other long-chain saturated acids are shown in Table 3; the values of $\bar{d}$ are compared in table 5 with the actual molecular dimensions obtained in x-ray diffraction studies. It is of interest that while the experimental values of $\bar{d}$-shown the correct overall trend, there are considerable irregularities and even a reversal of the expected order.   This reversal is avoided if the *amounts* of material per monolayer are estimated in terms of a "Lorentz-Lorenz" function, $(n^2-1)\bar{d}/(n^2+2)$: the values of this quantity, with increasing chain length, are 11.934, 13.705, 14.817, 16.045,

TABLE 3. *Spacing and refractive index of thin aliphatic acid films on* s-p *stepped reflector*

Ref.	Substance	C atoms	F	N	$\bar{d}$	n	$\bar{d}$-$\bar{d}$(cal)	n-n(cal)
			Dynes/cm					
[24]	BaH stearate	18	29	1–5			1.73	−0.012
[8]	BaCuH stearate		29	2			−.099	.002
				6			−.319	.001
[8]	BaCuH stearate		16	4	47.89	1.518		
	BaCuH stearate		9	4	45.16	1.528		
[24]	Stearic acid	18	29	1–2.5	41.9	1.537		
			29	2	41.0	1.535		
	BaCuH pentadecanoate	15	9	4	39.7	1.513		
	BaCuH palmitate	16	29	6	46.6	1.500		
[8]	BaCuH nonadecanoate	19	29	4	56.1	1.487		
	BaCuH arachidate	20	29	2	53.9	1.529		
				4	53.7	1.531		

F=film surface pressure at time of transfer to stepped reflector
N=number of double molecular layers used in measurement
d(cal), n(cal) refer to values for stearic acid used in stepped reflector calibration

    In ref. [24]: d(cal)=47.575 Åu, n(cal)=1.498
    In ref. [8]:   49.499   1.510

16.619. Some irregularity remains, but this may be due to differences in structure of films formed from the odd and even members of the aliphatic series. The improvement resulting from calculation of the Lorentz-Lorenz function is probably an example of the $n-d$ "coupling" discussed in the next paragraph.

b. Transferred Monolayers and Adsorbed Films of Protein

Two distinct procedures in the study of protein films, and their results [6, 7] are relevant to the present display of the stepped reflector method.

Direct adsorption. The stepped reflector is immersed in a solution of protein, the free remaining protein washed away in a stream of solvent, the solvent in turn displaced by water, and the reflector with adsorbed protein then dried. The entire process may be repeated.

Monolayer transfer. A monolayer of protein is formed upon an aqueous surface and the monolayer transferred by dipping, in the manner used in preparation of stearate films. According to the conditions of transfer the films produced may be "AB", double layers produced by attachment of the monolayer during both downward and upward passage of the slide through the interfaces, or "B", with attachment only during emergence.

A complete protocol of an experiment on direct adsorption of protein has been published [6]. Figure 13 shows that with successive transfers of bovine plasma albumin monolayers, the relative s- and p-fringe displacements remain constant, as does the corresponding increment in thickness per added monolayer. Other data on the thickness and refractive index of adsorbed and transferred films are given in table 4. In instances where several successive monolayer or double-layer transfers were made to the same reflector or pair of

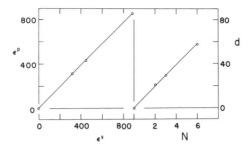

FIGURE 13. *Results of measuring s- and p-fringe shifts upon transfer of mono-layers of bovine plasma albumin to stepped reflector from distilled water surfaces.*

Film pressure, 9.5 dynes/cm. Left side: Abscissa, ϵ_s. Straight line is regression line that gives rough estimate of film refractive index by text eqs (89) or (90). Right side: apparent film thickness d and number of transferred monolayers N. Slope of regression line gives average thickness per monolayer, $\bar{d}$. (Diagram reproduced from [7].)

TABLE 4. *Thin protein films on s-p stepped reflector*

Solvent	pH	Concentration	X	n	d	$\bar{d}$
					Å	
Adsorbed Films of Bovine Plasma Albumin						
		percent				
Water		0.67	1	1.600±0.032	29.2±1.6	
Water		.67	1	1.588±0.042	27.8±2.0	
Acetate buffer, protein removed with water	4.7	.0067–10.00	6	1.598±0.018	20.2±10.6	
Water	5.5–6.0	.05–5.00	9	1.571±0.058	30.6±5.8	
HCl	5.0	.1	2	1.595	28.4	
(a) HCl	3.0	.1	2	1.27	14.5	
(b) Water, 2d exposure		.1	1	1.48	26.6	
Averages for water and HCl pH 5				*1.589*	*29.0*	
Adsorbed Films of Botulinum Toxins						
Type A in 0.05 M acetate	3.38	0.357	3	1.593, 1.574, 1.598 *avg. 1.588*	24.5, 26.1, 24.2 *avg. 24.9*	
Type B in 0.2 M succinate	5.5	0.06	3	1.530, 1.536, 1.513 *avg. 1.526*	31.1, 29.3, 29.9 *avg. 30.1*	
Transferred Monolayers of Bovine Plasma Albumin						
Liquid Substrate		Type				
Water	9	A B	1	1.526	20.9	10.45
		A B₂			29.2	9.73
		A B₅			57.6	9.60
Dilute zinc chloride	9	A B	2	1.583	19.97, 19.07	9.99, 9.54
		(A B)₂			36.10, 35.93	9.03, 8.98
Dilute zinc chloride	16	A B	2	1.600	17.67, 24.25	8.84, 12.13
		(A B)₂			36.22, 36.76	9.06, 9.19
		(A B)₃			54.35, —	9.06 —
Averages for ZnCl₂				*1.592*		*9.65*

n=Film refractive index.
d=Total thickness.
$\bar{d}$=Average thickness per monolayer.
X=Number of slides.
F=Surface pressure at time of transfer, dynes/cm.
A indicates film transferred during downward motion of slide.
B indicates transfer during emergence of slide from film tray.

reflectors, a single value of refractive index was obtained by calculating the linear regression lines of ϵ_s on ϵ_p. Individual values of d were then calculated for each experimental point.

A notable feature of the measurements on protein films is a marked coupling between film thickness and refractive index, of such a nature that, under similar conditions of deposition, rather wide variations of n and d are associated with highly reproducible values of the surface density, γ mg/m^2. For a protein film regarded as a mixture of solid protein and air, γ is given by the Lorentz-Lorenz equation in the form

$$\frac{n^2-1}{n^2+2}=\frac{\gamma}{d}\cdot\frac{1}{\rho}\cdot\frac{n_0^2-1}{n_0^2+2} \tag{13}$$

where $\rho\sim1.3$ [20] and $n_o\sim1.60$ [26, 13] for solid protein, giving

$$\frac{\gamma}{d}=0.38\frac{n^2-1}{n^2+2}. \tag{14}$$

The $n-d$ coupling has been confirmed by using 25 sets of data in which duplicate slides were coated with protein under various conditions. For each pair of slides, with protein films n_1, d_1, γ_1, and n_2, d_2, γ_2, the angle θ given by

$$\tan\theta=\delta\left(0.38\frac{n^2-1}{n^2+2}\right)/\delta(\gamma_1/d) \tag{15}$$

is a useful measure of the degree of coupling; in absence of coupling the average value will be zero, and with perfect coupling, 45°. The value obtained for the 25 pairs of slides was 38.3°.

c. Other Measurements

Several substances were deposited upon stepped reflectors by condensation *in vacuo*, and monolayers of one organic substance of high bulk index of refraction were successfully transferred. The results of these miscellaneous measurements are included in table 5.

d. Summary and Discussions

The evidence for the validity of the stepped reflector method rests upon the accumulation of data that can be considered in connection with auxiliary information that is not strictly comparable. For example (table 5): (a) Using calibration constants that are fairly close to values obtained by the s-fringe method, measurements of the thickness per monolayer of several other aliphatic soap films are in fair agreement with values anticipated on stereochemical grounds. (b) The corresponding indices of refraction are reasonable since (i) low values for the odd carbon acid, nonadecanoic, are found by both stepped reflector and s-fringe methods; (ii) some uncertainty as to the actual values arises from the presence of Ba and Cu, and from the

TABLE 5. *Summary of data on validity of* s-p *stepped reflector methods*

Substance	Stepped s-p reflector		Higher order s-fringes		Abelès method	Other values		
	n_{sp}	$d, \bar{d}$	n_s	$\bar{d}$	n_p''	$\bar{d}$	n bulk	n film
Stearic acid____	1.537±0.014	41.9±1.3	_____	_____	[a]1.549±0.006	[b]48.84	_____	[c]1.51
	1.535±0.023	41.0±1.4				(~41?)		
BaH stearate__	_____	_____	1.503	46.63$_8$	1.508±0.014	_____	_____	[d]1.4917
								1.551
BaCuH soaps								
pentadec-								
anoate____	1.513	39.7_	_____	_____	_____	[e](41.22)	_____	_____
palmitate___	1.500	46.6_	_____	_____	_____	(43.76)	_____	_____
stearate_____	_____	_____	[f]1.522$_5$	[f]48.53	_____	(48.84)	_____	[g](1.559)
nonadec-								
anoate____	1.487	56.1_	1.489	52.74	_____	(41.38)	_____	_____
arachidate__	1.530	53.8_	_____	_____	_____	(53.92)	_____	_____
Bovine								
plasma								
albumin								
Adsorbed [h]__	1.589	29.0_	_____	_____	_____	[i]>22	[j]1.6	_____
Mono-								
layers [k]____	1.592	9.6$_3$_	_____	_____	_____	[m]10.0	_____	_____
Botulinum								
toxins								
Adsorbed,								
type A____	1.588	24.9_	_____	_____	_____	[n]25.5	_____	_____
Adsorbed,								
type B____	1.526	30.1_	_____	_____	_____	_____	_____	_____
Fused ring								
compound[o]								
Monolayers_	1.676±0.028	_____	_____	_____	1.728±0.014	_____	[p]1.7	_____
CaF$_2$_____	1.362±0.015	258(±10)	_____	_____	1.250±0.022	_____	[q]1.434	[r]1.23−1.28
Cryolite,								
Na$_3$AlF$_6$_____	1.393±0.009	106−197__	_____	_____	1.405±0.006	_____	[s]1.364	[t]1.30−1.31
MgF$_2$_____	1.411±0.014	63,246___	_____	_____	1.412±0.006	_____	[u]1.384	1.400±0.002
CaCO$_3$_____	1.563±0.020	150____	_____	_____	1.596±0.006	_____	[v]1.572	_____
ZnS_____	1.51±0.06	93_____	_____	_____	1.98±0.02	_____	[w]2.37	_____
	1.50± (0.04)	~100	_____	_____	_____	_____	_____	_____

SYMBOLS:

n_{sp}=refractive index determined by stepped reflector method. Calibration with BaCuH stearate for all BaCuH compounds using n_3=1.510, $\bar{d}_3$=49.499 Å. For remaining experiments, calibration with BaH stearate using n_3=1.498, $\bar{d}_3$=47.575 Å.

n_s=refractive index by s-fringe method.

n_p=refractive index by Abeles method with directions of incidence and reflection parallel to long axis of film slide.

d=film thickness (evaporated films)

$\bar{d}$=thickness per double layer (fatty acids) or monolayer (proteins and ring compounds)

NOTES

[a] cf. ref [8], fig. 7.

[b] Stearic acid unit cell: c=48.84 Å, c sin β=43.75 or 39.75 [30].

[c] [10].

[d] n_o and n_e, respectively [10].

[e] Values in this column obtained by adding 2.54 Å per carbon atom to extended chain length of stearic acid. No allowance made for metal atoms.

[f] Values obtained with checkerboard reflector, with equal numbers of double layers deposited at right angles.

[g] n_s for BaPbH stearate [10].

[h] Adsorbed from HCl solution at pH 5.

[i] Molecule 22×49×106 Å [4] if deposited in orientation similar to that in unit cell would form film about 22 Å thick [6].

[j] Calculated for solid protein from refractive index increment of solutions, using Lorentz-Lorenz equation [26, 13].

[k] Protein spread on dilute ZnCl$_2$.

[m] Side chain spacing in extended β-form [20].

[n] From sedimentation and diffusion measurements, axial ratio ~18, molecular weight ~10^6, consistent with ellipsoid of revolution 460×25.5 Å [32].

[o] 8, 9, 10, 11—tetrahydro-benzanthracene; 8—malonic acid obtained from the laboratory of Dr. W. E. Bachmann through the Chemical Biological Coordination Center of the National Research Council. See [5].

[p] Assumed from structural resemblance to other fused ring compounds of refractive index around 1-7.

[q] [15].

[r] Range of values given for very thin films [18].

[s] Value for β index [15].

[t] n_p determined by Abelès [2].

[u] Average of n_o, 1.378 and n_e, 1.390 [15].

[v] Average of values given for calcite: 1.6583, β, 1.4864. Value for CaO=1.838 [15].

[w] Average of 2.36 and 2.38 [15].

fact that the ordinary and extraordinary indices are appreciably different. (c) Protein adsorbed films and monolayers prepared under optimum conditions appear to have refractive indices close to 1.60, the value for dry protein in bulk. (d) The thicknesses of adsorbed films of two different proteins are consistent with known molecular dimensions, while transferred monolayers have the thickness of extended polypeptide chains. (e) The refractive indices of several substances deposited *in vacuo*, and of a fused ring organic compound transferred in monolayer form, were in satisfactory agreement with values obtained on much thicker films prepared by similar methods and examined by the Abelès method. Agreement to be expected with bulk values is limited by the fact that the substances are not always isotropic, and by a possible decrease of refractive index in very thin layers.

Two discrepancies exist.

(a) Zinc sulfide, of bulk index ~ 2, appeared to be much less dense ($n \sim 1.5$) in very thin layers, while the Abelès method gave an intermediate value. Zinc sulfide is used routinely as a highly refractive material in preparing interference filters [31] and we know of no precedent for these low values.

(b) The apparent refractive index of stearic acid is unexpectedly high (1.536) by the stepped reflector method, and still higher (1.549) by the Abelès method. The first result has been explained [8] by calculating the s- and p-indices as a function of angle of molecular tilt and showing that the value 1.537 is compatible with the values of n_p and n_s expected when the molecules are tilted at an angle 30.3° to the slide normal. The still higher value obtained by the Abelès method becomes reasonable when one remembers that the slide was viewed parallel to the monolayer dipping direction at an angle of incidence $\tan^{-1} 1.549$ or 56.45°. The incident beam is nearly parallel to the molecular chains and a value approaching the extraordinary index, 1.55, is to be expected.

A final point of relevance to these tests is the coupling between n and d, which suggests, under carefully duplicated conditions, the formation of films having the same mass but different thicknesses. A result of this tendency, which has been noted with the aliphatic acids as well as the proteins, is that the reproducibility is less than that calculated for the known accuracy with which the fringe wavelengths can be measured. Mattuck [23] gives the following standard deviations upon the latter basis: for films 12 Å thick, $\sigma_n = \pm 0.054$, $\sigma_d = \pm 1.4$ Å; for films 142.5 Å thick, $\sigma_n = \pm 0.010$, $\sigma_d = \pm 3.2$ Å. Larger standard deviations in n and d in replicate experiments, with small deviations in γ, apparently show that with extremely thin films the orientation is far from perfect, although on the average the same number of molecules is always needed to "saturate" a receptor surface. This question needs further study, but for the moment we shall assume that it does not point to any shortcomings of the optical observations.

6. Theory of Stepped Interference Reflector

6.1. Derivation of Fringe Shift Equations

Having presented evidence of the usefulness of the s-p stepped reflector method, we now sketch the derivation of the fringe shift equations for those who are interested; the original derivations are spread over three papers [16, 22, 23] and a brief self-contained statement may be of value.

a. Stepped Reflector Without Test Film

We refer to the diagram of the stepped reflector given in figure 14, with the interfaces represented by lower case letters and the substances forming them by numbers. The letters s and p indicate the portion of the reflector under consideration, and the plane of polarization of the light impinging upon it.

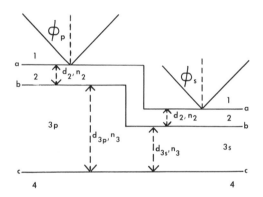

FIGURE 14. *Illustrating designation of films and interfaces in* s-p *stepped reflector.*

Medium 1 is air; 2, the test film; 3s, barium copper stearate of thickness suitable for production of s-extinction fringe in absence of film 2; 3p, barium stearate of thickness suitable for production of p-extinction fringe in absence of film 2; 4 is chromium or chromium-plated glass. ϕ_s and ϕ_p are angles of incidence appropriate to the extinction conditions; in the theoretical development given here, $\phi_s = \phi_p = \phi$ while in ref. [23] the distinction is maintained. Reflection at a single interface separating two semi-infinite media is designated with a numerical suffix. Reflection at an interface within the actual system shown in the diagram is designated by the number of the medium containing the incident beam, followed by the letter designating the interface—e.g. r_{1a}, the reflection coefficient for the whole reflector; r_{1c}, the reflection coefficient for a clean metal-coated glass slide in air.

Considering first the case of a dielectric film, 3, between a metal plate, 4, and air, 1, we repeat eq (11):

$$r_{1b} = \frac{r_{13} + r_{3c} \exp(-i\delta_3)}{1 + r_{13}r_{3c} \exp(-i\delta_3)} \tag{16}$$

where

$$r_{13s} = \frac{\cos\phi - (n_3^2 - \sin^2\phi)^{1/2}}{\cos\phi + (n_3^2 - \sin^2\phi)^{1/2}} \tag{17}$$

$$r_{13p}=\frac{n_3^2 \cos \phi-(n_3^2-\sin^2 \phi)^{1/2}}{n_3^2 \cos \phi+(n_3^2-\sin^2 \phi)^{1/2}} \tag{18}$$

$$\delta_3=(4\pi/\lambda)d_3(n_3^2-\sin^2 \phi)^{1/2} \tag{19}$$

while r_{3c} is given by equations similar to (17) and (18) using

$$\hat{n}_4=n_4-ik_4. \tag{20}$$

For present purposes it is sufficient to write

$$r_{3c}'=\rho_{3c} \exp (i\theta_{3c}) \tag{21}$$

giving

$$r_{1b}=\frac{r_{13}+\rho_{3c} \exp i(\theta_{3c}-\delta_3)}{1+r_{13}\rho_{3c} \exp i(\theta_{3c}-\delta_3)}=\rho_{1b} \exp i\theta_{1b}. \tag{22}$$

At a wavelength λ_b and a film thickness d_3' giving a phase change δ_3' at a suitable angle of incidence, the reflected amplitude will be zero (extinction fringe) if

$$r_{13}=\rho_{13} \exp i180°=\rho_{3c} \tag{23}$$

and

$$\theta_{3c}-\delta_3'=2\pi m \qquad (m=0, 1, 2 \ldots). \tag{24}$$

The condition for (23) has already been illustrated in figure 3; it is found empirically to be satisfied when ϕ is about 78° for the s-, and 81° for the p-vibration in the case of barium stearate films on chromium-plated glass. The second condition is satisfied when the s-layer has about 20 or 60 barium stearate double layers, while about 40 or 80 are required for the p-layer, because of the different value of θ_{3c} illustrated in figure 2.

b. Stepped Reflector With Test Film

If a film of substance 2, thickness d_2, is placed on the step reflector, the reflected amplitudes will now be given by

$$r_{1a}=\frac{r_{12}+r_{2b} \exp (-i\delta_2)}{1+r_{12}r_{2b} \exp (-i\delta_2)} \tag{25}$$

where

$$r_{2b}=\frac{r_{23}+r_{3c} \exp (-i\delta_3)}{1+r_{23}r_{3c} \exp (-i\delta_3)} \tag{26}$$

and δ_2, δ_3 are values appropriate to the wavelength of observation, λ, by equations similar to (19). By suitable manipulation the new fringe condition can now be calculated by differentiating (25) with respect to wavelength.

The original fringe condition can be used to define r_{3c} by equations (16), (23), and (24), and applying this to any wavelength λ by assuming no dispersion of the reflection coefficients:

$$r_{3c} = -r_{13} \exp i\delta_3' \qquad (27)$$

$$r_{2b} = \frac{r_{23} - r_{13} \exp i(\delta_3' - \delta_3)}{1 - r_{23}r_{13} \exp i(\delta_3' - \delta_3)}. \qquad (28)$$

Substitution in (25) and introducing some abbreviations then leads to

$$r_{1a} = \frac{a - b \exp (-i\delta) + c[\exp (-i\xi) - ab \exp (-i\eta)]}{1 - ab \exp (-i\delta) + c[a \exp (-i\xi) - b \exp (-i\eta)]} \qquad (29)$$

where

$$a = r_{12}$$

$$b = r_{13}$$

$$c = r_{23}$$

$$\epsilon = \delta_2 + \delta_3 - \delta_3' = \xi + \eta$$

$$\xi = \delta_2$$

$$\eta = \delta_3 - \delta_3'.$$

Multiplying r_{1a} by its complex conjugate we then obtain

$$r_{1a} \cdot r_{1a}^* = \frac{(a - b \cos \epsilon + c \cos \xi - abc \cos \eta)^2 + (b \sin \epsilon - c \sin \xi + abc \sin \eta)^2}{(1 - ab \cos \epsilon + ac \cos \xi - bc \cos \eta)^2 + (ab \sin \epsilon - ac \sin \xi + bc \sin \eta)^2} \qquad (30)$$

$$= \frac{A + f(\epsilon)}{B + f(\epsilon)} = \frac{A + f}{B + f} \qquad (31)$$

where

$$A = a^2 + b^2 + c^2 + a^2b^2c^2 \qquad (32)$$

$$B = 1 + a^2b^2 + a^2c^2 + b^2c^2 \qquad (33)$$

$$f = f(\epsilon) = -2ab[\cos \epsilon + c^2 \cos (\xi - \eta)] \\ + 2c[a(1 + b^2) \cos \xi - b(1 + a^2) \cos \eta]. \qquad (34)$$

The variables ξ and ϵ are readily expressed in terms of ϵ by introducing the phase shift δ_2' due to the new film at the *original* fringe wavelength λ_b and noting that

$$\delta_3/\delta_3' = \delta_2/\delta_2'. \tag{35}$$

One finds

$$\xi = \frac{\delta_2'(\epsilon + \delta_3')}{\delta_2' + \delta_3'} \tag{36}$$

$$\eta = \frac{\delta_3'(\epsilon - \delta_2')}{\delta_2' + \delta_3'}. \tag{37}$$

The fringe condition is now given by

$$\frac{d(r_{1a} \cdot r_{1a}^*)}{d\epsilon} = \frac{B - A}{(B+f)^2} \cdot \frac{df}{d\epsilon} = 0 \tag{38}$$

remembering that

$$d\epsilon/d\lambda \neq 0.$$

Hence

$$df/d\epsilon = 0. \tag{39}$$

Differentiation of (34), using (36) and (37), and applying the argument used in deriving eq (11) by placing

$$c = (b - a)/(1 - ab) \tag{40}$$

then gives

$$\sin \epsilon - \frac{b-a}{1-ab} \left[\frac{1+b^2}{b} \cdot \frac{\delta_2'}{\delta_3' + \delta_2'} \sin \xi + \frac{1+a^2}{a} \cdot \frac{\delta_3'}{\delta_3' + \delta_2'} \sin \eta \right.$$
$$\left. + \frac{b-a}{1-ab} \cdot \frac{\delta_3' - \delta_2'}{\delta_2' + \delta_2'} \sin (\eta - \xi) \right] = 0. \tag{41}$$

It is now convenient to eliminate ϵ, ξ, and η, using the definitions, eq (29), together with

$$\lambda_b/\lambda_a = \delta_3/\delta_3' = \delta_2/\delta_2' \tag{42}$$

where λ_a is the new fringe wavelength. It is also convenient to designate the two unknowns x and y:

$$x(n_2, d_2) \equiv \delta_2' \tag{43}$$

$$y(n_2) \equiv r_{12} \equiv a \tag{44}$$

and to define the fringe shift Δ:

$$\Delta = \lambda_a - \lambda_b. \tag{45}$$

Equation (41) then becomes

$$(\delta_3'+x) \sin (\omega x-\theta)+f_1(\delta_3'-x) \sin (-\omega x-\theta)$$
$$+f_2 x \sin \omega x+f_3\delta_3' \sin (-\theta)=0 \quad (46)$$

where

$$\omega=\lambda_b/\lambda_a=1-\Delta/\lambda_a \qquad (47)$$

$$\theta=\delta_3'\Delta/\lambda_a \qquad (48)$$

$$f_1=[(b-y)/(1-by)]^2 \qquad (49)$$

$$f_2=-(b-y)(1+b^2)/b(1-by) \qquad (50)$$

$$f_3=(b-y)(1+y^2)/y(1-by). \qquad (51)$$

6.2. Approximations

a. Simple Approximate Solution to the Fringe Shift Equation

An exact analytical solution to eq (46) has not been obtained, but expansion of the trigonometric functions and neglect of square and higher powers of ωx and θ and their products leads to a quadratic in x that can be solved. The result is

$$x\sim\delta_3' \frac{1-\omega}{\omega} \cdot \frac{b}{1-b^2} \cdot \frac{1-y^2}{y} \qquad (52)$$

and the approximation is equivalent to specifying that x must be less than 6° and the film thickness less than 150 Å. Also, by an equation similar to (14),

$$x=4\pi d_2\beta_2/\lambda_b \qquad (53)$$

where

$$\beta_2^2=n_2^2-\sin^2 \phi. \qquad (54)$$

Combining (52) and (53) one finds

$$d_2=\frac{\Delta}{4\pi\beta_2} \delta_3' \frac{b}{1-b^2} \cdot \frac{1-y^2}{y} \qquad (55)$$

where, it will be recalled, β_2 and y are both functions of the refractive index of the test substance, n_2; Δ is measured experimentally; δ_3' is determined by calibration; b can be calculated from the refractive index of substance 3 and the angle of incidence.

Equation (55) applies to both s- and p-vibrations, and it must now be shown that after inserting the appropriate reflection coefficients d_2 can be eliminated from the two resulting equations and an explicit solution for n_2 obtained.

Substituting (eqs (17) and (18)/,

$$y_s = (\cos\phi - \beta_2)/(\cos\phi + \beta_2) \qquad (56)$$

$$y_p = (n^2\cos_2\phi - \beta_2)/(n_2^2\cos\phi + \beta_2) \qquad (57)$$

one obtains

$$d_2 \sim \frac{1}{\pi}\frac{\cos\phi}{1-n_2^2}\cdot\frac{b_s}{1-b_s^2}\,\delta'_{3s}\Delta_s \qquad (58)$$

$$d_2 \sim \frac{1}{\pi}\cdot\frac{n_2^2\cos\phi}{n_2^4\cos^2\phi - n_2^2 + \sin^2\phi}\cdot\frac{b_p}{1-b_p^2}\,\delta'_{3p}\Delta_p. \qquad (59)$$

Neglecting $n_2^4\cos^2\phi$ and placing $\sin^2\phi \sim 1$,

$$n_2^2 = \frac{b_s}{1-b_s^2}\cdot\frac{1-b_p^2}{b_p}\frac{\delta'_{3s}}{\delta'_{3p}}\cdot\frac{\Delta_s}{\Delta_p} \qquad (60)$$

which gives, on substitution for b_s and b_p, eqs (17) and (18),

$$n_2^2 = \frac{n_3^2}{1+(1+n_3^2)\cos^2\phi}\cdot\frac{\delta'_{3s}}{\delta'_{3p}}\frac{\Delta_s}{\Delta_p}. \qquad (61)$$

If n_3 is 1.5 and ϕ is 81° (values used in the most recent work), we find, calculating the term in n_3 or placing it nearly equal to n_3^2, respectively,

$$n_2 \sim 1.444(\delta'_{3s}\Delta_s/\delta'_{3p}\Delta_p)^{1/2} \sim 1.50(\delta'_{3s}\Delta_s/\delta'_{3p}\Delta_p)^{1/2} \qquad (62)$$

while, from (58)

$$d_2 \sim 0.088\delta'_{3s}\Delta_s/(n_2^2-1). \qquad (63)$$

b. Calibration for Determination of δ'_3

The values of δ'_3 cannot be calculated reliably because the thickness of the dielectric film 3 is not determined solely by the number of double layers transferred; calibration, however, is a simple matter. This is done by measuring the fringe shifts produced by the last one or more substrate double layers prior to deposition of the test film. Preparation of the stepped reflector is stopped when fringes can be observed at some suitable wavelengths λ_{os}, λ_{op}. By eq (19), and abbreviating with

$$\beta_3 = (n_3^2 - \sin^2\phi)^{1/2} \qquad (64)$$

we find

$$\delta'_3 = 4\pi d_{30}\beta_3/\lambda_0. \qquad (65)$$

Upon transfer of N additional double layers of thickness $N\bar{d}$ to both steps of the reflector, the fringe wavelength shifts to the higher value

λ_b in order to keep δ'_3 constant:

$$\delta'_3 = 4\pi(d_{30} + N\bar{d})\beta_3/\lambda_b \tag{66}$$

$$= 4\pi d_3\beta_3/\lambda_b. \tag{67}$$

Eliminating d_{30} and placing

$$\lambda_b - \lambda_0 = \Delta_0 \tag{68}$$

$$\delta'_3 = 4\pi N\bar{d}\beta_3/\Delta_0. \tag{69}$$

Typically, if n_3 is 1.5 and $\bar{d}$ 50 Å,

$$\delta'_3 = 709N/\Delta_0 \tag{70}$$

where the fringe shift is in Å and δ'_3 in radians; δ'_{3s} is somewhat less than 180° and δ'_{3p} somewhat less than 360° (again, compare fig. 2).

c. A More Refined Approximation

For a given value of the fringe shift Δ the exact eq (46) and the simple analytical approximation (52) both represent curves $x(y)$ corresponding to pairs of values of n_2 and d_2. For the special case when the test film has the same refractive index, 1.5, as the substrate (i.e., $y = b$), the exact slope of this curve can be written in simple form and compared with the approximate slope obtained from eq (52). The latter is then modified to conform to the equation for the exact slope, and the modified equation (assumed also to be valid for other values of n_2) is integrated. The resulting improved approximation gives a curve $x(y)$ which (a) coincides with the exact curve when $n_2 = 1.5$; (b) has the same slope as the exact curve when $n_2 = 1.5$; and (c) has the same form as eq (52) in the limit as x approaches zero.

Differentiating (46) and setting $y = b$, one finds

$$f_1 = f_2 = f_3 = 0 \tag{71}$$

$$\sin(\omega x - \theta) \sim 0 \tag{72}$$

$$\cos(\omega x - \theta) \sim 1 \tag{73}$$

$$df_3/dn_2 = -df_2/dn_2 \tag{74}$$

$$df_2/dn_2 = -df_3/dn_2 = \frac{1}{b} \cdot \frac{1+b^2}{1-b^2} \cdot \frac{dy}{dn_2} \tag{75}$$

giving finally

$$\left(\frac{dx}{dn_2}\right)_{1.5} = -\frac{1}{b} \cdot \frac{1+b^2}{1-b^2} \cdot \frac{1}{\omega} (\sin\theta) \left(\frac{dy}{dn_2}\right)_{1.5}. \tag{76}$$

The result of a similar calculation with eq (52) is the same as (76) except for the replacement of sin (θ) by its argument. Assuming (76) to be approximately correct for any n_2 and integrating, we get

$$x = \frac{b}{1-b^2} \cdot \frac{1-y^2}{y} \cdot \frac{\sin \theta}{\omega} + K \tag{77}$$

and, finally, evaluating K by placing n_2 equal to 1.5,

$$x \sim \frac{1}{\omega} \frac{1-y^2}{y} \cdot \frac{b}{1-b^2} \cdot \sin \theta + \theta - \sin \theta. \tag{78}$$

As before, separate expressions for d_2 are now obtained by substituting for y_s and y_p:

$$d_2 = \frac{\lambda_a}{4\pi\beta_2} (\beta_2 F \sin \theta + \theta - \sin \theta) \tag{79}$$

where for the s-step we use λ_{as}, θ_s, and F_s, and for the p-step the corresponding p-terms:

$$F_s = \frac{b_s}{1-b_s^2} \cdot \frac{4 \cos \phi}{1-n_2^2} \tag{80}$$

$$F_p = \frac{b_p}{1-b_p^2} \cdot \frac{4n_2^2 \cos \phi}{n_2^4 \cos^2 \phi - n_2^2 + \sin^2 \phi}. \tag{81}$$

Eliminating d_2 and proceeding without further approximations,

$$\frac{F_s}{F_p} = \frac{D_p}{D_s} + B \cdot \frac{E_p - E_s}{D_s} \tag{82}$$

where

$$D = \lambda_a \sin \theta \tag{83}$$

$$E = \lambda_a(\theta - \sin \theta) \tag{84}$$

$$B = 1/\beta_2 F_p. \tag{85}$$

Equation (82) is quite suitable for calculation of n_2 from the measured fringe shifts, since an approximate value can be obtained by equating D_p/D_s to F_s/F_p, using this to calculate B (approximately) and then applying the complete equation to obtain a second, more accurate value of n_2. The film thickness can then be obtained by eq (79), which may be abbreviated:

$$4\pi d_2 = DF + E/\beta_2. \tag{86}$$

6.3. Methods of Computation; Numerical Examples

The fact that the s- and p-fringe shifts are sufficiently different to permit resolution of film thickness and refractive index is evident

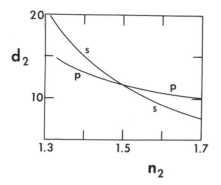

FIGURE 15.   *Plot of* d_2 *versus* n_2 *for* ¼ *added double layer of barium stearate.*

Letters s and p indicate curves obtained from s-fringe and p-fringe equations.   Each curve represents the solutions $d_2(n_2)$ that are compatible with a constant fringe shift, 52.5Å for the s-step and 26.25 Å for the p-step.   (Adapted from ref. 23, fig. 2.)

from the first crude approximation, eq (62), and is illustrated graphically in figure 15.   That the magnitudes of the fringe shifts are sufficient for experimental purposes is evident from the data already presented; some typical sets of values for quick reference are collected in table 6.

The choice of the approximation to use will depend upon the accuracy desired and the time available for computation.   For convenience we restate the several approximate equations for the refractive index and present examples of results obtained by the use of each:

$$F_s/F_p = (D_p/D_s) + B(E_p - E_s)/D_s \qquad (87)$$

$$n_2^2 = n_2^2 (F_s/F_p)(\epsilon_s/\epsilon_p) \qquad (88)$$

$$n_2^2 = b_s(1 - b_p)\ \epsilon_s/b_p(1 - b_s^2)\epsilon_p \qquad (89)$$

$$n_2^2 = 2.25\epsilon_s/\epsilon_p. \qquad (90)$$

In eqs (87) to (89),

$$F_s = [b_s/(1 - b_s^2)][4\ \cos\ \phi/(1 - n_2^2)] \qquad (91)$$

$$F_p = [b_p/(1 - b_p^2)][4n_2^2\ \cos\ \phi/(n_2^4\ \cos^2\ \phi - n_2^2 + \sin^2\ \phi)] \qquad (92)$$

TABLE 6.   *Approximate fringe shifts as a function of film thickness and refractive index*

Calculated by eqs (62) and (63) using $\Delta_s = 420$ and $\Delta_p = 220$ for calibration.

n_2	1.30		1.50		2.0	
d (Å)	Δ_s	Δ_p	Δ_s	Δ_p	Δ_s	Δ_p
23.7	59	40.7	105	55	257	77
95.0	236	163	(420)	(220)	1026	300

$$D = \lambda_a \sin \theta \tag{93}$$

$$E = \lambda_a (\theta - \sin \theta) \tag{94}$$

$$B = 1/\beta_2 F_p \tag{95}$$

$$\epsilon = \delta_3' \Delta = \delta_3' (\lambda_a - \lambda_b) \tag{96}$$

$$\theta = \delta_3' \Delta / \lambda_a = \epsilon / \lambda_a \tag{97}$$

$b \equiv r_{13}$ (eqs (17) and (18)).

The use of successive approximations with eq (87) has been outlined already. Equations (88) and (89) can be used similarly; (88) is simply, in other notation, the result of combining (58) and (59) without omitting $n_2^4 \cos^2 \phi$ and $\sin^2 \phi$, and can be used after a preliminary value of n_2 has been obtained by (89). Equation (90) is of little value since the numerical factor in eq (89) can always be used.

Examples of calculated values of n_2 for several values of Δ_s and Δ_p are collected in table 7. The most reliable values are those in the final column, since Mattuck [22] has shown by direct comparison with the exact eq (46) that eq (87) is reliable to 3 decimal places in n_2. If permanent tables of F_s/F_p are available, some time is saved by using (89) and (88); (90) or (89) alone give only a crude estimate.

TABLE 7. *Film refractive indices calculated from fringe shifts by approximate equations*

					n_2				
Δ_s	Δ_p	Δ_s/Δ_p	λ_{as}	λ_{ap}	Eq (90)	Eq (89)	Eq (88)	Eq (87)	
								1	2
59.0	40.7	1.4496	5059	5048	1.2770	1.3405	1.2956	1.2970	1.2967
105	55	1.0991	5105	5055	1.4655	1.5383	1.4759	1.4773	1.4772
420	220	1.9091	5420	5220	1.4655	1.5383	1.4759	1.4785	1.4768
257	77	3.3377	5257	5077	1.9378	2.0340	1.9055	1.9120	1.9159

$n_2 = 1.510$ and $\phi = 81°$ throughout.

$b_s/(1-b_s^2) = -1.791102.$

$b_p/(1-b_p^2) = -0.722482.$

7. Some Possible Sources of Error

7.1. Dispersion Effects

The dispersion of the metal base has been neglected in the development of the s-p stepped reflector. In this respect the choice of chromium appears to have been fortunate; moreover, it can be assumed

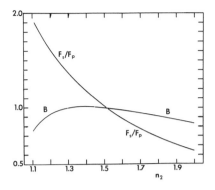

FIGURE 16. *Functions used in calculation of film thickness and refractive index from s-p stepped reflector data, using eq (87), defined in eqs (91), (92), and (95).*

Calculated for films of refractive index n_2 on dielectric of refractive index n_3 equal to 1.51. Angle of incidence, 81°.

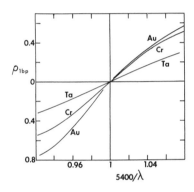

FIGURE 17. *Extinction fringe amplitude profiles for p-vibration incident upon metal slides coated with barium stearate.*

Calculated from eq (23); values for complex Fresnel reflection coefficients r_{3c} calculated from optical constants by equations given by Born and Wolf [11], p. 624 ff. In absence of dispersion effects, fringes are nearly parabolic in vicinity of the extinction position, giving a straight line when plotted in opposite quadrants as in diagram. This is true for Cr and Ta which give fairly symmetrical fringes, but not for Au which gives grossly distorted fringes. All extinctions normalized to occur at 5400 Å. Abscissa, 5400/λ. Ordinate, ρ_{1bp}.

that if the optical constants of the metal vary in a regular manner over the range of wavelengths used, the calibration procedure will minimize dispersion errors. When less regular variations occur, the fringes may become quite unsymmetrical, as shown in the case of gold in figure 17; the effect of this on the fringe shifts has not yet been calculated. Ideally, the angle of incidence for extinction fringes should be independent of wavelength; the extent of actual deviatioan from this is illustrated in figure 18.

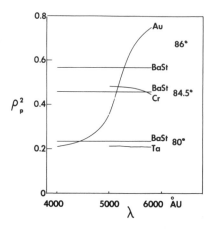

FIGURE 18.   *Reflection coefficients as a function of wavelength.*

The diagrams show that as a result of dispersion the first extinction fringe condition ($r_{13} = \rho_{3c}$, eq (23)) may be dependent upon wavelength.   The assumption that this is not so, used in the theory of the stepped reflector, is very nearly true for tantalum over the range 5000 to 6000 Å, and for chromium between 5000 and 5400, but not for gold at any wavelength between 4000 and 5800 Å.   Horizontal lines give $r_{13}{}^{2}(\equiv\rho_{13}{}^{2})$ for the air-barium stearate interface; closed circles give $\rho^{2}{}_{3c}$ assumed equal to $\rho^{2}{}_{34}$, for the stearate-metal interface. Optical constants of the metals from International Critical Tables and Landolt-Boernstein "Tabellen."

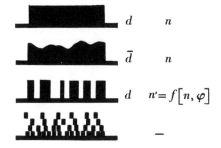

FIGURE 19.   *Film sections illustrating departures from uniformity of thickness and refractive index.*

Second from top, homogeneous film with irregular surface.   Third, film with random pores.   Fourth, film density decreasing with distance from substrate.   (Reproduced from [6].)

7.2. Anisotropy of Dielectric Substrate and Test Film

The theory has been developed for isotropic films, but it is certain that the refractive index of barium stearate, at an angle of incidence 81°, for the p-vibration is about 0.18 higher than for the s-vibration. Mattuck [23] has given approximate fringe shift equations appropriate to this difference and has concluded that errors arising from birefringence will usually be 1 percent or less.   The effects are nevertheless detectable, and some observations on aliphatic acid films already discussed in section 5 have been analyzed in terms of molecular orientation [8].

7.3. Film Heterogeneity

It has been pointed out [6] that the theory envisages plane-parallel homogeneous films with sharp boundaries. However, the existence of (a) skeleton films of stearate [10], (b) of incomplete or mosaic-like films of protein [6], changes in optical properties with thickness [18], and the *n-d* coupling already discussed, all suggest that various types of irregularity may be encountered (fig. 19) and that it may be difficult in practice to detect these or to characterize them. Chemical non-uniformity may exist in the stepped reflector itself; Schaefer [29] has observed periodic variations in the surface properties of BaH stearate multilayers, and it has been noted [8] that with respect to certain polycylic organic compounds the *s*- and *p*-surfaces behave quite differently, so that optical measurements on these substances were impossible.

8. Conclusion

The outcome of these investigations has been a method that, within certain clearly defined limits, should be very serviceable for the study of dielectric films of thickness greater than a few angstroms, and of index of refraction between 1.1 and 2.0. Certain technical improvements and certain other developments are of course to be expected. The former should include development of stepped reflectors with isotropic dielectric layers, preferably with zero and first-order steps on the same slide as an aid to the detection of differences of surface reactivity with changing thickness.

For the biologist two matters will be of special interest. The first is the need, in many types of investigation, to characterize thin test films placed upon the stepped reflector and then to observe their ability to take up additional material by adsorption or chemical attachment. The determination of the optical constants of a second or a third test film requires a modification of the fringe equations that has not yet been attempted, although the basic theory of multiple layers is available [18].

The second matter of biological interest is the possibility of characterizing films at the liquid-solid interface. This presents special difficulties because the extinction fringe condition ($r_{13} = r_{3c}$) occurs at rather higher angles of incidence than in air: $\phi_s \sim 88°$, $\phi_p \sim 83°$ for the system water-barium stearate-chromium. A solution to the problem exists in principle; if the reflector is composed of a dielectric material (medium 4 in fig. 15) of refractive index equal to that of water, r_{13} is equal to r_{34} at all angles of incidence, so that there should be no difficulty in obtaining extinction fringes with suitable thicknesses of barium stearate. In practice, the only solid substance said to have a sufficiently low refractive index, polytetrafluoroethylene, also possesses undesirable optical and chemical properties.

In all these matters, it need hardly be said, the biologist depends upon the work of the physicists, and we have made this contribution to the *Symposium on the Ellipsometer and Its Use in the Measurement*

332 BATEMAN

of Surfaces and Thin Films in the hope that the solutions to some of our problems may be present, or implicit, in the work that others will be describing on this interesting occasion.

In preparing this paper, the author has made use of the published work and the notebooks of his former colleagues R. E. Hartman and R. D. Mattuck. He also acknowledges with thanks the cooperation of E. D. Adams, T. T. Bannister, A. Calio, E. J. Covington, Roberta S. Hartman, K. Larson, R. L. Parker, R. D. Petti, and A. Rosen, who in varying degrees have been responsible for much of the experimental work, and that of H. R. Peplow in some of the calculations. The standard tables for the stepped reflector were calculated by the Biomathematics Division, Fort Detrick; the friendly help of Mr. V. S. Palmer and Mr. G. I. Eccles is acknowledged.

9. References

[1] F. Abelès, Sur la détermination des indices et des épaisseurs des couches minces, Compt. rend. Acad. Sci. (Paris) **228,** 553–555 (1949).
[2] F. Abelès, La détermination de l'indice et de l'épaisseur des couches minces transparentes, J. Phys. Rad. **11,** 310–314 (1950).
[3] F. Abelès, Methods for determining optical parameters of thin films, Progr. in Optics, **2,** 249–288 (1963).
[4] J. W. Anderegg, W. W. Beeman, S. Shulman, and P. Kaesberg, An investigation of the size, shape and hydration of serum albumin by small-angle X-ray scattering, J. Am. Chem. Soc. **77,** 2927–2937 (1955).
[5] W. E. Bachmann, The synthesis of compounds related to 1,2-benzanthracene and cholanthrene, J. Org. Chem. **3,** 434–447 (1938).
[6] J. B. Bateman, E. D. Adams, The thickness and refractive index of plasma albumin films on stearate, J. Phys. Chem. **61,** 1039–1049 (1957).
[7] J. B. Bateman, Continuous and disperse films of bovine plasma albumin on stearate, Proc. first nat. Biophysics Conf., 298–313 Yale Univ. Press, New Haven, Conn. (1959).
[8] J. B. Bateman, E. J. Covington, Molecular tilt in fatty acid multilayers, J. Coll. Sci. **16,** 531–548 (1961).
[9] K. B. Blodgett, Properties of built-up films of barium stearate, J. Phys. Chem. **41,** 975–984 (1937).
[10] K. B. Blodgett, I. Langmuir, Built-up films of barium stearate and their optical properties, Phys. Rev. **51,** 964–982 (1937).
[11] M. Born, E. Wolf, Principles of Optics, Pergamon Press, New York, N.Y., 1959.
[12] H. J. Deuel, The Lipids. Vol. I. Chemistry. Interscience Publishers, Inc., New York, p. 103 ff. (1961).
[13] P. Doty, and E. P. Geiduschek, Optical Properties of Proteins, in The Proteins, ed. H. Neurath and K. Bailey, Vol. I, Part A. Academic Press, New York (1953).
[14] P. Drude, Ueber Oberflaechenschichten. II. Theil. Ann. Physik u. Chem., Neue Folge **36,** 865–897 (1889).
[15] Handbook of Chemistry and Physics, 1961–2, 43d ed., Chemical Rubber Publishing Co., Cleveland, Ohio.
[16] R. E. Hartman, The fringes of equal reflection coefficient ratio and their application to the determination of the thickness and refractive index of monomolecular films. I. Theory. J. Opt. Soc. Am. **44,** 192–196 (1954).
[17] R. E. Hartman, R. S. Hartman, K. Larson, and J. B. Bateman, The fringes of equal reflection coefficient ratio and their application to the determina-

ation of the thickness and refractive index of monomolecular films. II. The determination of the thickness and refractive index of barium stearate double layers. J. Opt. Soc. Am. **44,** 197–198 (1954).

[18] O. S. Heavens, Optical Properties of Thin Solid Films, Academic Press, New York (1955).

[19] I. Langmuir, The Collected Works of Irving Langmuir, Vol. 9: Surface Phenomena. Pergamon Press, New York, N.Y. (1961).

[20] B. W. Low, The Structure and Configuration of Amino Acids, Peptides and Proteins, in The Proteins, ed. H. Neurath and K. Bailey, Vol. 1, Part A. Academic Press, New York (1953).

[21] F. A. Lucy, Studies of surface film by reflection of polarized light. I. A more rigorous algebraic method for computing results, J. Chem. Phys. **16,** 167–174, (1948).

[22] R. D. Mattuck, Recent attempts to determine the thickness and refractive index of unimolecular films, J. Opt. Soc. Am. **46,** 615–620 (1956).

[23] R. D. Mattuck, A stepped interference reflector for determining the optical constants of non-absorbing unimolecular films. I. Theory, J. Opt. Soc. Am. **46,** 621–628 (1956).

[24] R. D. Mattuck, R. D. Petti, J. B. Bateman, A stepped interference reflector for determining the optical constants of non-absorbing unimolecular films. films. II. Experimental, J. Opt. Soc. Am. **46,** 782–789 (1956).

[25] F. L. McCrackin, E. Passaglia, R. R. Stromberg, and H. L. Steinberg, Measurement of the thickness and refractive index of very thin films and the optical properties of surfaces by ellipsometry, J. Res. NBS **67A,** 363–377 (1963).

[26] P. Putzeys, and J. Brosteaux, L'indice de réfraction des protéides, Bull. Soc. Chim. Biol. **18,** 1681–1703 (1936).

[27] E. K. Rideal, Discussion on surface phenomena, Proc. Roy. Soc., London **A155,** 684–690 (1936).

[28] E. K. Rideal, Surface action in biology, Nature **140,** 671–672 (1937).

[29] V. J. Schaefer, Studies of surface properties by the light scattering of deposited liquid films, J. Phys. Chem. **45,** 681–701 (1941).

[30] T. Schoon, Polymorphe Formen kristalliner Kohlenstoffverbindungen mit langen gestreckten Ketten (Nach Strukturuntersuchungen durch Elektronenbeugung), Z. phys. Chem. **39B,** 385- 410 (1938); Strukturber. **6,** 238–240 (1938).

[31] A. F. Turner, Some current developments in multilayer optical films. J. Phys. Rad. **11,** 444–460 (1950).

[32] J. Wagman, and J. B. Bateman, The behavior of the botulinus toxins in the ultracentrifuge. Arch. Biochem. Biophys. **31,** 424–430 (1951).

Discussion

A. BAIDINS (E. I. du Pont de Nemours and Co.):

Generally it is assumed that large molecules are adsorbed vertically and weakly on surfaces of low energy and horizontally on surfaces of high energy. As barium stearate has a very low surface energy, I wonder why all the protein molecules are adsorbed horizontally.

J. B. BATEMAN:

The protein molecule can be considered to be an assembly of polar and nonpolar groups covalently linked. In an aqueous environment, the molecule assumes a configuration in which the ambient water has the greatest possible opportunity, consistent with stereochemical limitations, to interact with the polar groups, while the nonpolar groups participate in internal hydrophobic interactions. In presence of a hydrocarbon-water interface, however, it is thermodynamically advantageous for the nonpolar groups to form hydrophobic associa-

tions with the hydrocarbon since this decreases the area of the interface occupied by water molecules. This explanation, of course,
detracts somewhat from the significance of the apparent correlation
between film thickness and the small molecular dimension, since
emergence of the previously buried nonpolar groups is likely to be
accompanied by a certain amount of distortion of the "native"
molecule.

Blood Coagulation Studies With the Recording Ellipsometer

L. Vroman

Veterans Administration Hospital, Brooklyn, N.Y.

An ellipsometer was used which records the difference between outputs of one phototube receiving light passed by the polarizer only and one at the end of the light path. Polished silicon crystal slices and anodized tantalum sputtered glass slides were used as reflecting surfaces, with and without treatment to affect wettability. Out of solution, blood plasma was shown to be adsorbed, and then, only if containing both intact clotting factors XI and XII, partially desorbed again, in agreement with current coagulation theories. Other series demonstrated the adsorption and polymerization of fibrinogen by films of thrombin. Though macroscopically visible fibrin formed on the slides, instrument recordings and minimum settings revealed that only a film with a thickness equivalent to less than 400 Å of barium stearate was adsorbed, indicating that polymerization took place only at a fraction of the interface.

1. Introduction

The coagulation of blood is generally regarded as a chain of reactions among several proteins; it is thought to be initiated at glass or other wettable solid surfaces by adsorption of one specific protein, named factor XII. This adsorbed factor in turn apparently adsorbs factor XI, and the resulting "activation product" of the two proteins may stay at the interface [1] [1] or be released [2]. The problem appears to cry out for ellipsometric observations, but no studies have thus far been reported in which physical measurement of the adsorbed layer and its release was attempted.

The ellipsometrist should also be attracted by the last phase of· coagulation, in which the enzyme thrombin removes peptide groups from fibrinogen molecules, thus transforming them into fibrinogen monomers; these will then polymerize to form macroscopically visible fibrin.

Like other proteins, those involved in coagulation must contain amino acid residues with varying degree of polarity; after adsorption of a protein from bulk solution onto predominantly polar or apolar solid surfaces, and its more apolar or polar groups are exposed to reactants in solution, further reactivity of the film may indicate which type of residues is most involved [3]. Specific coagulation tests using hydrophobic and hydrophilic powders as adsorbents, as well as other approaches including ellipsometry to some extent, have suggested that certain coagulation factors are more active at hydrophilic interfaces, and that exposure of hydrophobic bonds may be involved in coagulation [4, 5, 6]. We therefore decided to obtain

---

[1] Figures in brackets indicate the literature references on p. 347.

ellipsometric recordings of surface "activation" and of the thrombin-fibrinogen reaction at both hydrophilic and hydrophobic interfaces.

2. Technique

2.1. Instrument

The elements of our recording ellipsometer (Rudolph & Sons, Inc., Caldwell, N.J.; model #436–200E) are arranged as follows: Mercury light source; filter passing the 5461 Å line; polarizer (reading to 0.1°); beamsplitter passing adjustable amount of light to photo-multiplier tube a (IP 21); specimen holder (see below); quarter-wave plate; analyzer (both reading to 0.01°); plate allowing selection between a telescope and photomultiplier tube b. The specimen holder consists of a clamp allowing a slide to be moved vertically along a scale and into a strainfree glass cuvette; a 300-rpm motor for stirring; and a base on which the assembly can rotate or slide in the horizontal plane for adjustment.

The signals from tubes a and b are amplified and their difference serves as input for a voltmeter (Photovolt #520SP) and a recorder (Honeywell #KSC153x17; recording speed ½ in. per minute).

2.2. Reflecting Surfaces

(a) Glass slides, vacuum sputtered with tantalum (kindly provided by Dr. B. H. Vromen, Bell Tel. Labs., Inc., Murray Hill, N.J.) were anodized in 0.01 percent nitric acid at room temperature until appearing violet (zero order) when viewed in air with daylight at about 45° incidence. The slides were washed, air-dried, and returned to the anodizing bath with only about ³⁄₁₆ in. submerged while the potential was increased less than 1 V, to create an oxide "step" near the end of the slide. This step served for calibration of the recorder (described below). Before use, the slides were cleaned with a detergent (Sparkleen, Fisher Sc., N.Y.), rinsed with tap and distilled water, air-dried, and passed five times over the blue section of a Bunsen flame. They were quite wettable and are indicated in this text as TaW. To render them hydrophobic, they were covered with a solution of ligno-ceric acid in benzene, dried, and then polished vigorously, or dipped in and out of a compressed film of barium lignocerate on a Langmuir tray. These nonwettable slides are indicated as TaN.

(b) Silicon crystal slices with one surface polished optically flat (kindly provided by Dr. R. J. Archer, Bell Tel. Labs., Murray Hill, N.J.) were cleaned as follows: washed three times in boiling benzene, placed in concentrated nitric acid which was then brought to near boiling, rinsed with large amounts of distilled water, dipped for 15 to 20 secs in concentrated HF, and again rinsed in distilled water. These hydrophobic surfaces are indicated below as SiN. They could be rendered wettable by again heating in concentrated nitric acid, followed by rinsing with large amounts of distilled water and air drying. Such slides are indicated as SiW.

(c) Other surfaces, which yielded curves of desired sensitivity but are not reported here, were titanium-coated glass slides, with and without oxide film, and anodized tantalum slides treated with ferric or barium stearate. The latter was avoided as a substrate in this study because of its possible removal by plasma albumin under our conditions [7].

2.3. Optimal Conditions

With the polarizer at 135° and our slides submerged in a mixture of 1 part veronal buffer (pH 7.4) to 4 parts of 0.85 percent NaCl at room temperature (22 to 26 °C), greatest sensitivity was obtained at 75° incidence. All observations reported below were made under these conditions. Optimal settings for recording were sought by plotting quarter-wave plate and analyzer positions against recorder readings, using first a blank surface and then one on which various proteins had been adsorbed (figs. 1 and 2). As a compromise between

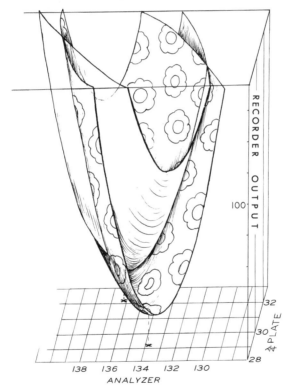

FIGURE 1. *Analyzer and quarter wave plate readings plotted against recorder output; values of the latter beyond 100 obtained by zero adjustment of instrument.*

Blank shape: blank TaW slide. Flowered shape: same surface after completing adsorption from 0.067% Thrombin Topical. 2 crosses on X/Y plane indicate minimum light settings for blank and coated slide.

maximum sensitivity as well as linearity, and ability of the beam-splitter to balance a large light output, a position of the analyzer 6° above or below minimum setting was decided upon; the quarter-wave plate was maintained at minimum position, and a 1-mm aperture was used to collimate the reflected light.

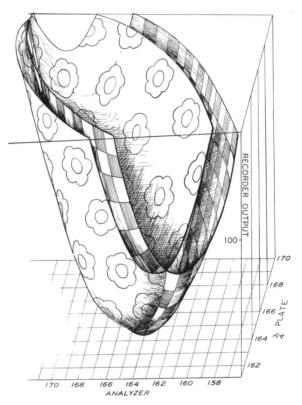

FIGURE 2.   *Construction as of figure 1.*

Checkered shape: blank SiW surface. Flowered shape: same surface after completing adsorption from 1.3% serum.

2.4. Calibration

Barium stearate layers, compressed by 23.5 dynes, were prepared on a modified Langmuir trough [8], and deposited as 1, 3, and 5 monomolecular layers on clean TaW and SiW, and as 2 and 4 layers onto TaN and SiN slides. Ta slides were dipped at right angles to their extra oxide steps, so that the effects of stearate and oxide steps, upon the minimum transmitted light position of the analyzer could be compared.   The stearate layers were then removed and the oxide step could serve as a permanent calibrated property of the slide, allowing adjustment of the recorder span at the onset of each experiment as described below. Since the Si slices could not be provided with permanent steps, the relationship between blank surface and stearate layer was noted by its effect on minimum transmitted light position of the analyzer as well as by the recorded change in light output when the slide was shifted from stearate to blank under experimental conditions. Both the specific anodized *Ta* slide used in the present experiments, and the Si slides, happened to demand a change of 0.1° in analyzer position per 3 Å of barium stearate, when observed under the conditions given above. However, we would be disregarding the large differences between refractive indices of tantalum oxide, barium stearate, and protein if we listed the recorded light and analyzer changes as changes in actual film thickness. Instead, we will use the term *basta* to indicate Ba Stearate Ångström, being the number of Ångströms of compressed barium stearate film which would cause the same change in Δ and ψ (ψ being the analyzer azimuth), and the same recorder pen travel under the same recording conditions.

2.5. Experiments

Actual tests were run as follows: the slide was lowered in buffer mixture as described and positioned for light incident at 75°; minimum position of analyzer and quarter-wave plate were determined; the analyzer was turned 6° up or down; the beamsplitter filter was adjusted to bring the meter back to 0; the recorder was actuated; when Ta oxide surface was used, the slide was moved up briefly, causing the recorder to deflect so that its span could be set to the desired value (80% of total scale for an oxide step of 24 basta); if an Si slice was used, the recorder span was adjusted to give a certain deviation when the analyzer was moved from 6° to 7° off minimal position (1° giving 80% of total scale). The recorder was run for several minutes with the blank slide in buffer mixture; then the sample was added. When the recording indicated that adsorption or desorption had ceased, the instrument was briefly switched from recorder to meter, and minimum positions of quarter-wave plate and analyzer were determined. The values obtained, as well as our ability to record more or less symmetrical recordings when repeating experiments with the analyzer at symmetrical deviations from minimum, indicated that the direction of recorder deviations represented that of actual optical thickness changes at the film and not turbidity or other phenomena that would affect light output.

3. Results

3.1. Surface Activation

If certain presumptions quoted in our introduction [1, 2] are correct, it must be possible to show a difference between adsorption of intact and of glass-activated plasma. For example, if intact factor XII,

TABLE 1. *Change in compensating analyzer position, and its barium stearate equivalent in angstroms, after adsorption and desorption of intact plasma*

Slide	Sample	Degree change in analyzer	±	Std. dev.	Equivalent of compressed BaStea	N*
					$\overset{\circ}{A}$	
TaW	Intact normal plasma_____	1.90	±	0.25	57	13
TaW	Spontaneous desorption of intact normal plasma___	.44	±	.27	13	13
TaW	Intact Ba stearate treated plasma_____	1.91	±	.18	57	11
SiW	Intact normal plasma _____	1.13	±	.07	34	4
SiW	Spontaneous desorption of intact normal plasma___	.16	±	.04	5	4

*N=number of experiments.

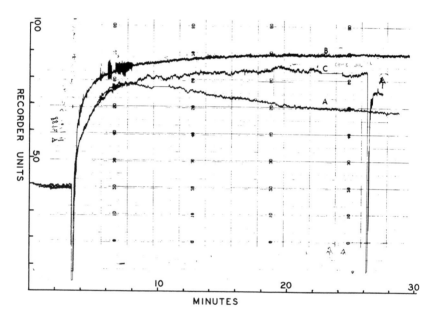

FIGURE 3. *Superimposed photocopies of recordings.*

Curve A: adsorption and spontaneous desorption of intact plasma. B: adsorption of activated plasma. C: adsorption of barium stearate treated plasma.

once adsorbed, will in turn adsorb intact factor XI, after which the XI–XII product is released, the adsorption of intact plasma at the proper concentration will come to an optimum, and then show a decrease, while no decrease will be shown by plasma which has been activated. This was indeed found (table 1; fig. 3, curves A & B): when 1 ml of citrated, intact plasma was added to the 60 ml buffer mixture in the cuvette, adsorption onto TaW and onto Si slides started at a rate of much more than 10 basta per minute but decreased rapidly and appeared to cease after about 2 to 6 min, when about 40 to 60 basta had been adsorbed; this was followed by slow desorption of about 5 to 15 basta (fig. 3, curve A). Adsorption of plasma which had been shaken gently with 1 part of quartz powder (3 to 5 μ, Engelhard, Newark, N.J.) or Speedex (Great Lakes Carbon Corp., Los Angeles, Calif.) for 10 min and then centrifuged, was not followed by desorption (fig. 3, curve B). Specific coagulation tests, to be published elsewhere, indicated that the quartz or Speedex treatment had indeed activated our plasma. Presumably, the "activation product" of factors XII and XI had formed and was at least partially released by the powder; during subsequent ellipsometry, either no intact factor XII was left available for adsorption, or no intact factor XI was left to remove adsorbed factor XII.

It appeared likely that desorption began before adsorption of the intact plasma was completed; separation of the two processes in time to reveal the full extent of each would be possible if plasma could be prepared which contained intact factor XII but no factor XI activity. Treatment of normal intact plasma with barium stearate powder (neutral, Witco Chem. Co., N.Y.) did yield such a preparation [9]. Fifty milligrams of the powder per milliliter of plasma was rubbed into suspension at room temperature, and removed by high-speed centrifugation after 20 min. Such plasma showed adsorption onto our slides; no spontaneous desorption followed (fig. 3, curve C). About 10 min after adsorption had ceased, 1 ml untreated intact plasma (therefore containing intact factor XI as well as XII), was

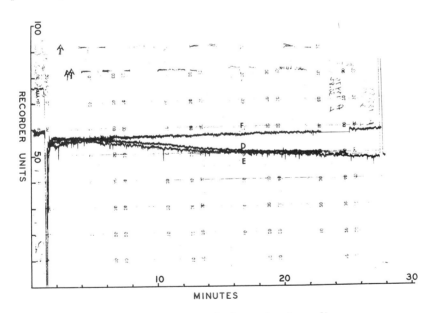

FIGURE 4. *Superimposed photocopies of recordings.*

Effect of the following upon films of barium stearate treated intact plasma. Curve D. removal of film by whole intact plasma. E: removal of film by "activated" congenitally factor XII deficient plasma. F: no removal by whole activated plasma.

added to the cuvette; removal of some of the substrate followed (fig. 4, curve D).   A substrate which lacked intact factor XII, such as a film deposited by barium stearate-treated *serum* instead of plasma, or by barium stearate-treated *activated* plasma, could not be removed by untreated intact plasma.   This would indicate that intact factor XI does not remove substrate unless it contains intact factor XII.

A substrate which presumably did contain intact factor XII (being deposited by barium stearate treated intact plasma) could not be removed by plasma which had been activated with Speedex or quartz (fig. 4, curve F).   All factor XI in this plasma may have been changed during its reaction with factor XII by the activating Speedex treatment.   However, when congenitally factor XII deficient plasma was treated with Speedex, it was still able to remove adsorbate left by barium stearate-treated intact plasma (fig. 4, curve E).   This finding fits the theory that in absence of factor XII, factor XI cannot be activated [1, 2].   On TaN slides, adsorption of intact plasma was only rarely followed by measurable desorption, but results were erratic and better temperature control for this substrate may be required.

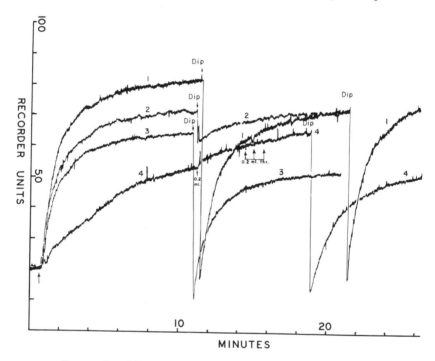

FIGURE 5.   *Adsorption of Thrombin Topical; recorder tracings.*

Curve 1: TaW slide, 1 ml 0.4% thrombin added to cuvette at 0 minutes.   Dipping causes second adsorption curve.   Curve 2: TaN slide, same treatment.   Dipping causes instantaneous increment.   Curve 3: as curve 2, but liquid in cuvette covered with plastic film.   Instantaneous increment prevented.   Curve 4: 0.2 ml amounts of thrombin added at zero, 14 and 18 to 20 minutes.   Upon dipping, new adsorption slope reflects total thrombin concentration.   (Reproduced from [6].)

3.2. Thrombin-Fibrinogen Reaction

(a) Adsorption of Thrombin

Two preparations of thrombin were used: Thrombin topical (bovine, approximately 5,000 N.I.H. units per 200 mg, Parke Davis & Co., Detroit, Mich.), a rather crude preparation, and resin thrombin (7,100 U/ml, 25,400 U/mg tyrosine), kindly supplied by Dr. W. H. Seegers, Detroit, Mich. One milliliter of a 0.4 percent solution of the former in saline or 0.1 ml of the latter were added per 60 ml buffer mixture. The crude preparation yielded rather convex adsorption curves (fig. 5, curves 1–3), while the purified (resin thrombin) sample showed quite linear adsorption rates (fig. 6). Into both preparations, TaW and TaN slides could be dipped deeper after adsorption at the observed site appeared complete; thus, whereas the first observation was made on the slide placed into buffer mixture before protein solution was added, the second observation showed adsorption upon a section of the slide submerged more than 20 min after protein solution had been admixed.

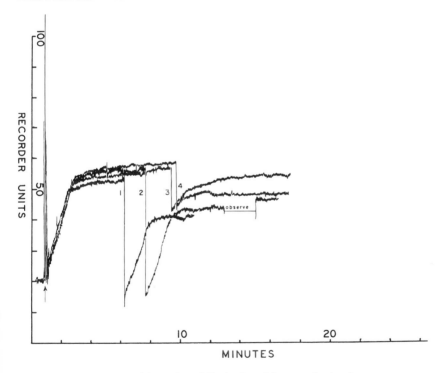

FIGURE 6.   *Adsorption of Resin thrombin; recorder tracings.*

Curves 1 and 2: adsorption onto TaW; curves 3 and 4: adsorption onto TaN.   At "observe", instrument was switched temporarily to observe by telescope, or to read analyzer and quarter wave plate angles at minimum light transmission.   (Reproduced from [6].)

This technique revealed that adsorption upon sections of TaW slides submerged after adding the thrombin proceeded quite similarly to adsorption upon sections which had been submerged into the buffer mixture before thrombin was added; but when TaN slides were dipped deeper in the protein solution, they appeared to have become coated immediately with a layer of about 20 to 35 basta (fig. 5, curve 2; fig. 6, curves 3 and 4), upon which only a small additional amount was adsorbed. By floating a fitted piece of polyethylene film on the thrombin solution in the cell and dipping the TaN slide through a narrow slot in this plastic film, "instantaneous adsorption" could be prevented, and the initial adsorption curve repeated itself completely after dipping (fig. 5, curve 3). These findings suggest that a film, presumably of protein, had formed at the air/liquid interface; it was dragged down by the hydrophobic slides but not by the hydrophilic ones.

The progressive dipping technique also allowed a comparison between adsorption rates at various concentrations in the same cuvette. For example, repeated addition of 0.2 ml amounts of thrombin yielded a lower rate of adsorption onto a TaW slide; dipping the slide deeper showed an adsorption rate corresponding to the total concentration of added thrombin (fig. 5, curve 4).

Under these conditions 45 to 70 basta of thrombin were adsorbed on TaW and TaN slides in 30 min, and 30 to 40 basta onto SiW and SiN slides. In one experiment, a TaW slide was dipped into 400 mg/100 ml instead of 6.7 mg/100 ml crude thrombin, and a total of 54 basta was adsorbed rapidly.

(b) Adsorption of Fibrinogen Onto Thrombin

As a source of fibrinogen, either a fresh, centrifuged, and decanted 0.3 percent solution of human fraction I (Mann Res. Labs., N.Y.) in 0.85 percent NaCl, or normal ACD plasma was used as follows. Slides onto which thrombin had been adsorbed to equilibrium, were rinsed with buffer mixture and, while wet, submerged into a clean cuvette of buffer mixture; the stirrer too was cleaned before reuse. Recording and minimum quarter-wave plate and analyzer readings rarely revealed significant thickness changes of thrombin as a result of this treatment; if these were found, the experiment was repeated. When a thrombin coated slide had shown no change for several minutes, 1 ml of fraction I or 0.2 ml of plasma was added to the cuvette.

In a few experiments, adsorption of concentrated fibrinogen onto thrombin was observed by dipping thrombin coated slides into undiluted plasma or into a 300 mg/100 ml solution of fraction I. From the dilute solutions, all types of thrombin-coated slides except TaN adsorbed about 50 basta in 50 min (fig. 7), and from the concentrated samples, about 150 to 250 basta. In all instances however, after about 40 min of contact between thrombin film and fibrinogen or plasma solution, the TaW, SiW, and SiN slides began to grow grossly visible beards of fibrin, waving in the stirred solution and causing the light output to oscillate and to decrease; yet Δ and ψ did not con-

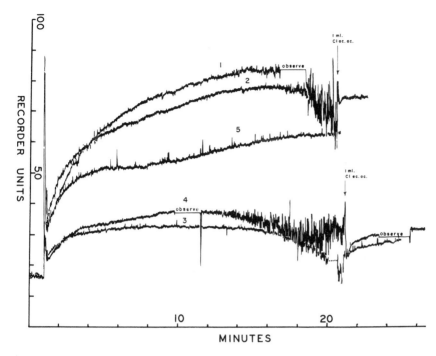

FIGURE 7.   *Adsorption of plasma onto Resin thrombin; recorder tracings.*

Curves 1 to 4 are continuations of the correspondingly numbered curves in Fig. 6.   Curves 1, 2 and 5: plasma on thrombin on TaW slides.   Curves 3 and 4: plasma on thrombin on TaN slides.   Cl ac.ac.: nonochloro-acetic acid 1½, 1 ml added at arrow.   Note absence of oscillations from then on.   (Reproduced from [6].)

tinue changing beyond the indication that the equivalent of a mono molecular layer of fibrinogen had been deposited upon the thrombin [6].

When thrombin had been deposited upon TaN slides, it appeared able to attract the usual amount of fibrinogen in a fibrinogen solution and cause it to form fibrin, but out of whole plasma such thrombin films could only adsorb about 20 basta and did not form visible fibrin.

4. Evaluation of Results

4.1. Optical Versus Actual Thickness of Films

Some of the preceding papers in this volume have dealt thoroughly with the problem of obtaining both thickness and refractive index by ellipsometer measurements.   By merely noting Δ and ψ values on our recordings where an obtained equilibrium allowed time for such observations, we have delayed our encounter with this problem until computer programs such as described here by McCrackin and Colson [11], Archer [12], and others may be available to us; we are not reporting these values now. We did gain the impression that the most delicate change recorded, namely the "desorption" of intact plasma, was accompanied by analyzer (see table 1) and quarter-wave plate setting changes which were too small to show statistically significant mutual relationships; from these we must predict that our measurements could not have been accurate enough to tell whether thickness or refractive index was affected most during desorption.

In our use of barium stearate steps for the calibration of slides, too, we confined ourselves to the values of compensating analyzer position and recorded light output, without referring to quarter-wave plate settings. We may therefore not be allowed to equate basta units on Ta with those on Si slides.

4.2. Validity and Meaning of Results

In spite of the restrictions given above, correlation between recording and analyzer values indicates that true optical thickness changes were observed though not accurately measured. If so, the finding that only a substrate containing intact factor XII can be removed in part only by a solution containing intact factor XI, agrees alarmingly well with the current opinion of coagulationists, that intact factor XI must form a complex with adsorbed intact factor XII. Release of the complex (activation product) then may leave holes in the film that can be refilled by more intact factor XII, and the process may continue—as some preliminary ellipsometry studies are indicating—until the supply of intact factors XI and/or XII is exhausted.

Plasma or serum treated with barium stearate powder was found to have solubilized a significant amount of fatty acid. It was conceivable that such plasma would carry this contaminant to the interface, and that subsequently added intact plasma would remove this stearic acid. The various control tests, including use of stearate treated serum instead of plasma as a substrate, or of albumin instead of intact plasma to remove the adsorbate with, and of various states of activation, all yielded results pointing away from implication of such a nonspecific interaction. Yet, further studies, preferably with purified intact factor XII, may yield further information, such as its need for orientation at the interface. Our intact plasma behaved similarly on SiW and on SiN; this may have been due to its rather high dilution, allowing factor XII to spread upon the surface with all its amino acid residues available, whether resting prone or supine. Studies with higher plasma concentrations, as well as with metal interfaces (allowing application of electrostatic charges) are in progress. We are hoping that others will develop some rapid technique for actual thickness measurement; we shall be eager to see then if our spontaneous desorption of intact plasma is actually the production of small holes in our film, accompanied by a drop of refractive index only.

The thrombin-fibrinogen reaction, though perhaps not interfacial by nature, was a rewarding subject for ellipsometry because of the apparent discrepancy between progressive macroscopic fibrin formation and unchanging optical thickness. The most likely explanation for this finding may be that once a monomolecular layer of fibrinogen is deposited upon the thrombin film, rapid polymerization of the now forming fibrinogen monomers takes place only at certain points on the film; thus, the isolated strands of fibrin growing to relatively very great and random lengths will merely be recorded as a loss of total light, but they will not affect the Δ and ψ values of undisturbed film.

The complex of events leading from surface activation to thrombin formation have not been discussed here, because measurements in this area were not yet attempted. Some involve a phospholipid. Its physiological orientation in suspension, as well as that of proteins reacting with it during clotting, will be tested in future by observing their interactions at hydrophilic and hydrophobic interfaces in the ellipsometer, and compared with "breath pattern" [10, 4] and other studies.

The technical assistance of Miss Ann Lukosevicius is gratefully acknowledged.

5. References

[1] B. A. Waaler, Scand. J. Clin. & Lab. Invest **11** (Suppl. 37), 1–130 (1959).
[2] P. Ollendorff, Scand. J. Clin. & Lab. Invest **14** 641–647 (1962).
[3] J. B. Bateman, H. E. Calkins, and L. A. Chambers, J. Immunol. **41** 321–341 (1941).
[4] L. Vroman, Nature **196** 476 (1962).
[5] L. Vroman, A possible role of hydrophobic bonds in coagulation proteins, 11th Annual Symp. on Blood, Wayne State Univ. Coll. of Medicine, Detroit (1963).
[6] L. Vroman, Effects of hydrophobic surfaces upon blood coagulation, Thromb. Diath. Haemorrhag. **10** 455–493 (1964).
[7] H. Sobotka, R. Santamaria, and M. Demeny, Interactions of molecular layers of fatty acids with urea treated serum albumin, Proc. 2d Intern. Congr. of Surface activity, 307–309 (1957).
[8] I. H. Sher, and J. D. Chanley, Rev. Sci. Instr. **26** 266–268 (1955).
[9] L. Vroman, Surface Contact and Thromboplastin Formation, Thesis, Utrecht, The Netherlands (1958).
[10] A. Rothen, Surface Film Techniques, in Physical Techniques in Biological Research, ed. G. Oster and A. W. Pollister, Academic Press, New York (1956). Vol. II, 193–194.
[11] F. L. McCrackin, and J. P. Colson, this publication, p. 61.
[12] R. J. Archer, J. Opt. Soc. Am. **52** 970–977 (1962).

Ellipsometry for Frustrated Total Reflection

T. R. Young and J. M. Fath

National Bureau of Standards
Washington, D.C. 20234

In the field of precise length measurement there exists the need to measure precisely the proximity of two surfaces, nominally "in contact." Often at least one of these surfaces transmits light. For instance, in the interferometric determinations of the lengths of metallic end standards, called gage blocks, one of the end surfaces may be contacted to a transparent plate and the optical length between the plate and the other end surface of the gage block is determined. By correcting for the phase-change difference of the two dissimilar surfaces, the practical length may be determined from the optical length. Therefore the practical length of the gage block is dependent upon the thickness of the film between the two contacting surfaces. The relationship between this wringing film thickness and its effect upon incident parallel and perpendicular polarization has been theoretically determined for the case where the light is incident upon the first surface (transmitting surface) at an angle greater than the critical angle and where the second surface is metallic (complex index). The theoretical results indicate that when the optical constants of the two contacting surfaces and the wringing film are known, a polarization analysis of the reflected light by the methods of ellipsometry offers an extremely sensitive and unique determination of the wringing film thickness. Attempts to verify the theory experimentally are discussed.

1. Theory

In the field of precise length measurement there exists the need to measure precisely the proximity of two surfaces that are " n contact." Frequently at least one of the surfaces transmits light. For instance, in the interferometric determinations of the lengths of metallic end standards, called gage blocks, one of the end surfaces may be contacted to a transparent plate and the optical length between the plate and the other end surface of the gage block is determined. After correction of the phase-change difference between the two dissimilar surfaces, the practical length is obtained from the optical length. This practical length is therefore dependent upon the thickness of the film between the two contacting surfaces.

Measured values of wringing film thicknesses range from -2.4 to $+2.8$ μin. for lapped metallic surfaces [1].[1] The negative values are explained as being caused by an intermeshing of the high points of the surfaces. Some of this inconsistency in results might be due to the use of questionable assumptions; however, there is a distinct possibility that wringing film thickness is dependent upon the material forming the surface, the planeness of the surfaces involved, and the surface finish. There is agreement among many investigators

---

[1] Figures in brackets indicate the literature references on p. 358.

that the thickness of a wringing film between two given surfaces is repeatable to a fraction of a microinch [1, 2, 3].

Thus it is obvious that in the measurement of the practical length of gage blocks to an accuracy of 0.1μ in., stringent control and measurement of wringing film thicknesses are required. What seems to be required is a measurement facility that will directly determine the wringing film thickness between two surfaces to an accuracy better than 0.01 interference fringe (0.1 μin.). Extension of fundamental physical theory led to the method of frustrated total reflection to measure these quantities to a high degree of accuracy.

As light travels from a dense medium of index of refraction μ_1 to a rarer medium of index μ_2, making an incident angle θ_1 with the normal, the light is refracted away from the normal by an angle θ_2. This phenomena is governed by Snell's Law: $\mu_1 \sin \theta_1 = \mu_2 \sin \theta_2$. As the angle of incidence θ_1 is increased the critical angle is approached beyond which all the light is totally reflected back into the incident medium. The energy of the light is not reflected exactly at the boundary surface; it is carried in an attenuated manner into the rarer medium [4]. The magnitude of energy rapidly damps off exponentially with increasing d, d being the normal distance measured from the boundary into the rarer medium.

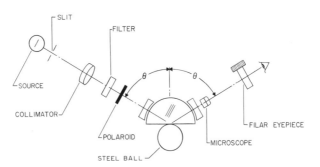

FIGURE 1. *Schematic outline of apparatus used in experimental verification of theory.*

The basic equipment consists of a spectrometer with the vertical axis of rotation being perpendicular to the plane of the paper. The prism, end caps, and ball rests on the spectrometer table with the ball held against the prism by a 0.1 g force due to a 1 deg tilt in the table.

By bringing up a third medium of index μ_3, e.g., the steel ball in figure 1, some of this energy is frustrated in the sense of prevention of its return to the first medium. The third medium will absorb or transmit part of the frustrated energy, depending on whether μ_3 is real or complex. This will naturally affect the light reflected back into the first medium. For an all dielectric system, such as glass-air-glass, the relative amount of energy intercepted is known to depend upon the polarization of the incident light, the thickness of the wringing film, the three refractive indices, μ_1, μ_2, μ_3, the wavelength of the incident light, and the angle of incidence θ_1 [5]. The effect of conducting surfaces (complex μ_3) was investigated recently [6].

For light polarized perpendicular to the plane of incidence, no unexpected phenomena occur when conductors are used as the third medium. However, for parallel polarized light a minimum in reflectivity occurs when μ_3 has a complex index, figure 2. These curves, plotted from an equation [6] developed in an analysis of electromagnetic wave theory, indicate a sensitive method of determining d by measuring the reflectivity of the light. This presumes a knowledge of the indices of refraction of all the media, the wavelength, and the angle of incidence θ_1. Each one of these values can be determined by measurement with the possible exception of μ_2, the index of the wringing film. By methods of ellipsometry μ_3, the index of the frustrating medium, may be measured even if it is complex. The pertinent questions are the value of the index of refraction and the thickness of the wringing film. From the form of the curves in figure 2, it is apparent that for a very thin film increasing from zero in

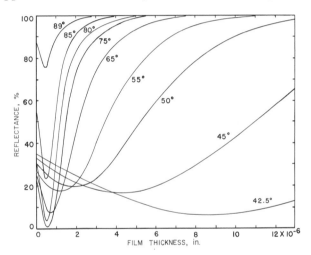

FIGURE 2. *Variation of reflectance with film thickness of air at various angles of incidence of parallel polarized light for the case where μ_3 is of complex index.*

thickness a pattern of minimum reflectance should be obtained resembling an interference fringe of equal thickness. Unlike an interference fringe pattern, only one minimum can be obtained, corresponding to a thickness of film dependent upon the angle of incidence. Therefore no ambiguity concerning the order of interference will exist. Other important differences are the increased sharpness of the reflectance dip obtained for larger angles of incidence, and, for an increase in the index ratio μ_1/μ_2, the minimum occurs at smaller d and the system becomes very sensitive since there is a rapid change in reflectivity for small changes in d.

Starting with Maxwell's equations and modifying them for the total reflection case one obtains for the perpendicular polarization,

$$\frac{-A'_{1s}}{A_{1s}}=$$

$$\frac{\left[\begin{array}{l}\sinh u\left[\sin^2\theta_1-n_{12}^2-\rho^{1/2}\cos\theta_1\cos\dfrac{\phi}{2}\right]-\rho^{1/2}(\sin^2\theta_1-n_{12}^2)^{1/2}\sin\dfrac{\phi}{2}\cosh u\\[2mm]-i\left[\rho^{1/2}\cos\theta_1\sin\dfrac{\phi}{2}\sinh u-(\sin^2\theta_1-n_{12}^2)^{1/2}\left(\cos\theta_1+\rho^{1/2}\cos\dfrac{\phi}{2}\right)\cosh u\right]\end{array}\right]}{\left[\begin{array}{l}\sinh u\left[\sin^2\theta_1-n_{12}^2+\rho^{1/2}\cos\theta_1\cos\dfrac{\phi}{2}\right]-\rho^{1/2}(\sin^2\theta_1-n_{12}^2)^{1/2}\sin\dfrac{\phi}{2}\cosh u\\[2mm]+i\left[\rho^{1/2}\cos\theta_1\sin\dfrac{\phi}{2}\sinh u-(\sin^2\theta_1-n_{12}^2)^{1/2}\left(\cos\theta_1-\rho^{1/2}\cos\dfrac{\phi}{2}\right)\cosh u\right]\end{array}\right]}$$

$$(1)$$

and for the parallel polarization,

$$\frac{A'_{1p}}{A_{1p}}=\frac{\left[\begin{array}{l}\left[n_{12}^2\mu_2^2\rho^{1/2}\cos\theta_1\cos\dfrac{\phi}{2}-n^2(1-\alpha^2)(\sin^2\theta_1-n_{12}^2)\right]\sinh u\\[2mm]+\left[\mu_2^2\rho^{1/2}\sin\dfrac{\phi}{2}-2n_{12}^2n^2\alpha\cos\theta_1\right](\sin^2\theta_1-n_{12}^2)^{1/2}\cosh u\\[2mm]+i\left\{\sinh u\left[n_{12}^2\mu_2^2\rho^{1/2}\cos\theta_1\sin\dfrac{\phi}{2}+2n^2\alpha(\sin^2\theta_1-n_{12}^2)\right]\right.\\[2mm]\left.-\cosh u\left[\mu_2^2\rho^{1/2}\cos\dfrac{\phi}{2}+n_{12}^2n^2(1-\alpha^2)\cos\theta_1\right][\sin^2\theta_1-n_{12}^2]^{1/2}\right\}\end{array}\right]}{\left[\begin{array}{l}\left[n_{12}^2\mu_2^2\rho^{1/2}\cos\theta_1\cos\dfrac{\phi}{2}+n^2(1-\alpha^2)(\sin^2\theta_1-n_{12}^2)\right]\sinh u\\[2mm]-\left[\mu_2^2\rho^{1/2}\sin\dfrac{\phi}{2}+2n_{12}^2n^2\alpha\cos\theta_1\right][\sin^2\theta_1-n_{12}^2]^{1/2}\cosh u\\[2mm]+i\left\{\sinh u\left[n_{12}^2\mu_2^2\rho^{1/2}\cos\theta_1\sin\dfrac{\phi}{2}-2n^2\alpha(\sin^2\theta_1-n_{12}^2)\right]\right.\\[2mm]\left.+\cosh u\left[\mu_2^2\rho^{1/2}\cos\dfrac{\phi}{2}-n_{12}^2n^2(1-\alpha^2)\cos\theta_1\right][\sin^2\theta_1-n_{12}^2]^{1/2}\right\}\end{array}\right]}$$

$$(2)$$

where

$$n_{12}=\frac{\mu_2}{\mu_1}$$

$$n_{23}=\frac{\mu_3}{\mu_2}=\frac{n(1-i\alpha)}{\mu_2}$$

$$n=\text{refractive index}$$

$$\alpha=\text{absorption index}$$

$$u = \frac{-i2\pi\mu_2 d \cos \theta_2}{\lambda_0}$$

$\lambda_0 =$ vacuum wavelength

$$\rho = +\sqrt{\left[\frac{n_{12}^2 n_{23}^2 (1-\alpha^2)}{\mu_2^2} - \sin^2 \theta_1\right]^2 + \frac{4n_{12}^4 n^4 \alpha^2}{\mu_2^4}}$$

$$\sin \phi = -\frac{2n_{12}^2 n^2 \alpha}{\mu_2^2 \rho}$$

$$\cos \phi = \frac{n_{12}^2 n^2 (1-\alpha^2) - \mu_2^2 \sin^2 \theta_1}{\mu_2^2 \rho}.$$

Equations (1) and (2) may be used to determine the magnitude and phase of the reflected electric vectors.

These theoretical equations have been qualitatively and quantitatively verified by placing a steel ball against the boundary surface as in figure 1. The minimum indicated by theory has been observed and its formation verified with respect to film thickness. This minimum is formed because as the surface of the ball recedes from the

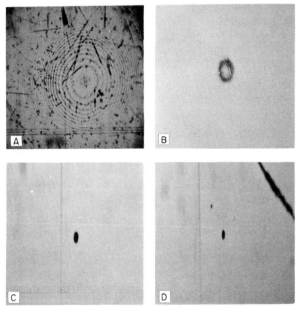

FIGURE 3. *Newton's rings obtained by interference between glass boundary surface and steel ball of figure 1.*

(A) angle of incidence less than the critical angle.
(B, C, & D) reflectance patterns obtained by frustrated total reflection at angles of incidence 45, 65, and 75°.

total reflecting surface, d increases and the reflectivity decreases, goes through a minimum, and then increases as predicted by theory. Figure 3 shows a series of patterns formed between a glass surface and a steel ball.

Preliminary investigation and results indicate the method of frustrated total reflection applicable to the precise measurement of thin films such as those existing between a dielectric and a conductor. There are two areas of investigation of thin films in which this method of frustrated total reflection can be significantly employed. One is a reflectometer to measure the intensity of the reflected light, and the other is an ellipsometer to analyze the polarization characteristics of the reflected light. As can be seen in figure 4, if the optical constants of the metallic surface (these determine the terminal point of the family of curves) and the index of the wringing film are known, and a polarization analysis of the reflected light is made, an extremely sensitive and single-valued determination of the wringing film thickness can be obtained. This sensitivity can be shown by assuming a hypothetical case of the wringing film index being 1.3 and the thickness going from 0 to 1.0 μ in. Over this range of film thickness, for this particular index, the relative phase change of the reflected light changes by 70 deg and the azimuth angle by 19 deg. Whereas if the intensity of the reflected light is measured with a reflectometer, figure 2, the result obtained is not single-valued, since it can not be determined on which side of the minimum the measured reflectivity value falls. Thus there will be two film thicknesses for each reflectivity value that is experimentally determined. The problem of knowing the index of the wringing film still exists if a reflectometer is used. This, and the fact that with an ellipsometer the optical constants of a conducting material can be measured, led to the selection of an ellipsometer for investigating the thickness of a film existing between two surfaces that are nominally "in contact."

2. Procedures

Various techniques have been used for the cleaning and preparation of the end surfaces of the gage blocks employed in this investigation. Initially the surface of the gage block was cleaned with trichloroethylene, to remove any organic contaminates, and then with ethyl alcohol to remove any residue from the trichloroethylene. The polarization characteristics of the reflected light were then measured for this cleaned surface. Although the angle of incidence was not changed, and the surface was not disturbed, the measurements were found to vary considerably throughout the day. From the characteristics of the variations in the measurements it seemed likely that a transparent film was building up on the surface throughout the day. By directing a beam of microwave radiation at normal incidence upon the surface while it was being measured this film was "boiled off" the surface without any heating effects to the surface. The measurements of the light reflected from the surface, at the same angle of incidence, were then found to be highly reproducible, showing random character and having variations limited to about 0.05°. Another cleaning solution that was tried was spectral grade acetone. The experimental results of surfaces cleaned with acetone showed that a film was being deposited upon the surface. When the cleaning was repeated the thickness of the film increased. A third method that was tried was flaming. The surface was cleaned with trichloroethylene and alcohol and then rapidly passed through a flame several times.

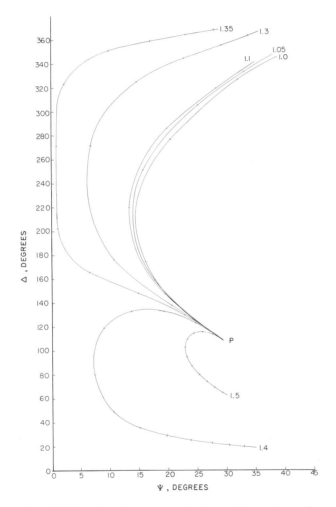

FIGURE 4. *Relative phase change* vs. *azimuth angle for various values of* μ_2.

Numbers on curves represent index of refraction of wringing film. Each successive point, beginning at P, represents an increase in d of 0.5 μ in.

$\theta_1 = 65°$, $\mu_1 = 1.576$, $\mu_3 = 2.41\ (1 - 3.326i\ )$, $\lambda = 21.50$ microinches.

This made the surface hydrophilic for about an hour, at the end of which it again became hydrophobic. This method produced a clean surface, but it was found that after flaming a surface could not be wrung. In the following experimental results the method mentioned above of cleaning a surface with trichloroethylene and alcohol and then placing it in a beam of microwave radiation was employed.

By using the following formula, the measured polarization characteristics of the reflected light can be utilized to determine the complex index of refraction of the metallic surface under study.

$$\mu_3 = \mu_1 \tan \theta_1 \left[1 - \frac{4\beta \sin^2 \theta_1}{(\beta+1)^2} \right]^{1/2}$$

where,

$$\mu_3 = n(1 - i\alpha)$$

$$\beta = \tan \psi e^{i\Delta}$$

$\theta_1 =$ angle of incidence

$\psi =$ azimuth angle

$\Delta =$ relative phase shift.

As stated above the measurements of optical constants of the surfaces prepared with this cleaning procedure were found to be highly reproducible at the same angle of incidence. However, when the angle of incidence was changed the optical constants of the surface were found to vary slightly. The possibility that this variation could be due to the formation of an oxide film on the surface was investigated. This investigation consisted of a thorough study of a theoretical case of a surface with a transparent oxide film of complex index on it. Upon the completion of this study it was found that this variation in the index of refraction of the metallic surface could not be explained by an oxide film, regardless of the thickness of the film. At the present time this variation of index with angle of incidence is still unexplained.

If the complex index of the metallic surface is measured and the index of the glass to which the surface is to be wrung is known, the index of the wringing film must still be determined in order to measure the thickness of the film. In figure 4 the starting point, P, of the curves is the point at which the film thickness is zero. It is dependent upon the wavelength of the light, the angle of incidence, the index of the glass, and the index of the metallic surface. Starting at this point of zero thickness the curves then undergo a separation dependent upon the index of the film. If the index of the film is known the thickness of the film can then be computed from the polarization analysis of the reflected light.

3. Results

The first approach to this problem was to measure the bulk index of the fluid (e.g. kerosene) used to deliberately contaminate the surfaces in order to wring them together. Using this measured index, approximately 1.4, and the polarization characteristics of the reflected light from the wrung combination of glass and metallic surfaces a film thickness for this index was calculated, using an electronic computer program [7]. The measured polarization for different angles of incidence for this combination of glass and gage block indicated a rather large variation in the derived film thickness even though the complex index of the metallic surface was corrected for the angle of incidence at which the film was being measured. Both the film thicknesses and refractive indices were then calculated from the experimental data for each angle of incidence. The film index which gave the minimum spread of film thicknesses for various angles of incidence was in the range 1.00 to 1.02.

The index of the film being equivalent to the index of air instead of approximately 1.4, the index of the contaminate used to wring the combination together, seems reasonable when two facts are considered. One, the surface of a gage block is not a completely smooth finish, but a series of irregularities. The arithmetical average surface finish is defined as the average value of the departure of the surface from a centerline, whether above or below it, over the length of the block. It is the sum of all the areas of the peaks and valleys divided by the length. The average height of the irregularities with respect to the centerline, for the type of surface used in this investigation, was about $0.07~\mu$ in. Since the metallic surface was contaminated by putting a drop of the fluid on it and then rubbing the surface with a lens tissue until the contimate was no longer visible, the possibility existed that the contaminating fluid had flowed into the valleys of the surface. If this were the case the material immediately adjacent to the glass surface would be a thin layer of air. Second, since the real Poynting vector, or the real energy flow, is parallel to the surfaces of the glass and the gage block, the real energy would be radiating in the thin layer of air and would not encounter the contaminating fluid in the valleys. However, when the film index was taken to be 1.00 to 1.02, the deviations of the measured polarization characteristics, the azimuth angle and the relative phase change, from theoretical curves similar to those of figure 4 were too large to be attributed to experimental errors.

The next phase of the investigation of the film index was to use a "dry" wring to contact the surfaces. That is, the surfaces were cleaned with trichloroethylene and alcohol, wiped dry with a lens tissue and then wrung together. A series of measurements was then taken of this wringing film at an angle of 65 deg. Film indices and corresponding film thicknesses which fell within experimental errors were then calculated. For a wringing combination that had been wrung for a period of 18 hr the film index was in the range 1.35 to 1.36, and the film thickness was 0.615 to 0.654 μ in. After a total wringing time of 41 hr another measurement of this film was made. The index had now increased to the range 1.43 to 1.44 and the thickness to the range 1.217 to 1.340 μ in. After a lapse of another 96 hr the index was still about 1.43 to 1.44 but the thicknesses had increased to the range 1.378 to 1.519 μ in.

Since the last cleaning fluid used on the surfaces was alcohol and alcohol has an affinity for water the initial index value of about 1.35 seems realistic. A visual observation of the metallic surface after it had been pulled free from the glass revealed that some unknown substance had seeped in between the metallic surface and the glass. This seepage appeared to have originated at the edge of the metallic surface. Further investigation of this phenomenon revealed that the amount of seepage increased with time. Experimental attempts to identify the index of this substance proved unsuccessful, but they did reveal that the index was rather high, approximately 1.5. This high index value would explain the increase of the film index observed experimentally. The observed continual seepage of this substance would explain the index value appearing to reach a plateau of 1.43 to 1.44, while the thickness of the film continued to increase. This specimen was a 405 nitrided stainless steel gage block. The four non-gaging surfaces of the block had not been subjected to any finishing process. The unfinished sides of the specimen probably served as a reservoir for the unknown substance that seeped into the wringing area existing between the glass and the gage block.

The reported results are of a preliminary nature. The investigation of the index of refraction and the thickness of the thin films existing between two surfaces nominally "in contact" with each other will be continued along the same lines of investigation indicated in this paper.

4. References

[1] C. F. Bruce and B. S. Thornton, J. Appl. Phys. **27,** 853 (1956).
[2] A. M. Dexter, ASTE 59, Tech. Paper 195 (1959).
[3] F. H. Rolt and H. Barrell, Proc. Roy. Soc. **A116,** 401 (1927).
[4] R. W. Ditchburn, Light, Interscience Publishers, Inc., N.Y., p. 434 (1955).
[5] E. E. Hall, Phys. Rev. **15,** 73 (1902).
[6] T. R. Young and B. D. Rothrock, J. Res. NBS **67A,** 115 (1962).
[7] F. L. McCrackin and J. Colson, NBS Tech. Note 242 (1964).

Discussion

C. DEL CARLO (Chrysler Corp.):
If I understand you correctly, the variation of the length of the gage block can be as much as a 10th of a wavelength whereas the thickness of the wringing film is about an order of magnitude less than this. In view of this difference, I can't understand your concern about an exact measurement for the thickness of the film.

T. R. YOUNG:
The thickness of the film must be measured at one point. If

there is a convexity of the surface the forces of attraction working on the surfaces tend to draw them together.

R. J. ARCHER (Bell Telephone Laboratories):

Recognizing that the surface of the metal gage block is not perfectly flat, it must be considered that an irregular surface region can constitute a film on the gage block. The thickness of this film is the height of the irregularities, and its optical constants are a combination of the optical constants of the metal and of the medium that fills the "valleys" of the irregular region. Thus, the net change in Δ and ψ following the formation of a wringing film results from the combined effect of the wringing film plus the change in the optical constants of the film constituted by the irregular surface region due to the change in the index of refraction of the medium that fills the irregularities. It follows that the properties of the wringing film calculated from changes in Δ and ψ would be incorrect if the irregular surface region were not taken into account. The likely effect would be for the calculated thickness and index of refraction to be smaller than the true values.

T. R. YOUNG:

This irregular surface region of the gage block we feel is taken into account since the optical constants of the "clean" block are measured and the block is then wrung to the glass without the use of any wringing lubricant or agent. Therefore, the effective surface of the gage block in the wrung combination is essentially the same surface for which the optical constants were determined.

A. B. WINTERBOTTOM (Norges Tekniska Hogskole):

Experiments have indicated that all surfaces have a contaminated film therefore the actual model that would closely resemble the physical model would be a three-film case. This may explain the discrepancy in your results.

T. R. YOUNG:

In the measurement of the optical constants of the surfaces involved we have undoubtedly obtained some resultant effects, hopefully the optical constants of an effective surface.

U.S. GOVERNMENT PRINTING OFFICE; 1964—O-728-101